It's another great book from CGP...

GCSE Edexcel Additional Science is all about **understanding how science works**.
And not only that — understanding it well enough to be able to **question**
what you hear on TV and read in the papers.

But don't panic. This book includes all the **science facts** you need to learn,
and shows you how they work in the real world. It even includes
a **free** Online Edition you can read on your computer or tablet.

How to get your free Online Edition

Just go to **cgpbooks.co.uk/extras** and enter this code...

3795 8909 9790 5497

By the way, this code only works for one person. If somebody else has used
this book before you, they might have already claimed the Online Edition.

CGP — still the best! ☺

Our sole aim here at CGP is to produce the highest
quality books — carefully written, immaculately presented
and dangerously close to being funny.

Then we work our socks off to get them
out to you — at the cheapest possible prices.

Contents

Published by CGP

From original material by Richard Parsons.

Editors:
Luke Antieul, Charlotte Burrows, Ben Fletcher, Helena Hayes, Felicity Inkpen,
Rosie McCurrie, Jane Sawers, Karen Wells, Sarah Williams.

Contributors:
Paddy Gannon

ISBN: 978 1 84762 768 1

With thanks to Ian Francis, David Hickinson, Sue Hocking, Peter Schofield and Dawn Wright
for the proofreading.
With thanks to Jan Greenway, Laura Jakubowski and Laura Stoney for the copyright research.

With thanks to Getty Images for permission to use the image on page 31.

Data used to construct stopping distance diagram on page 88 from the Highway Code.
© Crown Copyright re-produced under the terms of the Click-Use licence.

Pages 99 and 100 contain public sector information published by the Health and Safety
Executive and licensed under the Open Government Licence v1.0.

Printed by Elanders Ltd, Newcastle upon Tyne.
Clipart from Corel®

The Scientific Process

You need to know a few things about how the world of science works. First up is the <u>scientific process</u> — how a scientist's <u>mad idea</u> turns into a <u>widely accepted theory</u>.

Scientists Come Up with <u>Hypotheses</u> — Then <u>Test</u> Them

About 100 years ago, scientists hypothesised that atoms looked like this.

1) Scientists try to <u>explain</u> things. Everything.

2) They start by <u>observing</u> something they don't understand — it could be anything, e.g. planets in the sky, a person suffering from an illness, what matter is made of... anything.

3) Then, they come up with a <u>hypothesis</u> — a <u>possible explanation</u> for what they've observed.

4) The next step is to <u>test</u> whether the hypothesis might be <u>right or not</u> — this involves <u>gathering evidence</u> (i.e. <u>data</u> from <u>investigations</u>).

5) To gather evidence the scientist uses the hypothesis to make a <u>prediction</u> — a statement based on the hypothesis that can be <u>tested</u>.

6) If data from experiments or studies <u>backs up the prediction</u>, you're one step closer to figuring out if the hypothesis is true.

Other Scientists Will <u>Test</u> the Hypotheses Too

1) <u>Other</u> scientists will use the hypothesis to make their <u>own predictions</u>, and carry out their <u>own experiments</u> or studies.

2) They'll also try to <u>reproduce</u> the original investigations to check the results.

3) And if <u>all the experiments</u> in the world back up the hypothesis, then scientists start to think it's <u>true</u>.

4) However, if a scientist somewhere in the world does an experiment that <u>doesn't</u> fit with the hypothesis (and other scientists can <u>reproduce</u> these results), then the hypothesis is in trouble.

5) When this happens, scientists have to come up with a new hypothesis (maybe a <u>modification</u> of the old hypothesis, or maybe a completely <u>new</u> one).

After more evidence was gathered scientists changed their hypothesis to this.

If <u>Evidence</u> Supports a Hypothesis, It's <u>Accepted</u> — for Now

1) If pretty much every scientist in the world believes a hypothesis to be true because experiments back it up, then it usually goes in the <u>textbooks</u> for students to learn.

2) Accepted hypotheses are often referred to as <u>theories</u>.

Now we think it's more like this.

3) Our <u>currently accepted</u> theories are the ones that have survived this 'trial by evidence' — they've been tested many, many times over the years and survived (while the less good ones have been ditched).

4) However... they never, <u>never</u> become hard and fast, totally indisputable <u>fact</u>. You can never know... it'd only take <u>one</u> odd, totally inexplicable result, and the hypothesising and testing would start all over again.

<u>You expect me to believe that — then show me the evidence...</u>

Scientific <u>ideas</u> are <u>changing</u> all the time as a result of <u>new evidence</u> being uncovered. It's the role of the <u>scientific community</u> (all the world's scientists) to <u>test</u> and <u>evaluate</u> these ideas and decide whether or not they should be <u>accepted</u> as theories — so you don't have to waste your time learning stuff that's absolute rubbish.

Your Data's Got to Be Good

Evidence is the key to science — but not all evidence is equally good.
The way evidence is gathered can have a big effect on how trustworthy it is...

Lab Experiments and Studies Are Better Than Rumour

1) Results from controlled experiments in laboratories are great. A lab is the easiest
place to control variables so that they're all kept constant (except for the one you're
investigating). This makes it easier to carry out a fair test.

2) For things that you can't investigate in the lab (e.g. climate) you conduct scientific studies.
As many of the variables as possible are controlled, to make it a fair test.

3) Old wives' tales, rumours, hearsay, "what someone said", and so on, should be taken with a
pinch of salt. Without any evidence they're NOT scientific — they're just opinions.

There's more about variables and fair tests on page 5.

The Bigger the Sample Size the Better

Data based on small samples isn't as good as data based on large samples.
A sample should be representative of the whole population (i.e. it should share as many of
the various characteristics in the population as possible) — a small sample can't do that as well.

Evidence Needs to be Reliable (Reproducible)

Evidence is only reliable if other people can repeat it. If they can't, then you can't believe it.

RELIABLE means that the data can be reproduced by others.

EXAMPLE: In 1989, two scientists claimed that they'd produced 'cold fusion' (the energy
source of the Sun — but without the enormous temperatures). It was huge news — if true,
this could have meant energy from seawater — the ideal energy solution for the world... forever.
However, other scientists just couldn't get the same results — i.e. the results weren't reliable.
And until they are, 'cold fusion' isn't going to be generally accepted as fact.

Evidence Also Needs to Be Valid

VALID means that the data is reliable AND answers the original question.

EXAMPLE: DO POWER LINES CAUSE CANCER?
Some studies have found that children who live near overhead power lines are more likely to develop
cancer. What they'd actually found was a correlation (relationship) between the variables "presence of
power lines" and "incidence of cancer" — they found that as one changed, so did the other. But this
evidence is not enough to say that the power lines cause cancer, as other explanations might be possible.
For example, power lines are often near busy roads, so the areas tested could contain different levels of
pollution from traffic. Also, you need to look at types of neighbourhoods and lifestyles of people
living in the tested areas (could diet be a factor... or something else you hadn't thought of...).
So these studies don't show a definite link and so don't answer the original question.

Does the data really say that?...

If it's so hard to be definite about anything, how does anybody ever get convinced about anything?
Well, what usually happens is that you get a load of evidence that all points the same way. If one study
can't rule out a particular possibility, then maybe another one can. So you gradually build up a whole
body of evidence, and it's this (rather than any single study) that convinces people.

Benefits, Risks and Decision Making

Science is all about the <u>balance</u> between benefit and risk — a bit like life really...

Developments <u>in Science</u> Usually Have Benefits and Drawbacks...

Scientists have created loads of <u>new technologies</u> that could <u>improve</u> our lives.
For example, generating electricity using <u>nuclear power</u> has lots of <u>benefits</u>:

1) The <u>national population</u> benefits from a <u>reliable source of electricity</u>.

2) There's a <u>global benefit</u> because generating electricity this way <u>doesn't</u> contribute to <u>global warming</u> (like coal-fired power stations do).

3) <u>Construction companies</u> benefit from years of work in building the power station.

4) <u>Local people</u> benefit from new jobs.

However, it's not all good news. One of the <u>drawbacks</u> is:

Nuclear power stations are <u>very expensive</u>. Perhaps the money that goes into building them would be better spent on things like building new wind turbines or hydroelectric plants.

...and They're Never Risk Free

1) Most technologies have some <u>risks</u>.
   For example, for a <u>new nuclear power station</u>:

   - Local people might suffer from <u>higher radiation exposure</u>, which could affect their health.

   - There could be a <u>major accident</u>, like the Chernobyl disaster, which would affect large areas.

2) To make a <u>decision</u> about a course of action (e.g. whether or not to build a new nuclear power station) society has to <u>weigh up</u> the benefits, drawbacks and risks involved for everyone.

Loads of Other Factors Can Influence Decisions Too

Here are some other factors that can influence decisions about science, and the way science is used:

Economic issues: Society <u>can't</u> always <u>afford</u> to do things scientists recommend without <u>cutting back elsewhere</u> (e.g. investing heavily in alternative energy sources).

Social issues: Decisions based on scientific evidence affect <u>people</u> — e.g. should fossil fuels be taxed more highly (to invest in alternative energy)? Should alcohol be banned (to prevent health problems)? <u>Would the effect on people's lifestyles be acceptable...</u>

Environmental issues: <u>Genetically modified crops</u> may help us <u>produce more food</u> — but some people think they could cause <u>environmental problems</u>.

Ethical issues: There are a lot of things that scientific developments have made possible, but <u>should we do them</u>? E.g. clone humans, develop better nuclear weapons.

Not revising — a definite drawback in the exam...

Developments in science involve a lot of <u>weighing up</u> — new technologies have risks, but the benefits are often huge. Then there are the economic, social, environmental and ethical issues to think about...

Science Has Limits

Science can give us amazing things — cures for diseases, space travel, heated toilet seats...
But science has its limitations — there are questions that it just can't answer.

Some Questions Are Unanswered by Science — So Far

1) We don't understand everything. And we never will. We'll find out more, for sure — as more hypotheses are suggested, and more experiments are done. But there'll always be stuff we don't know.

   EXAMPLES:
   - Today we don't know as much as we'd like about the impacts of global warming. How much will sea level rise? And to what extent will weather patterns change?
   - We also don't know anywhere near as much as we'd like about the universe. Are there other life forms out there? And what is the universe made of?

2) These are complicated questions. At the moment, scientists don't all agree on the answers because there isn't enough evidence.

3) But eventually, we probably will be able to answer these questions once and for all...
   ...all we need is more evidence.

4) But by then there'll be loads of new questions to answer.

Other Questions Are Unanswerable by Science

1) Then there's the other type... questions that all the experiments in the world won't help us answer — the "Should we be doing this at all?" type questions. There are always two sides...

2) Take embryo screening (which allows you to choose an embryo with particular characteristics). It's possible to do it — but does that mean we should?

3) Different people have different opinions.

   For example...
   - Some people say it's good... couples whose existing child needs a bone marrow transplant, but who can't find a donor, will be able to have another child selected for its matching bone marrow. This would save the life of their first child — and if they want another child anyway... where's the harm?

   - Other people say it's bad... they say it could have serious effects on the new child. In the above example, the new child might feel unwanted — thinking they were only brought into the world to help someone else. And would they have the right to refuse to donate their bone marrow (as anyone else would)?

   THE GAZETTE
   BONE MARROW BABY'S BROTHER SAVED

   THE POST
   BONE MARROW BABY BORN: WHAT RIGHTS DOES HE HAVE?

4) This question of whether something is morally or ethically right or wrong can't be answered by more experiments — there is no "right" or "wrong" answer.

5) The best we can do is get a consensus from society — a judgement that most people are more or less happy to live by. Science can provide more information to help people make this judgement, and the judgement might change over time. But in the end it's up to people and their conscience.

Chips or rice? — totally unanswerable by science...

Right — get this straight in your head — science can't tell you whether you should or shouldn't do something. That kind of thing is up to you and society to decide. There are tons of questions that science might be able to answer in the future — like how much sea level might rise due to global warming, what the Universe is made of and whatever happened to those pink stripy socks with Santa on that I used to have.

Planning Experiments

That's all the dull stuff about the world of science over — now to the hands-on part. The next few pages show how <u>experiments</u> should be carried out — by both <u>professional scientists</u> and <u>you</u>.

An <u>Experiment</u> Must be a <u>Fair Test</u>

1) One of the most important parts of planning an experiment is making sure that the <u>evidence</u> you collect is <u>valid</u> and <u>reliable</u> (see page 2). This means that your experiment must be a <u>fair test</u>.

2) The only way to make it a fair test is to <u>change</u> only <u>one variable</u> (factor) in the experiment. All the <u>other variables</u> should <u>be controlled</u> — they should <u>stay exactly the same</u> throughout the experiment and each time the experiment is repeated.

3) For example, if you're looking at the effect of <u>temperature</u> on the rate of an enzyme-controlled reaction you need to keep the <u>pH</u> the same each time (otherwise you won't know if any change in the rate of reaction is caused by the change in temperature, or the change in pH).

The <u>Equipment</u> Used Has to be <u>Right for the Job</u>

When you're planning an experiment, you need to make sure you choose the <u>right equipment</u>. For example, the measuring equipment you use has to be <u>sensitive enough</u> to accurately measure the chemicals you're using, e.g. if you need to measure out 11 ml of a liquid, you'll need to use a measuring cylinder that can measure to 1 ml, not 5 or 10 ml.

An <u>Experiment Must be</u> Safe

1) Part of planning an experiment is making sure that it's <u>safe</u>.

2) There are lots of <u>hazards</u> you could be faced with during an experiment, e.g. <u>microorganisms</u>, <u>chemicals</u>, <u>radiation</u>, <u>electricity</u>, <u>gas</u> and <u>fire</u>.

3) You should always make sure that you <u>identify</u> all the hazards that you might encounter.

4) You should also come up with ways of <u>reducing the risks</u> from the hazards you've identified.

5) One way of doing this is to carry out a <u>risk assessment</u>:

For an experiment involving a <u>Bunsen burner</u>, the risk assessment might be something like this:

<u>Hazard:</u> Bunsen burner is a fire risk.

<u>Precautions:</u>
- Keep flammable chemicals away from the Bunsen.
- Never leave the Bunsen unattended when lit.
- Always turn on the yellow safety flame when not in use.

<u>Repeats</u> affect <u>Reliability, and Range of Measurements</u> affects <u>Validity</u>

1) One way to make data <u>more reliable</u> is to <u>repeat</u> the measurements and take an <u>average</u> (see next page).

2) Also, the <u>range of data</u> collected has to be <u>suitable</u>, and you need to take <u>enough measurements</u> throughout the <u>whole</u> of the range — otherwise you won't be able to identify the <u>pattern</u> you're looking for. For example, if your hypothesis is that temperature affects the rate of an enzyme-controlled reaction, you'd need to measure the rate of reaction at a wide range of temperatures, e.g. 0 °C to 50 °C, and in 5 °C steps throughout the range.

3) If the range isn't big enough, or you don't take enough measurements throughout the range, your data <u>won't</u> be <u>valid</u> for the <u>hypothesis</u> you're supposed to be testing.

Take a look back at page 2 if you can't remember what reliability and validity are.

Reliable data — it won't ever forget your birthday...

All this stuff is really important — without <u>good quality</u> data an investigation will be totally <u>meaningless</u>. So give this page a read through a couple of times and your data will be the envy of the whole scientific community.

Collecting, Processing and Presenting Data

After you've collected your data you'll have <u>oodles of info</u> that you have to <u>make some kind of sense of</u>. You need to <u>process</u> and <u>present</u> it so you can look for <u>patterns</u> and <u>relationships</u> in it.

Data Needs to be Organised

1) <u>Tables</u> are dead useful for <u>recording results</u> and <u>organising data</u>.

2) When you draw a table, make sure that <u>each column</u> has a <u>heading</u> and that you've included the <u>units</u>.

3) Annoyingly, tables are about as useful as a chocolate teapot for showing <u>patterns</u> or <u>relationships</u> in data. You need to use some kind of graph for that (see below).

Check For Mistakes Made When Collecting Data

1) When you've collected all the results for an experiment, you should have a look to see if there are any results that <u>don't seem to fit</u> in with the rest.

2) Most results vary a bit, but any that are totally different are called <u>anomalous results</u>.

3) If you ever get any anomalous results, you should investigate them to try to <u>work out what happened</u>. If you can work out what happened (e.g. you measured something wrong) you can <u>ignore</u> them when processing and presenting your data.

Data Can be Processed Using a Bit of Maths

1) When you've done repeats of an experiment you should always calculate the <u>mean</u> (average). To do this <u>ADD TOGETHER</u> all the data values and <u>DIVIDE</u> by the total number of values in the sample.

2) You might also need to calculate the <u>range</u> (how spread out the data is). To do this find the <u>LARGEST</u> number and <u>SUBTRACT</u> the <u>SMALLEST</u> number from it. *Ignore anomalous results when calculating these.*

EXAMPLE:

Test tube	Repeat 1 (g)	Repeat 2 (g)	Repeat 3 (g)	Mean (g)	Range (g)
A	28	37	32	(28 + 37 + 32) ÷ 3 = 32.3	37 – 28 = 9
B	47	51	60	(47 + 51 + 60) ÷ 3 = 52.7	60 – 47 = 13
C	68	72	70	(68 + 72 + 70) ÷ 3 = 70.0	72 – 68 = 4

If Your Data Comes in Categories, Present it in a Bar Chart

1) If one of the variables is <u>categoric</u> (comes in distinct categories, e.g. blood types, metals) you should use a <u>bar chart</u> to display the data.

2) You can also use a bar chart if one of the variables is <u>discrete</u> (the data can only take whole values and there are no in-between ones, e.g. number of people is discrete because you can't have half a person).

3) There are some <u>golden rules</u> you need to follow for <u>drawing</u> bar charts:

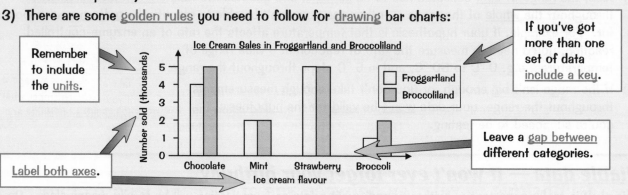

Remember to include the <u>units</u>.

If you've got more than one set of data <u>include a key</u>.

Label both axes.

Leave a <u>gap between</u> different categories.

Ice Cream Sales in Froggartland and Broccoliland

Number sold (thousands)

Chocolate   Mint   Strawberry   Broccoli

Ice cream flavour

Froggartland
Broccoliland

Collecting, Processing and Presenting Data

If Your Data is Continuous, Plot a Line Graph

1) If both the variables are continuous (numerical data that can have any value within a range, e.g. length, volume, temperature) you should use a line graph to display the data.

2) Here are the rules for drawing line graphs:

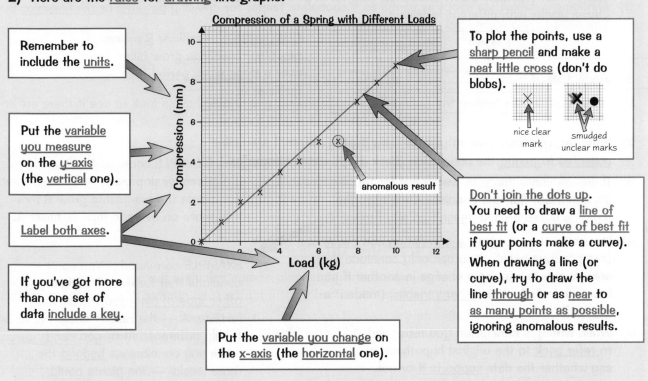

Remember to include the units.

Put the variable you measure on the y-axis (the vertical one).

Label both axes.

If you've got more than one set of data include a key.

Put the variable you change on the x-axis (the horizontal one).

Compression of a Spring with Different Loads

Compression (mm) — Load (kg)

anomalous result

To plot the points, use a sharp pencil and make a neat little cross (don't do blobs).

nice clear mark — smudged unclear marks

Don't join the dots up. You need to draw a line of best fit (or a curve of best fit if your points make a curve).

When drawing a line (or curve), try to draw the line through or as near to as many points as possible, ignoring anomalous results.

Line Graphs Can Show Relationships in Data

1) Line graphs are used to show the relationship between two variables (just like other graphs).

2) Data can show three different types of correlation (relationship):

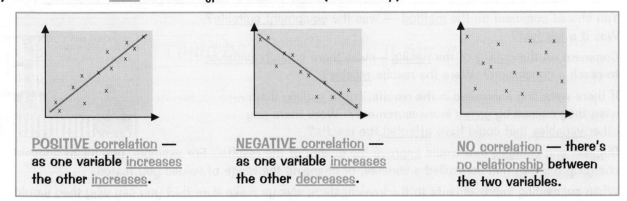

POSITIVE correlation — as one variable increases the other increases.

NEGATIVE correlation — as one variable increases the other decreases.

NO correlation — there's no relationship between the two variables.

3) You've got to be careful not to confuse correlation with cause though. A correlation just means that there's a relationship between two variables. It doesn't mean that the change in one variable is causing the change in the other (there might be other factors involved).

There's a positive correlation between age of man and length of nose hair...

Collect, process, present... data's like a difficult child — it needs a lot of attention. Go on, make it happy.

Drawing Conclusions and Evaluating

At the end of an experiment, the conclusion and evaluation are waiting. Don't worry, they won't bite.

You Can Only Conclude What the Data Shows and NO MORE

1) Drawing a conclusion can be quite straightforward — just look at your data and say what pattern you see between the variables.

EXAMPLE: The table below shows the heights of pea plant seedlings grown for three weeks with different fertilisers.

Fertiliser	Mean growth / mm
A	13.5
B	19.5
No fertiliser	5.5

CONCLUSION: Fertiliser B makes pea plant seedlings grow taller over a three week period than fertiliser A.

2) However, you also need to use the data that's been collected to justify the conclusion (back it up).

EXAMPLE continued... Over the three week period, Fertiliser B made the pea plants grow 6 mm more on average than fertiliser A.

3) There are some things to watch out for too — it's important that the conclusion matches the data it's based on and doesn't go any further.

4) Remember not to confuse correlation and cause (see previous page). You can only conclude that one variable is causing a change in another if you have controlled all the other variables (made it a fair test).

EXAMPLE continued... You can't conclude that fertiliser B makes any other type of plant grow taller than fertiliser A — the results could be totally different. Also, you can't make any conclusions beyond the three weeks — the plants could drop dead.

5) When writing a conclusion you also need to refer back to the original hypothesis — say whether the data supports it or not.

6) Then explain what's been found using your own scientific knowledge (what you've learnt in class).

Evaluation — Describe How You Could Improve the Investigation

1) You should comment on the method — was the equipment suitable? Was it a fair test?

2) Comment on the quality of the results — was there enough evidence to reach a conclusion? Were the results reliable?

3) If there were any anomalies in the results, try to explain them — were they caused by errors in measurement? Were there any other variables that could have affected the results?

I'd value this E somewhere in the region of 250-300k

4) Suggest any changes that would improve the quality of the results. For example, you might suggest changing the way you controlled a variable, or changing the range of values you tested.

5) When suggesting improvements to the investigation, always make sure that you say why they would make the results better.

Evaluation — next time, I will make sure I don't burn the lab down...

I know it doesn't seem very nice, but writing about where you went wrong is an important skill — it shows you've got a really good understanding of what the investigation was about. It's difficult for me — I'm always right.

The Controlled Assessment

You'll probably carry out a few investigations as you go through the course, but at some point you'll have to do the one that counts... the <u>controlled assessment</u>. Here's a bit about it, but make sure you can recite all the stuff we've covered in this section first — it'll really help you out.

The Controlled Assessment is Split into Three Parts

Part A — Planning

For this part you'll be given some information about a topic. Then you'll have to develop a <u>hypothesis</u> and <u>plan an experiment</u> to <u>test it</u>. You'll need to decide:

There's lots of help on all of these things on page 5.

1) What <u>variables</u> you're going to <u>control</u> — and <u>how</u> you're going to control them.
2) What <u>equipment</u> to use — and say <u>why</u> you've chosen each bit of kit.
3) What <u>risks</u> are involved in the experiment — and say <u>how</u> you're going to <u>reduce</u> each of them.
4) The <u>range of measurements</u> you're going to take — and say <u>why</u> you've chosen that range.
5) How many times you'll <u>repeat</u> each measurement. You should do <u>at least two</u> repeats to make your data <u>more reliable</u>.

Part B — Observations

For this part you'll be given a new hypothesis and an experiment plan.
You then <u>follow the plan</u> and <u>carry out the experiment</u>.

You'll need to:

1) Take an appropriate <u>number</u> and <u>range</u> of measurements (see page 5).
2) <u>Repeat</u> your measurements to get more <u>reliable data</u> (if possible) — <u>two times</u> is a good idea.
3) <u>Record</u> your data clearly in a nice, neat <u>table</u> (see page 6 for table tips).

Part C — Conclusions

This part involves <u>processing</u> data, <u>presenting</u> data, drawing <u>conclusions</u> and <u>evaluating</u>.
You'll have to do these things for your data (<u>primary data</u>), but also for data collected by other people (<u>secondary data</u>). You'll be given the secondary data when you need it.
You'll need to:

1) <u>Process all the data</u> (both primary and secondary), e.g. calculate the mean (see page 6).
2) <u>Present all the data</u> using the right type of <u>graph</u> for each (see pages 6-7 for help with this).
3) Identify any <u>anomalous results</u> and explain why you didn't include them when you processed and presented your data (they'd reduce the validity of your results). If there <u>aren't</u> any anomalous results, then you need to <u>say so</u>.
4) Write a <u>conclusion</u> for <u>both sets of data</u> (see previous page for what to say). Make sure you <u>back up</u> your conclusion using the data, say <u>whether it supports the hypothesis</u> or not and <u>explain what's been found</u> using your own knowledge.
5) Write an <u>evaluation</u> (see previous page for what to include). Don't forget to say <u>how</u> the method affected the results, and how any improvements would make the results better.

Keep your assessment under control — read this page...

Pretty straightforward, eh? As long as you've <u>learnt everything</u> on the previous few pages, you should be fine. Make sure you <u>know</u> each section like the <u>back of your hand</u> before you come to do the assessment itself.

Cells and Microscopy

<u>All</u> living things are made of <u>cells</u>. When someone first peered down a microscope at a slice of cork and drew the <u>boxes</u> they saw, little did they know that they'd seen the <u>building blocks</u> of <u>every organism on the planet</u>.

Plant <u>and</u> Animal Cells have Similarities <u>and</u> Differences

Animal Cell

4 THINGS THEY BOTH HAVE IN COMMON:

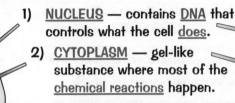

1) <u>NUCLEUS</u> — contains <u>DNA</u> that controls what the cell <u>does</u>.

2) <u>CYTOPLASM</u> — gel-like substance where most of the <u>chemical reactions</u> happen.

3) <u>CELL MEMBRANE</u> — holds the cell together and controls what goes <u>in</u> and <u>out</u>.

4) <u>MITOCHONDRIA</u> — these are where most of the reactions for <u>respiration</u> take place (see page 22). Respiration releases <u>energy</u> that the cell needs to work.

Plant Cell

3 EXTRAS THAT ONLY THE PLANT CELL HAS:

1) <u>RIGID CELL WALL</u> — made of <u>cellulose</u>, gives support for the cell.

2) <u>LARGE VACUOLE</u> — contains <u>cell sap</u>, a weak solution of sugar and salts.

3) <u>CHLOROPLASTS</u> — where <u>photosynthesis</u> occurs. They contain a green substance called <u>chlorophyll</u>.

Bacterial Cells Have No Nucleus

<u>Bacterial cells</u> are a lot <u>smaller</u> than plant or animal cells and have these <u>features</u>:

1) <u>Chromosomal DNA</u> (<u>one</u> long circular chromosome) controls the cell's <u>activities</u> and <u>replication</u>. It <u>floats free</u> in the <u>cytoplasm</u> (not in a nucleus).

2) <u>Plasmids</u> are <u>small loops</u> of <u>extra DNA</u> that aren't part of the chromosome. Plasmids contain genes for things like <u>drug resistance</u>, and can be <u>passed</u> between bacteria.

3) The <u>flagellum</u> (plural <u>flagella</u>) is a long, hair-like structure that <u>rotates</u> to make the bacterium <u>move</u>.

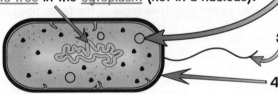

4) The cell is <u>supported</u> by a <u>cell wall</u>.

Cells are Studied Using Microscopes

1) <u>Microscopes</u> let us see things that we <u>can't see</u> with the <u>naked eye</u>.

2) <u>Light microscopes</u> were invented in the 1590s. They let us see things like <u>nuclei</u>, <u>chloroplasts</u> and <u>mitochondria</u>.

3) <u>Electron microscopes</u> were invented in the 1930s. They let us see much <u>smaller things</u> in <u>more detail</u> like the <u>internal structure</u> of mitochondria and chloroplasts, and even <u>tinier</u> things like <u>plasmids</u>.

4) You need to be able to calculate <u>magnification</u>. Magnification is how much <u>bigger</u> the <u>image</u> is than the <u>specimen</u> (the sample you're looking at). It's calculated using this formula:

$$\text{magnification} = \frac{\text{length of image}}{\text{length of specimen}}$$

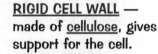

Look through the eyepiece

Focus the microscope, then finely tune the focus

Select the lowest powered objective lens, then choose a higher magnification if needed

Put the sample on the stage

Adjust the mirror to make sure there's plenty of light

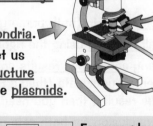

5 mm

For example:
If you have a magnified image that's 5 mm wide and your specimen is 0.05 mm wide, the magnification is:

$$\frac{5}{0.05} = 100, \text{ so it's} \times 100 \text{ magnification.}$$

There's quite a bit to learn in biology — but that's life, I guess...

On this page are <u>typical cells</u> with all the typical bits you need to know. If you look at cells under a <u>microscope</u>, they may look a bit different because they're specialised for different jobs — but they'll have the main features.

DNA

Once people had found out that <u>DNA</u> was the <u>molecule</u> that carried the <u>instructions</u> for <u>characteristics</u> from <u>your parents</u> to <u>you</u>, scientists did loads of studies to try and work out its <u>structure</u>. Here are their results...

DNA — a Double Helix of Paired Bases

1) A DNA molecule has <u>two strands</u> coiled together in the shape of a <u>double helix</u> (two spirals), as shown in the diagram opposite.

2) The two strands are held together by chemicals called <u>bases</u>. There are <u>four</u> different bases (shown in the diagram as different colours) — <u>adenine</u> (A), <u>cytosine</u> (C), <u>guanine</u> (G) and <u>thymine</u> (T).

3) The bases are <u>paired</u>, and they always pair up in the same way — it's always <u>A-T</u> and <u>C-G</u>. This is called <u>base-pairing</u>.

4) The <u>base pairs</u> are joined together by <u>weak hydrogen bonds</u>.

5) A <u>gene</u> is a <u>section</u> of DNA, and the <u>sequence of bases</u> in a gene <u>code</u> for a <u>specific protein</u> — see page 12 for more.

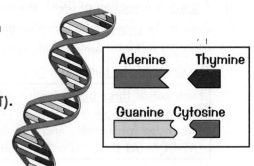

Adenine   Thymine

Guanine   Cytosine

Watson, Crick, Franklin and Wilkins Discovered The Structure of DNA

1) <u>Rosalind Franklin</u> and <u>Maurice Wilkins</u> worked out that DNA had a <u>helical structure</u> by directing beams of <u>x-rays</u> onto <u>crystallised DNA</u> and looking at the <u>patterns</u> the x-rays formed as they bounced off.

2) <u>James Watson</u> and <u>Francis Crick</u> used these ideas, along with the knowledge that the amount of <u>adenine + guanine</u> matched the amount of <u>thymine + cytosine</u>, to make a <u>model</u> of the DNA molecule where all the pieces <u>fitted together</u>.

You Can Do a Practical To Extract DNA From Cells

1) Chop up some <u>onion</u> and put it in a beaker containing a solution of <u>detergent</u> and <u>salt</u>. The detergent will <u>break down</u> the <u>cell membranes</u> and the salt will make the <u>DNA stick together</u>.

2) Put the beaker into a water bath at <u>60 °C</u> for <u>15 minutes</u> — this <u>denatures enzymes</u> (see p.14) that could digest the DNA and helps <u>soften</u> the onion cells.

3) Put the beaker in <u>ice</u> to <u>cool</u> the mixture down — this <u>stops</u> the DNA from <u>breaking down</u>.

4) Once the mixture is ice-cold, put it into a <u>blender</u> for a <u>few seconds</u> to <u>break open</u> the cell walls and <u>release</u> (but not break up) the DNA.

5) <u>Cool</u> the mixture down again, then <u>filter it</u> to get the froth and big bits of cell out.

6) <u>Gently</u> add some <u>ice-cold alcohol</u> to the filtered mixture. The <u>DNA</u> will start to <u>come out</u> of solution as it's <u>not soluble</u> in cold alcohol. It will appear as a <u>stringy white substance</u> that can be carefully fished out with a <u>glass rod</u>.

+ detergent + salt

ICE

ICE

+ alcohol

My band has a great rhythm section — it has paired basses...

Hope you enjoyed <u>extracting</u> all that DNA and learning about its <u>structure</u>. Sadly, though, you won't be getting a <u>Nobel prize</u> for your efforts — you're too late. Crick, Watson and Wilkins were awarded the Nobel prize for their work in <u>1962</u>. Unfortunately, by then Franklin had died and couldn't be nominated for the prize.

Protein Synthesis

Your DNA is basically a long list of instructions on how to make <u>all the proteins</u> in your body.

A Gene Codes for a Specific Protein

1) A <u>gene</u> is a <u>section</u> of DNA. It contains the <u>instructions</u> to make a <u>specific protein</u>.

2) Cells make <u>proteins</u> by stringing <u>amino acids</u> together in a particular order.

3) Only <u>20</u> different amino acids are used to make up <u>thousands</u> of different <u>proteins</u>.

4) The <u>order of the bases</u> in a gene simply tells cells <u>in what order</u> to put the amino acids together:

> Each set of <u>three bases</u> (called a <u>triplet</u>) <u>codes</u> for a <u>particular amino acid</u>.
> Here's an <u>example</u> (don't worry — you don't have to remember the specific codes):
> TAT codes for tyrosine and GCA for alanine. If the order of the bases in the gene is
> TAT-GCA-TAT then the order of amino acids in the protein will be tyrosine-alanine-tyrosine.

5) DNA also determines which genes are <u>switched on or off</u> — and so which <u>proteins</u> the cell <u>produces</u>, e.g. haemoglobin or keratin. That in turn determines what <u>type of cell</u> it is, e.g. red blood cell, skin cell.

6) Some of the proteins <u>help to make</u> all the other things that <u>aren't made of protein</u> (like cell membranes) from substances that come from your diet (like fats and minerals).

Proteins are Made by Ribosomes

Proteins are made in the cell by <u>organelles</u> called <u>ribosomes</u>. DNA is found in the cell <u>nucleus</u> and can't move out of it because it's <u>really big</u>. The cell needs to get the information from the DNA to the <u>ribosome</u> in the cell cytoplasm. This is done using a molecule called <u>mRNA</u>, which is very similar to DNA, but it's shorter and only a <u>single strand</u>. Also, <u>instead</u> of <u>thymine</u>, mRNA has the base <u>uracil</u> (U), which pairs with <u>adenine</u>. mRNA is like a <u>messenger</u> between the DNA in the nucleus and the ribosome. Here's how it's done:

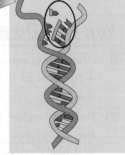

mRNA molecule forming

1) The two DNA strands <u>unzip</u>. The DNA is used as a <u>template</u> to make the <u>mRNA</u>. Base pairing ensures it's <u>complementary</u> (an exact match to the opposite strand). This step is called <u>TRANSCRIPTION</u>.

2) The mRNA molecule <u>moves out</u> of the nucleus and <u>joins</u> with a ribosome.

3) <u>Amino acids</u> that match the mRNA code are <u>brought</u> to the ribosome by molecules called <u>tRNA</u>.

4) The job of the ribosome is to <u>stick amino acids together</u> in a chain to make a <u>polypeptide</u> (protein). This follows the order of the triplet of bases (called <u>codons</u>) in the mRNA. This step is called <u>TRANSLATION</u>.

ribosome

mRNA

protein   amino acids

The result of all this molecular jiggery-pokery is that each type of <u>protein</u> gets made with its own specific <u>number</u> and <u>sequence</u> of <u>amino acids</u> — the ones described by its <u>DNA base sequence</u>. This is what makes it <u>fold up into the right shape</u> to do its specific <u>job</u>, e.g. as a particular <u>enzyme</u> (see the next page).

Mutations can be Harmful, Beneficial or Neutral

A <u>mutation</u> is a <u>change</u> to an organism's <u>DNA base sequence</u>. This could affect the sequence of <u>amino acids</u> in the protein, which could affect the <u>shape</u> of the protein and so its <u>function</u>. In turn, this could affect the <u>characteristics</u> of an organism. Mutations can be <u>harmful</u>, <u>beneficial</u> or <u>neutral</u>:

HARMFUL   A mutation could cause a <u>genetic disorder</u>, for example <u>cystic fibrosis</u>.

BENEFICIAL   A mutation could produce a <u>new characteristic</u> that is <u>beneficial</u> to an organism, e.g. a mutation in genes on bacterial plasmids can make them <u>resistant</u> to <u>antibiotics</u>.

NEUTRAL   Some mutations are <u>neither harmful nor beneficial</u>, e.g. they don't affect a protein's function.

4 bases, 20 amino acids, 1000s of proteins...

The <u>order of bases</u> says what amino acid is added and the <u>order of amino acids</u> determines the type of protein.

Enzymes

Chemical reactions are what make you work. And enzymes are what make them work.

Enzymes Are Catalysts Produced by Living Things

1) Living things have thousands of different chemical reactions going on inside them all the time.

2) These reactions need to be carefully controlled — to get the right amounts of substances.

3) You can usually make a reaction happen more quickly by raising the temperature.
    This would speed up the useful reactions but also the unwanted ones too... not good.

4) So... living things produce enzymes which act as biological catalysts. Enzymes reduce the need for high temperatures and we only have enzymes to speed up the useful chemical reactions in the body.

> A CATALYST is a substance which INCREASES the speed of a reaction,
> without being CHANGED or USED UP in the reaction.

5) Enzymes are all proteins, and they all work in the same way to catalyse various reactions.
    They can work inside or outside cells, for example:

    • DNA replication — enzymes help copy a cell's DNA before it divides by mitosis or meiosis (see p.17-18).

    • Protein synthesis — enzymes hold amino acids in place and form bonds between them (see p.12).

    • Digestion — various enzymes are secreted into the gut to digest different food molecules (see p.36).

Enzymes Have Special Shapes So They Can Catalyse Reactions

1) Chemical reactions usually involve things either being split apart or joined together.

2) The substrate is the molecule changed in the reaction.

3) Every enzyme has an active site — the part where it joins on to its substrate to catalyse the reaction.

4) Enzymes are really picky — they usually only work with one substrate. The posh way of saying this is that enzymes have a high specificity for their substrate.

5) This is because, for the enzyme to work, the substrate has to fit into the active site. If the substrate's shape doesn't match the active site's shape, then the reaction won't be catalysed. This is called the 'lock and key' mechanism, because the substrate fits into the enzyme just like a key fits into a lock.

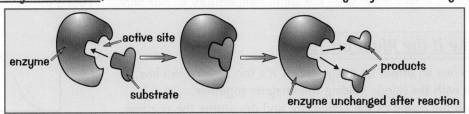

enzyme   active site   products
substrate   enzyme unchanged after reaction

Measuring the Rate of an Enzyme-Controlled Reaction — Method

1) You can measure the rate of a reaction by using amylase as the enzyme and starch as the substrate.

2) Amylase catalyses the breakdown of starch, so you can time how long it takes for the starch to disappear.

3) To do this, regularly take a drop of the amylase and starch mixture, and put it onto a drop of iodine solution on a spotting tile. Record the colour change — it'll turn blue-black if starch is present. Note the time when the iodine solution no longer turns blue-black — the starch has then been broken down by the amylase.

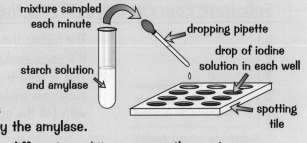

mixture sampled each minute   dropping pipette
starch solution and amylase   drop of iodine solution in each well
spotting tile

4) You can use the times to compare reaction rates under different conditions — see the next page.

If the lock & key mechanism fails, you get in through a window...

Just like you've got to have the correct key for a lock, you've got to have the right substrate for an enzyme.

More on Enzymes

Now it's time to take the <u>method</u> you've just learnt for an <u>enzyme-controlled reaction</u> and put it into <u>practice</u>...

Measuring *the Rate of an* Enzyme-Controlled *Reaction* — Variables

In the amylase/starch experiment from the last page you need to choose which variable to change.
For example:

* to investigate the effect of <u>temperature</u>, put the test tubes into <u>water baths</u> at a range of temperatures
* to investigate the effect of <u>pH</u>, use a range of different <u>pH buffers</u>
* to investigate the effect of <u>substrate concentration</u>, vary the initial <u>concentrations</u> of the <u>starch solutions</u>.

Remember to keep all the variables you're not investigating constant, e.g. use the same amylase concentration each time.

Measuring *the Rate of an* Enzyme-Controlled *Reaction* — Results

Enzymes *Like it* Warm *but* Not Too Hot

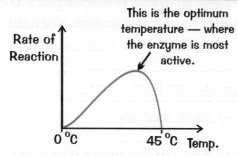

This is the optimum temperature — where the enzyme is most active.

1) Changing the <u>temperature</u> changes the <u>rate</u> of an enzyme-catalysed reaction.

2) Like with any reaction, a higher temperature <u>increases</u> the rate at first. This is because more <u>heat</u> means the enzymes and the substrate particles have more <u>energy</u>. They <u>move about</u> more, so they're more likely to meet up and react.

3) If it gets <u>too hot</u> though, some of the <u>bonds</u> holding the enzyme together <u>break</u>.

4) This makes the enzyme <u>lose its shape</u>. Its <u>active site</u> doesn't fit the shape of the substrate any more, so it <u>can't</u> catalyse the reaction and the reaction <u>stops</u>.

5) The enzyme is <u>denatured</u> — it won't go back to its normal shape if things <u>cool down</u> again.

6) Each enzyme has its own <u>optimum temperature</u> when the reaction goes <u>fastest</u>. This is the temperature just before it gets too hot and starts to denature. The optimum temperature for the most important <u>human</u> enzymes is about <u>37 °C</u> — the <u>same</u> temperature as our bodies. Lucky for us.

Enzymes *Like it the Right* pH *Too*

1) The <u>pH</u> also has an effect on enzymes. If it's too high or too low, it interferes with the <u>bonds</u> holding the enzyme together. This changes the shape of the <u>active site</u> and <u>denatures</u> the enzyme.

2) All enzymes have an <u>optimum pH</u> that they work best at. It's often <u>neutral pH 7</u>, but <u>not always</u>. For example, <u>pepsin</u> is an enzyme used to break down <u>proteins</u> in the <u>stomach</u>. It works best at <u>pH 2</u>, which means it's well-suited to the <u>acidic conditions</u> in the stomach.

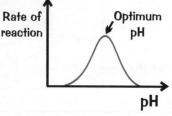

Substrate Concentration *Affects the Rate of Reaction* Up to a Point

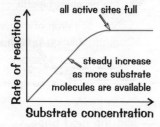

1) The <u>higher</u> the substrate concentration, the <u>faster</u> the reaction — it's <u>more likely</u> the enzyme will meet up and react with a substrate molecule.

2) This is only true up to a <u>point</u> though. After that, there are so many substrate molecules that the enzymes have about as much as they can cope with (all the <u>active sites</u> are <u>full</u>), and adding <u>more</u> makes <u>no difference</u>.

If only enzymes could speed up revision...

Changing the <u>shape</u> of a protein totally changes it. <u>Egg white</u> contains lots of protein — think what happens when you boil an egg and <u>denature</u> the protein. It goes from clear and runny to white and solid.

The Human Genome Project

The Human Genome Project is one of the <u>most exciting</u> things to happen in science for ages. Some people have even called it "more exciting than the first moon landing". Alright, maybe they should get out more...

The Idea was to Map the 25 000 (or so) Human Genes

<u>Thousands</u> of scientists from all over the world <u>collaborated</u> (worked <u>together</u>) on the Human Genome Project. The big idea was to <u>find every single human gene</u>. Human DNA is made up of about <u>25 000 genes</u> curled up to form 23 chromosomes (the other 23 will have the same genes — but maybe different versions).

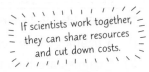
If scientists work together, they can share resources and cut down costs.

The collaboration of lots of scientists meant that all the genes were found <u>more quickly</u> and the data could be made <u>public</u>. Now we've found all the genes, the next thing is to try to figure out what they all <u>do</u>...

> If you get an exam question on this stuff, they'll probably ask you what's <u>good</u> about it, what's <u>bad</u> about it, or what's <u>good and bad</u> about it.

The Good Stuff — Improving Medicine and Forensic Science

1) <u>PREDICT AND PREVENT DISEASES</u>
   If doctors knew <u>what genes</u> predisposed people to <u>what diseases</u>, we could all get <u>individually tailored</u> advice on the best diet and lifestyle to avoid our likely problems. And doctors could <u>check</u> us regularly to ensure early treatment if we do develop the diseases we're susceptible to. Better still, <u>cures</u> could be found for genetic diseases like cystic fibrosis and sickle cell anaemia.

2) <u>DEVELOP NEW AND BETTER MEDICINES</u>
   Maybe one day we'll all have <u>medicines</u> designed <u>especially for us</u> — these will be based on the way our <u>individual</u> body will react to the <u>disease</u> and to the possible <u>treatments</u>. More generally, knowing how a disease affects us on a molecular level makes it possible to design <u>more effective</u> treatments.

3) <u>ACCURATE DIAGNOSES</u>
   Some diseases are hard to <u>test</u> for (e.g. you can only tell for sure if someone has Alzheimer's after they die), but if we know the <u>genetic</u> cause, accurate testing will be a lot <u>easier</u>.

4) <u>IMPROVE FORENSIC SCIENCE</u>
   Forensic scientists can produce a '<u>DNA fingerprint</u>' from biological material found at a <u>crime scene</u>. If this <u>matches</u> your suspect's DNA... he or she was <u>almost certainly</u> present.

   In the <u>future</u>, it might even be possible to figure out what a suspect <u>looks like</u> from DNA found at the scene of a crime (e.g. their eye, hair and skin colour).

The Bad Stuff — It Could be a Scary World If You're not Perfect

1) <u>INCREASED STRESS</u>
   If someone knew from an early age that they're susceptible to a nasty brain disease, they <u>could</u> panic every time they get a headache (even if they never get the disease).

2) <u>GENE-ISM</u>
   People with genetic problems <u>could</u> come under pressure not to have children.

3) <u>DISCRIMINATION BY EMPLOYERS AND INSURERS</u>
   Life insurance <u>could</u> become impossible to get (or blummin' expensive at least) if you have any genetic likelihood of serious disease. And employers may discriminate against people who are genetically likely to get a disease.

DNA lipstick is part of my genetic make-up...

Remember that these are only <u>possibilities</u> — some may happen <u>soon</u>, some will take <u>ages</u>, and others might not happen at all. But it's exciting stuff (medicines just for you — gosh). But before you can come to a sensible decision about the ethics of it all, you must know the <u>facts</u>. No problem — you were going to learn it all anyway.

Genetic Engineering

Scientists can now <u>change</u> an organism's <u>genes</u> to alter its characteristics.
This is a new science with exciting possibilities, but there might be <u>dangers</u> too...

Genetic Engineering <u>Uses</u> Enzymes <u>to Cut and Paste</u> Genes

The basic idea is to move <u>useful genes</u> from one organisms's chromosomes into the cells of another...

1) A useful gene is "<u>cut</u>" out from one organism's chromosome using <u>enzymes</u>.

2) <u>Enzymes</u> are then used to <u>cut</u> another organism's chromosome and then to <u>insert</u> the useful gene.

3) This technique produces <u>genetically modified</u> (<u>GM</u>) organisms.
   E.g. <u>human genes</u> can be used to make <u>GM bacteria</u>:

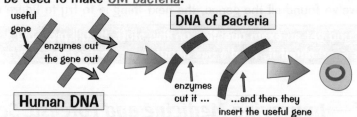

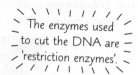

The enzymes used to cut the DNA are 'restriction enzymes'.

Genetic Engineering <u>Can Benefit</u> Humans

Here are three examples of <u>uses</u> of <u>GM organisms</u>:

1 Reducing vitamin A deficiency

1) Beta-carotene is used by our bodies to make <u>vitamin A</u>. Vitamin A <u>deficiency</u> is a <u>big problem</u> in parts of south Asia and Africa — up to <u>500 000 children per year</u> go <u>blind</u> due to vitamin A deficiency.

2) <u>Golden Rice</u> is a variety of GM rice. It contains <u>two genes</u> from other organisms which together enable the rice to produce <u>beta-carotene</u>.

3) So growing Golden Rice in these places means <u>fewer people</u> will suffer from <u>vitamin A deficiency</u>.

2 Producing human insulin

1) The <u>human insulin gene</u> can be inserted into <u>bacteria</u> to <u>produce human insulin</u>.

2) <u>Lots</u> of human insulin can be produced <u>quickly</u> and <u>cheaply</u> to <u>treat diabetes</u>.

3 Increasing crop yield

1) <u>GM crops</u> have had their genes modified, e.g. to make them <u>resistant to herbicides</u> (chemicals used to kill weeds).

2) Fields of these crops can be <u>sprayed</u> with a herbicide and <u>all the plants</u> except the <u>GM crop</u> are <u>killed</u>. This can <u>increase the yield</u> of the crop, making <u>more food</u>.

But Genetic Engineering is a <u>Controversial Topic...</u>

There are <u>worries</u> about the long-term effects of genetic engineering — that it might <u>accidentally</u> create unplanned <u>problems</u>. For example, here are some of the concerns that people have about <u>GM crops</u>:

1) Some people say that growing GM crops will affect the number of <u>weeds</u> and <u>flowers</u> (and therefore wildlife) that usually lives in and around the crops — <u>reducing</u> farmland <u>biodiversity</u> (number of species in an ecosystem).

2) Not everyone is convinced that GM crops are <u>safe</u>. People are worried they may develop <u>allergies</u> to the food — although there's probably no more risk for this than for eating usual foods.

3) A big concern is that <u>transplanted genes</u> may get out into the <u>natural environment</u>. For example, the <u>herbicide resistance</u> gene may be picked up by weeds, creating a new '<u>superweed</u>' variety.

I say it's great.

GM crops — that's nothing... my American cousin had a GM car...

Some people are worried about the <u>impact</u> of genetic engineering. Other people think that the <u>benefits</u> of genetic engineering outweigh the <u>disadvantages</u>. You need to be able to give <u>both sides</u> of the argument.

Mitosis

The cells of your body <u>divide</u> to <u>produce more cells</u>. This is so that your body can <u>grow</u> and <u>repair</u> damaged tissues. Of course, cell division doesn't just happen in humans — animals and plants do it too.

Mitosis *Makes New Cells for* Growth *and* Repair

1) <u>Human body cells</u> are <u>diploid</u>. This means they have <u>two versions</u> of each <u>chromosome</u> — one from the person's <u>mother</u>, and one from their <u>father</u>. This diagram shows the <u>23 pairs of chromosomes</u> in a human cell.

2) When a cell <u>divides</u> it makes <u>two</u> cells <u>identical</u> to the <u>original</u> cell — each with a <u>nucleus</u> containing the <u>same number</u> of chromosomes as the original cell.

3) This type of cell division is called <u>mitosis</u>. It's used when humans (and animals and plants) want to <u>grow</u> or to <u>replace</u> cells that have been <u>damaged</u>.

Mitosis *Results in* Two Identical Cells

In a cell that's not dividing, the DNA is all spread out in <u>long strings</u>.

If the cell gets a signal to <u>divide</u>, it needs to <u>duplicate</u> its DNA — so there's one copy for each new cell. The DNA is copied and forms <u>X-shaped</u> chromosomes. Each 'arm' of the chromosome is an <u>exact duplicate</u> of the other.

The left arm has the same DNA as the right arm of the chromosome.

The chromosomes then <u>line up</u> at the centre of the cell and <u>cell fibres</u> pull them apart. The <u>two arms</u> of each chromosome go to <u>opposite ends</u> of the cell.

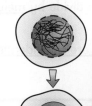

Membranes form around each of the sets of chromosomes. These become the <u>nuclei</u> of the two new cells.

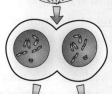

Lastly, the <u>cytoplasm</u> divides.

You now have <u>two new diploid cells</u> containing exactly the same DNA — they're <u>genetically identical</u>.

Asexual Reproduction *Also Uses* Mitosis

1) Some organisms also <u>reproduce</u> by mitosis, e.g. strawberry plants form runners in this way, which become new plants.

2) This is an example of <u>asexual reproduction</u>.

3) The offspring have exactly the <u>same genes</u> as the parent — so there's <u>no genetic variation</u>.

Now that I have your undivided attention...

The next page is about meiosis, which is quite similar to mitosis. It's easy to get them confused if you're not careful. So make sure you've <u>learnt mitosis really thoroughly</u>, before moving on. The best way to do this is to: 1) learn the diagram on this page, 2) cover it over, 3) sketch it out.

Meiosis

You thought mitosis was exciting. Hah. <u>You ain't seen nothing yet</u>.

Gametes Have Half the Usual Number of Chromosomes

1) <u>Gametes</u> are 'sex cells'. They're called <u>ova</u> (single, ovum) in females, and <u>sperm</u> in males. During <u>sexual reproduction</u>, two <u>gametes combine</u> to form a <u>new cell</u> which will grow to become a new organism.

2) <u>Gametes</u> are <u>haploid</u> — this means they only have <u>one copy</u> of each <u>chromosome</u>. This is so that when <u>two gametes combine</u> at fertilisation, the resulting cell (zygote) has the <u>right number of chromosomes</u>. Zygotes are <u>diploid</u> — they have <u>two copies</u> of each <u>chromosome</u>.

3) For example, human body cells have <u>46 chromosomes</u>. The <u>gametes</u> have <u>23 chromosomes each</u>, so that when an egg and sperm combine, you get 46 chromosomes again.

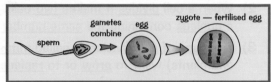

Meiosis Involves Two Divisions

1) To make new cells which only have <u>half</u> the original number of chromosomes, cells divide by <u>meiosis</u>.

2) Meiosis <u>only</u> happens in the <u>reproductive organs</u> (e.g. ovaries and testes).

3) <u>Meiosis</u> is when a cell divides to produce <u>four haploid nuclei</u> whose <u>chromosomes are NOT identical</u>.

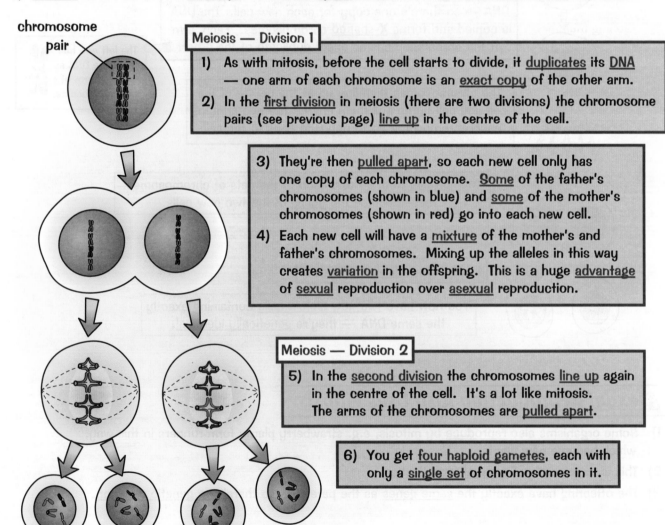

chromosome pair

Meiosis — Division 1

1) As with mitosis, before the cell starts to divide, it <u>duplicates</u> its <u>DNA</u> — one arm of each chromosome is an <u>exact copy</u> of the other arm.

2) In the <u>first division</u> in meiosis (there are two divisions) the chromosome pairs (see previous page) <u>line up</u> in the centre of the cell.

3) They're then <u>pulled apart</u>, so each new cell only has one copy of each chromosome. <u>Some</u> of the father's chromosomes (shown in blue) and <u>some</u> of the mother's chromosomes (shown in red) go into each new cell.

4) Each new cell will have a <u>mixture</u> of the mother's and father's chromosomes. Mixing up the alleles in this way creates <u>variation</u> in the offspring. This is a huge <u>advantage</u> of <u>sexual</u> reproduction over <u>asexual</u> reproduction.

Meiosis — Division 2

5) In the <u>second division</u> the chromosomes <u>line up</u> again in the centre of the cell. It's a lot like mitosis. The arms of the chromosomes are <u>pulled apart</u>.

6) You get <u>four haploid gametes</u>, each with only a <u>single set</u> of chromosomes in it.

Relegation to the Second Division is inevitable...

Again, the best thing to do is to <u>learn the diagram</u>. Cover it up and sketch it out.

Cloning Mammals

If you've cloned a sheep before then you won't need to learn this page. If not, you'd better <u>read on</u>...

Cloned Mammals Can be Made by Adult Cell Cloning

<u>Cloning</u> is a type of <u>asexual reproduction</u> (see page 17). It produces cells that are <u>genetically identical</u> to an original cell. Here's how it's done:

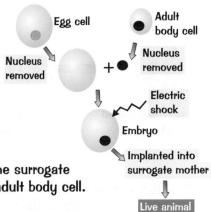

1) <u>Adult cell cloning</u> involves taking an unfertilised <u>egg cell</u> and removing its <u>nucleus</u> (the egg cell is <u>enucleated</u>).

2) A nucleus is taken from an <u>adult body cell</u> (e.g. skin cell). This is a <u>diploid nucleus</u> containing the full number of <u>chromosomes</u>.

3) The diploid nucleus is <u>inserted</u> into the 'empty' egg cell.

4) The egg cell is then stimulated by an <u>electric shock</u> — this makes it <u>divide</u> by mitosis, like a normal embryo.

5) When the embryo is a ball of cells, it's <u>implanted</u> into an <u>adult female</u> (the surrogate mother) to grow into a genetically identical copy (clone) of the original adult body cell.

6) This technique was used to create <u>Dolly</u> — the famous <u>cloned sheep</u>.

Cloning Has Many Uses

1) Cloning mammals could help with the <u>shortage</u> of <u>organs</u> for <u>transplants</u>. For example, genetically-modified pigs are being bred that could provide <u>suitable organs</u> for humans. If this is successful, then <u>cloning</u> these pigs could help to meet the <u>demand</u> for organ transplants.

2) The <u>study</u> of animal clones could lead to greater <u>understanding</u> of the development of the <u>embryo</u>, and of <u>ageing</u> and <u>age-related disorders</u>.

3) Cloning could also be used to help preserve <u>endangered species</u>.

There are Many Issues Surrounding Cloning

1) Cloning mammals leads to a "<u>reduced gene pool</u>" — this means there are <u>fewer different alleles</u> in a population.

   • If a population are all <u>closely related</u> and a <u>new disease</u> appears, they could all be <u>wiped out</u> — because there may be no allele in the population giving <u>resistance</u> to the disease.

2) Cloned mammals mightn't <u>live as long</u> — Dolly the sheep only lived for <u>6 years</u> (half as long as many sheep).

   • She was put down because she had <u>lung disease</u>, and she also had <u>arthritis</u>. These diseases are more usual in <u>older sheep</u>.

   • Dolly was <u>cloned</u> from an <u>older sheep</u>, so it's been suggested her '<u>true' age</u> may have been <u>older</u>.

   • But it's possible she was <u>just unlucky</u> — and that her illnesses weren't linked to her being a clone.

3) There are other <u>risks</u> and problems associated with cloning:

   • The cloning process <u>often fails</u>. It took hundreds of attempts to clone Dolly.

   • Clones are often born with <u>genetic defects</u>.

   • Cloned mammals' <u>immune systems</u> are sometimes unhealthy — so they suffer from <u>more diseases</u>.

Thank goodness they didn't do that with my little brother...

Cloning can be a <u>controversial</u> topic — especially when it's to do with cloning mammals. More <u>large-scale</u>, <u>long-term studies</u> into cloned mammals are needed to find out what the <u>dangers</u> are.

Stem Cells

Cells divide to make you grow. They also <u>differentiate</u> (specialise) so they can do different jobs.

Embryonic Stem Cells Can Turn into Any Type of Cell

1) A fertilised egg can divide by mitosis to produce a bundle of cells — the <u>embryo</u> of the new organism.

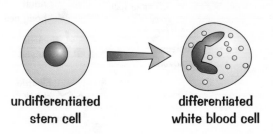

undifferentiated
stem cell

differentiated
white blood cell

2) To start with, the <u>cells</u> in the embryo are <u>all the same</u> (<u>undifferentiated</u>). They are called <u>embryonic stem cells</u>.

3) Stem cells are <u>able to divide</u> to produce either more stem cells or <u>different types</u> of <u>specialised cell</u> (e.g. blood cells).

4) The process of stem cells <u>becoming specialised</u> is called <u>differentiation</u>. It is by this process that the embryo starts to develop a recognisably human body with <u>organs</u> and <u>systems</u>.

5) In most <u>animal</u> cells, the ability to differentiate is <u>lost</u> at an early stage, but lots of <u>plant</u> cells <u>don't</u> ever lose this ability.

6) <u>Adult</u> humans only have <u>stem cells</u> in certain places like the <u>bone marrow</u>. These stem cells <u>aren't as versatile</u> as the stem cells in embryos — they can only differentiate into certain types of cell.

Stem Cells May be Able to Cure Many Diseases

1) Doctors already use <u>adult stem cells</u> to cure some <u>diseases</u>. E.g. <u>sickle cell anaemia</u> can sometimes be cured with a <u>bone marrow transplant</u> (containing adult stem cells which produce new blood cells).

2) Scientists have experimented with <u>extracting stem cells</u> from very early <u>human embryos</u> and <u>growing</u> them. Under certain conditions the stem cells will differentiate into <u>specialised cells</u>.

3) It <u>might</u> be possible to use stem cells to create specialised cells to <u>replace</u> those which have been <u>damaged</u> by <u>disease</u> or <u>injury</u>, e.g. new cardiac muscle cells to help someone with heart disease. This <u>potential</u> for <u>new cures</u> is the reason for the huge scientific interest in stem cells.

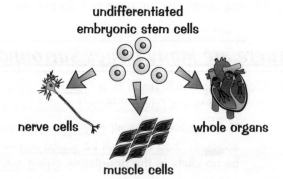

undifferentiated
embryonic stem cells

nerve cells

muscle cells

whole organs

4) Before this can happen, a lot of <u>research</u> needs to be done — and there are <u>ethical concerns</u> about this:

- Some people are strongly <u>against</u> embryonic stem cell research. They argue that human embryos <u>shouldn't</u> be used for experiments because each one is a <u>potential human life</u>. They say that scientists should find <u>other sources of stem cells</u>.
- Other people think that the aim of <u>curing patients</u> who are <u>suffering</u> should be <u>more important</u> than the potential life of the embryos. They point out that the embryos used are often <u>unwanted</u> ones from <u>fertility clinics</u> — if they weren't used for research, they would probably be <u>destroyed</u>.
- In some countries stem cell research is <u>banned</u>. It's allowed in the UK under <u>strict guidelines</u>.

But florists cell stems, and nobody complains about that...

These topics often <u>make people feel emotional</u>. Which isn't the best mindset for scientific thought... The potential of stem cells is huge — but it's early days yet. Research has recently been done into getting stem cells from <u>alternative sources</u>. For example from <u>umbilical cords</u>.

Revision Summary for B2 Topic 1

There's a lot to remember from this section and some of the topics are controversial, like cloning and genetic engineering. You need to know all sides of the story, as well as all the facts... so, here are some questions to help you figure out what you know. If you get any wrong, go back and learn the stuff.

1) Name four parts of a cell that both plants and animal cells have.
   What three things do plant cells have that animal cells don't?
2) Name four features of a cell that bacteria have.
3)* A magnified image is 7.5 mm wide. The specimen is 0.3 mm wide. What is the magnification?
4) What shape is a molecule of DNA?
5) Name the four different bases found in DNA. How do they pair up?
6) Name the four scientists who had major roles in discovering the structure of DNA.
7) What is a gene?
8) What does a triplet of DNA bases code for?
9) Describe the stages of protein synthesis.
10) Are mutations always harmful? Explain your answer.
11) Give a definition of a catalyst.
12) Name three enzyme-catalysed chemical reactions that happen inside living organisms.
13) Describe the "lock and key mechanism" of enzymes.
14) Explain why an enzyme-catalysed reaction stops
    when the reaction mixture is heated above a
    certain temperature.
15)* The graph on the right shows how the rate of
    an enzyme-catalysed reaction depends on pH:
    a) State the optimum pH of the enzyme.
    b) In which part of the human digestive system
       would you expect to find the enzyme?

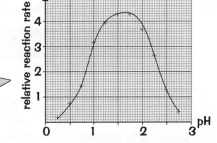

16) What is the Human Genome Project? Write down four good things and three bad things about it.
17) Describe how genetic engineering works.
18) State three useful applications of genetic engineering.
19) Why are some people concerned about genetic engineering?
20) What is mitosis used for in the human body? Describe the four stages of mitosis.
21) Where does meiosis take place in the human body?
22) How many cells are produced from an original cell when it divides by meiosis?
    Are the new cells diploid or haploid?
23) Describe the process of cloning a mammal from an adult cell (e.g. cloning a sheep).
24) Give three possible uses of cloning mammals.
25) Describe three risks associated with trying to clone mammals.
26) What is meant by the 'differentiation' of cells?
27) How are the stem cells in an embryo different from the stem cells in an adult?
28) Give an example of how embryonic stem cells could be used to cure diseases.

*Answers to these questions are given on p.107.

Respiration

Respiration might not sound very 'rock n roll' but it's pretty fundamental to life as we know it. So roll up your sleeves, take a deep breath (sorry), and get stuck in...

Respiration *is NOT 'Breathing In and Out'*

1) Respiration is really important — it's the process used by all living organisms to release energy from organic molecules (usually glucose).

2) Respiration is how all living things get energy from food.

> This energy is used to do things like:
> • build up larger molecules (like proteins)
> • contract muscles (see next page)
> • maintain a steady body temperature

> RESPIRATION is the process of BREAKING DOWN GLUCOSE TO RELEASE ENERGY, which goes on IN EVERY LIVING CELL

Aerobic *Respiration Needs Plenty of* Oxygen

Aerobic respiration is respiration using oxygen ('aerobic' just means 'with air'). It's the most efficient way to release energy from glucose. (You can also have anaerobic respiration, which happens without oxygen — see next page). You need to learn the word equation for aerobic respiration:

> Glucose + Oxygen → Carbon Dioxide + Water (+ ENERGY)

Raw Materials *and* Waste Diffuse *In and Out of Cells*

1) The circulatory system carries glucose, oxygen and CO_2 around the body in the blood.

2) The glucose needed for respiration comes from breaking down food in the digestive system.

3) The oxygen comes from air breathed into the lungs. CO_2 is breathed out.

4) The smallest blood vessels in the body are the capillaries. All the cells in the body have capillaries nearby to supply them with glucose and oxygen, and to take away the waste carbon dioxide.

5) These substances move between the cells and the capillaries by a process called diffusion.

6) 'Diffusion' is really simple. It's just the gradual movement of particles from places where there are lots of them to places where there are fewer of them. That's all it is — it's just the natural tendency for stuff to spread out. Unfortunately you also have to learn the fancy way of saying this, which is:

> DIFFUSION is the MOVEMENT OF PARTICLES from an area of HIGHER CONCENTRATION to an area of LOWER CONCENTRATION

7) When cells respire they use up oxygen and glucose, so the concentration of these inside the cells is low. The concentration of these substances in the blood is higher, so they diffuse from the capillaries into the cells.

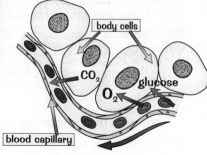

8) When cells respire they produce lots of carbon dioxide, so the concentration of this in the cells is high. This means carbon dioxide diffuses from the cells into the blood, where the concentration is lower.

9) The bigger the difference in concentration, the faster the rate of diffusion.

Revision by diffusion — you wish...

Wouldn't that be great — if all the ideas in this book would just gradually drift across into your mind, from an area of high concentration (in the book) to an area of low concentration (in your mind — no offence). Actually, that probably will happen if you read it again. Why don't you give it a go...

Respiration and Exercise

Your rate of respiration depends on what you're doing...

When You Exercise You Respire More

1) Muscles need energy from respiration to contract. When you exercise some of your muscles contract more frequently than normal so you need more energy. This energy comes from increased respiration.

2) The increase in respiration means you need to get more oxygen into the cells.

3) Your breathing rate increases to get more oxygen into the blood, and to get this oxygenated blood around the body faster your heart rate increases. This removes CO_2 more quickly at the same time.

4) To deal with the increased demand, the rate of diffusion of carbon dioxide and oxygen at the lung surface and in muscle cells increases.

5) When you do really vigorous exercise (like sprinting) your body can't supply oxygen to your muscles quickly enough, so they start respiring anaerobically.

You need to know this equation: CARDIAC OUTPUT = HEART RATE × STROKE VOLUME

You need to be able to use it too — e.g. if you're told heart rate is 80 bpm and stroke volume is 70 cm³, cardiac output is 80 × 70 = 5600 cm³ per min.

Cardiac output is the volume of blood the heart pumps in one minute — it increases as heart rate increases.

Anaerobic Respiration Doesn't Use Oxygen At All

1) Anaerobic respiration happens when there's not enough oxygen available. Anaerobic just means without air.

2) You need to learn the overall word equation. Glucose → Lactic Acid (+ ENERGY)

3) Anaerobic respiration does not release as much energy as aerobic respiration (but it's useful in emergencies).

4) It also produces a build-up of lactic acid in the muscles, which gets painful and can give you cramp.

5) The advantage is that at least you can keep on using your muscles for a while longer.

6) After resorting to anaerobic respiration, when you stop exercising you'll have an oxygen debt.

7) In other words you have to 'repay' the oxygen which you didn't manage to get to your muscles in time. The amount of oxygen required is called the excess post-exercise oxygen consumption (EPOC).

8) This means you have to keep breathing hard for a while after you stop to get more oxygen into the blood. Your heart rate also stays high to get the oxygen to your muscles, where it's used to convert the toxic lactic acid to harmless CO_2 and water.

You Can Investigate The Effect of Exercise on Breathing and Heart Rate

1) You can measure breathing rate by counting breaths, and heart rate by taking the pulse.

2) E.g. you could take your pulse after:
   - sitting down for 5 minutes,
   - then after 5 minutes of gentle walking,
   - then again after 5 minutes of slow jogging,
   - then again after running for 5 minutes,
   and plot your results in a bar chart.

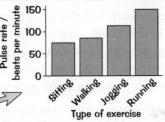

You put two fingers on the inside of your wrist or your neck and count the number of pulses in 1 minute.

3) Your pulse rate will increase the more intense the exercise is, as your body needs to get more oxygen to the muscles and take more carbon dioxide away from the muscles.

4) To make the experiment more reliable, do it as a group and plot the average pulse rate for each exercise.

Oxygen debt — cheap to pay back...

So, your heart rate and breathing rate go up when you exercise. But remember, they don't go straight back to normal when you stop — they'll return to normal gradually as your body recovers and gets the oxygen it needs.

Photosynthesis

You don't know photosynthesis 'til you know its <u>equation</u>. It's in a <u>nice green box</u> so you can't possibly miss it.

Plants are Able to Make Their Own Food by Photosynthesis

1) <u>Photosynthesis</u> is the process that produces '<u>food</u>' in <u>plants</u>. The 'food' it produces is <u>glucose</u>.
2) Photosynthesis happens in the leaves of all <u>green plants</u> — this is what the leaves are for.
3) Photosynthesis happens inside the <u>chloroplasts</u>. They contain <u>chlorophyll</u>, which absorbs <u>energy</u> in <u>sunlight</u> and uses it to convert <u>carbon dioxide</u> and <u>water</u> into <u>glucose</u>. <u>Oxygen</u> is also produced as a by-product. You need to learn the equation:

$$\text{Carbon dioxide} + \text{water} \xrightarrow[\text{chlorophyll}]{\text{SUNLIGHT}} \text{glucose} + \text{oxygen}$$

Leaves are Adapted for Efficient Photosynthesis

1) Leaves are <u>broad</u>, so there's a <u>large surface area</u> exposed to <u>light</u>.
2) Leaves contain lots of <u>chlorophyll</u> in <u>chloroplasts</u> to <u>absorb light</u> (see above).
3) Leaves are full of little holes called <u>stomata</u>. They open and close to let gases like CO_2 and O_2 in and out. They also allow <u>water vapour</u> to escape — which is known as <u>transpiration</u> (see page 27).

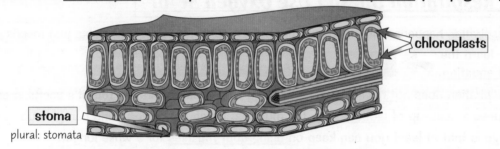

chloroplasts

stoma
plural: stomata

The Limiting Factor for Photosynthesis Depends on the Conditions

1) The rate of photosynthesis is affected by the <u>light</u> intensity, the concentration of CO_2 and the <u>temperature</u>.
2) Any of these three factors can become the <u>limiting factor</u>. This just means that it's stopping photosynthesis from happening any <u>faster</u>.
3) Which factor is limiting at a particular time depends on the <u>environmental conditions</u>:
   - at <u>night</u> it's pretty obvious that <u>light</u> is the limiting factor,
   - in <u>winter</u> it's often the <u>temperature</u>,
   - if it's warm enough and bright enough, the concentration of CO_2 is usually limiting.

1) You can do <u>experiments</u> to work out the <u>ideal conditions</u> for photosynthesis in a particular plant. The easiest type to use is a water plant like <u>Canadian pondweed</u> — you can easily measure the amount of <u>oxygen produced</u> in a given time to show how <u>fast</u> photosynthesis is happening (remember, oxygen is made during photosynthesis).
2) You could either count the <u>bubbles</u> given off, or if you want to be a bit more <u>accurate</u> you could <u>collect</u> the oxygen in a <u>gas syringe</u>.
3) You can then <u>measure</u> how <u>different factors</u> affect the <u>rate of photosynthesis</u> — see the next page...

bubbles of oxygen

pondweed

If you don't do much revision, it's time to turn over a new leaf...

Plants also need <u>water</u> for photosynthesis, but when a plant is so short of water that there's not enough for photosynthesis to take place, it's already in such <u>trouble</u> that this is the least of its worries...

The Rate of Photosynthesis

Before you start on this page, make sure you've read the <u>photosynthesis experiment</u> from the last page. OK...

Three Important Graphs for Rate of Photosynthesis

❶ Not Enough <u>LIGHT</u> Slows Down the Rate of Photosynthesis

1) Light provides the <u>energy</u> needed for photosynthesis.

2) As the <u>light level</u> is raised, the rate of photosynthesis <u>increases steadily</u> — but only up to a <u>certain point</u>.

3) Beyond that, it <u>won't</u> make any difference — it'll be either the <u>temperature</u> or the <u>CO_2 level</u> which is the limiting factor.

4) In the lab you can change the light intensity by <u>moving a lamp</u> closer to or further away from your plant.

5) But if you just plot the rate of photosynthesis against "distance of lamp from the beaker", you get a <u>weird-shaped graph</u>. To get a graph like the one above you either need to <u>measure</u> the light intensity at the beaker using a <u>light meter</u> or do a bit of nifty maths with your results.

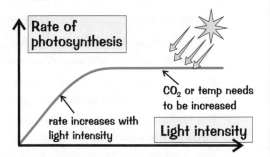

❷ Too Little <u>CARBON DIOXIDE</u> Also Slows it Down

1) CO_2 is one of the <u>raw materials</u> needed for photosynthesis.

2) As with light intensity the concentration of <u>CO_2</u> will only increase the rate of photosynthesis up to a point. After this the graph <u>flattens out</u> showing that CO_2 is no longer the <u>limiting factor</u>.

3) As long as <u>light</u> and <u>CO_2</u> are in plentiful supply then the factor limiting photosynthesis must be <u>temperature</u>.

4) There are loads of different ways to control the concentration of CO_2. E.g. dissolve different amounts of <u>sodium hydrogencarbonate</u> (which <u>gives off</u> CO_2) in the water.

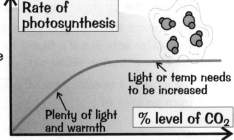

❸ The <u>TEMPERATURE</u> has to be Just Right

1) Usually, if the temperature is the <u>limiting factor</u> it's because it's <u>too low</u> — the <u>enzymes</u> needed for photosynthesis work more <u>slowly</u> at low temperatures.

2) But if the plant gets <u>too hot</u>, the enzymes it needs for photosynthesis and its other reactions will be <u>denatured</u> (see page 14).

3) This happens at about <u>45 °C</u> (pretty hot for outdoors, but <u>greenhouses</u> can get that hot if you're not careful).

4) Experimentally, the best way to control the temperature of the flask is to put it in a <u>water bath</u>.

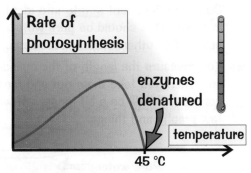

In all these experiments, you have to try and keep all the variables <u>constant</u> apart from the one you're investigating, so it's a <u>fair test</u>:

• use a <u>bench lamp</u> to control the intensity of the light (careful not to <u>block the light</u> with anything)

• keep the flask in a <u>water bath</u> to help keep the temperature constant

• you <u>can't</u> really do anything about the CO_2 levels — you just have to use a <u>large flask</u>, and do the experiments as <u>quickly</u> as you can, so that the plant doesn't use up too much of the CO_2 in the flask. If you're using sodium hydrogencarbonate make sure it's changed each time.

Don't blame it on the sunshine, don't blame it on the CO_2...

...don't blame it on the temperature, blame it on the plant. Right, and now you'll never forget the three limiting factors in photosynthesis. No... well, make sure you read these pages over and over again till you do.

Osmosis

Particles move about <u>randomly</u>, and after a bit they end up <u>evenly spaced</u>. But <u>cell membranes</u> only let some molecules, like <u>water</u>, move through. <u>Osmosis</u> is just the <u>water concentration evening up</u> across a membrane.

Osmosis is Movement of Water Molecules Across a Membrane

> <u>OSMOSIS</u> is the <u>movement of water molecules</u> across a <u>partially permeable membrane</u> from a region of <u>high water concentration</u> to a region of <u>low water concentration</u>.

1) A <u>partially permeable</u> membrane is just one with very small holes in it. So small, in fact, only tiny <u>molecules</u> (like water) can pass through them, and bigger molecules (e.g. <u>sucrose</u>) can't.

2) The water molecules actually pass <u>both ways</u> through the membrane during osmosis. This happens because water molecules <u>move about randomly</u> all the time.

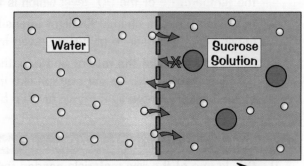

3) But because there are <u>more</u> water molecules on one side than on the other, there's a steady <u>net flow</u> of water into the region with <u>fewer</u> water molecules, i.e. into the <u>stronger</u> sugar solution.

4) This means the <u>strong sugar</u> solution gets more <u>dilute</u>. The water acts like it's trying to "even up" the concentration either side of the membrane.

Net movement of water molecules

5) Osmosis is a special type of <u>diffusion</u> (see page 22) — passive movement of <u>water particles</u> from an area of <u>high water concentration</u> to an area of <u>low water concentration</u>.

You Can do a Practical To Show Osmosis

You can do a fairly dull practical to show osmosis at work:

1) Cut up an innocent <u>potato</u> into identical cylinders, and get some beakers with <u>different sugar solutions</u> in them. One should be <u>pure water</u>, another should be a <u>very concentrated sugar solution</u>. Then you can have a few others with concentrations <u>in between</u>.

2) You measure the <u>length</u> of the cylinders, then leave a few cylinders in each beaker for half an hour or so. Then you take them out and measure their lengths <u>again</u>. If water has moved into the cylinders by osmosis, they'll be a bit <u>longer</u>. If water has moved out, they'll have <u>shrunk</u> a bit. Then you can plot a few <u>graphs</u> and things.

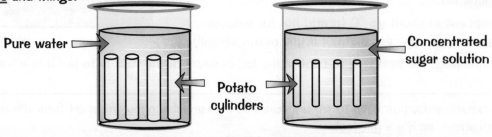

Pure water

Potato cylinders

Concentrated sugar solution

3) The <u>dependent variable</u> is the <u>chip length</u> and the <u>independent variable</u> is the <u>concentration</u> of the sugar solution. All <u>other</u> variables (volume of solution, temperature, time, type of sugar used, etc. etc.) must be kept the <u>same</u> in each case or the experiment won't be a <u>fair test</u>. See, told you it was dull.

And to all you cold-hearted potato murderers...

Cells in your body are surrounded by <u>tissue fluid</u>. It usually has a different concentration to the fluid <u>inside</u> a cell, so water either moves into or out of the cell by <u>osmosis</u>. That's why it's bad to drink <u>sea-water</u>. The high <u>salt</u> content means you end up with a much <u>lower water concentration</u> in your tissue fluid than in your cells. All the water moves out of your cells and they <u>shrivel and die</u>. So next time you're stranded at sea, remember this page.

Water Uptake and Loss in Plants

If you don't water a house plant for a few days it starts to go <u>all droopy</u>. Then it <u>dies</u>, and the people from the Society for the Protection of Plants come round and have you <u>arrested</u>. Plants need water.

Root Hairs **Take in Water by Osmosis**

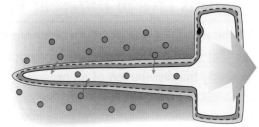

1) The cells on plant roots grow into long '<u>hairs</u>' which stick out into the soil. Each branch of a root will be covered in <u>millions</u> of these microscopic hairs.

2) This gives the plant a <u>big surface area</u> for <u>absorbing water</u> from the soil.

3) There's usually a <u>higher concentration</u> of water in the soil than there is inside the plant, so the water enters the root hair cell by <u>osmosis</u> (see page 26).

Root Hairs **Take In Minerals Using Active Transport**

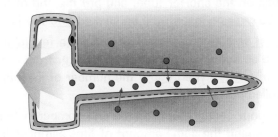

1) <u>Root hairs</u> also absorb minerals from the soil.

2) But the <u>concentration</u> of minerals in the <u>soil</u> is usually pretty <u>low</u>. It's normally <u>higher</u> in the <u>root hair cell</u> than in the soil around it.

3) So normal diffusion <u>doesn't</u> explain how minerals are taken up into the root hair cell.

4) The answer is that a different process called '<u>active transport</u>' is responsible.

5) Active transport uses <u>energy</u> from <u>respiration</u> to help the plant pull minerals into the root hair <u>against the concentration gradient</u>. This is essential for its growth.

Plants have <u>tube networks</u> to move substances to and from individual cells quickly:
- <u>XYLEM</u> tubes transport <u>water and minerals</u> from the <u>root</u> to the <u>rest of the plant</u> (e.g. the <u>leaves</u>).
- <u>PHLOEM</u> tubes transport <u>sugars</u> from the <u>leaves</u> (where they're made) to <u>growing</u> and <u>storage</u> tissues.

Transpiration **is the Loss of Water from the Plant**

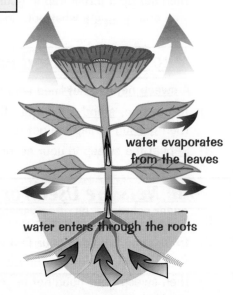

water evaporates from the leaves

water enters through the roots

1) Transpiration is caused by the <u>evaporation</u> and <u>diffusion</u> of water from inside the leaves.

2) This creates a slight <u>shortage</u> of water in the leaf, and so more water is drawn up from the rest of the plant through the <u>xylem vessels</u> to replace it.

3) This in turn means more water is drawn up from the <u>roots</u>, and so there's a constant <u>transpiration stream</u> of water through the plant.

4) Transpiration is just a <u>side-effect</u> of the way leaves are adapted for <u>photosynthesis</u>. They have to have <u>stomata</u> in them so that gases can be exchanged easily (see page 24). Because there's more water <u>inside</u> the plant than in the <u>air outside</u>, the water escapes from the leaves through the stomata.

5) But, the transpiration stream does provide the plant with a constant supply of water for <u>photosynthesis</u>.

Transpiration — the plant version of perspiration...

A big tree loses about <u>1000 litres</u> of water from its leaves <u>every day</u>. That's as much as an average person drinks in a year. The <u>roots</u> have to be very effective at drawing in water... which is why they have all those root <u>hairs</u>.

Distribution of Organisms

This is where the <u>fun</u> starts. Studying <u>ecology</u> gives you the chance to <u>rummage around</u> in bushes, get your hands <u>dirty</u> and look at some <u>real organisms</u>, living in the <u>wild</u>. Hold on to your hats folks...

Organisms Live in Different Places

1) A habitat is the place where an organism <u>lives</u>, e.g. a playing field.

2) The <u>distribution</u> of an organism is <u>where</u> an organism is <u>found</u>, e.g. in a part of the playing field.

3) To <u>study</u> the distribution of an organism, you can <u>measure</u> how common an organism is in <u>two sample areas</u> and compare them.

4) There are various ways to <u>measure</u> how common an organism is — you need to know about <u>five</u> of them.

(There's another one on the next page.)

Pooters Are For Collecting Ground Insects*

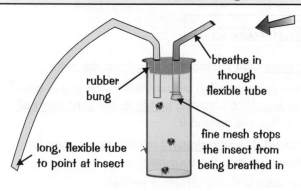

rubber bung

breathe in through flexible tube

long, flexible tube to point at insect

fine mesh stops the insect from being breathed in

1) <u>Pooters</u> are jars that have rubber bungs sealing the top, and <u>two tubes</u> stuck through the bung.

2) If you <u>suck</u> on the shorter tube, and put the end of the longer tube <u>over an insect</u>, it'll be sucked <u>into</u> the jar.

3) In your <u>first sample area</u>, crawl around for a <u>few minutes</u> sucking up as many insects as you can, e.g. from around the <u>base of a tree</u>. Then <u>count</u> the number of insects you've collected.

4) Do this in your <u>second</u> sample area and <u>compare</u> what you find. Spend the <u>same</u> amount of <u>time</u> sampling in each area, and choose sample areas of a <u>similar size</u>.

Pitfall Traps Are Another Way to Investigate Ground Insects

1) <u>Pitfall traps</u> are <u>steep-sided containers</u> that are sunk in a <u>hole</u> in the ground. The top is <u>partly open</u>.

2) Leave the trap <u>overnight</u> in your first sample area. Insects that come along <u>fall</u> into the container and <u>can't get out</u> again, so you can <u>count</u> them.

3) Then set up a pitfall trap in your second sample area and <u>compare</u> what you find.

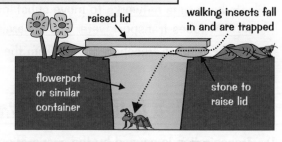

raised lid

walking insects fall in and are trapped

flowerpot or similar container

stone to raise lid

Sweep Nets Are Used For Collecting Animals From Long Grass

1) A <u>sweep net</u> is a net lined with <u>strong cloth</u> for collecting insects, spiders, etc. from <u>long grass</u>.

2) To use one, <u>stand still</u> in your first sample area and sweep the net <u>once</u> from <u>left to right</u> through the grass. Then <u>quickly</u> sweep the net up and turn the insects out into a <u>container</u> to <u>count</u> them.

3) <u>Repeat</u> the sweep in your second sample area and <u>compare</u> the numbers of organisms you find.

Pond Nets Are Used For Collecting Animals From... Ponds

1) A <u>pond net</u> is a net used for collecting insects, water snails, etc. from <u>ponds</u> and <u>rivers</u>.

2) To use one, stand in your first sample area and sweep the net <u>along the bottom</u> of the pond or river. Turn the net out into a <u>white tray</u> with a bit of water in to <u>count</u> the organisms you've caught.

3) Then sweep your pond net in your second sample area and <u>compare</u> what you find.

Traps have their pitfalls, nets have catches and pooters really suck...

For these experiments, you should <u>repeat</u> the measurements <u>several times</u> and then take the <u>average</u> result. But setting up a pitfall trap the <u>same way</u> over and over again is a lot more <u>tricky</u> than doing a regular lab experiment.

*That's insects on the ground, not some kind of powdered wasp and ant mixture.

More on the Distribution of Organisms

If this page makes no sense, turn back. Turn back a page, I mean, not abandon hope all ye who enter here...

Use a Quadrat to Study The Distribution of Small Organisms

A quadrat is a square frame enclosing a known area, e.g. 1 m². To compare how common an organism is in two sample areas, just follow these simple steps:

1) Place a 1 m² quadrat on the ground at a random point within the first sample area. E.g. divide the area into a grid and use a random number generator to pick coordinates. Otherwise, if all your samples are in one spot and everywhere else is different, the results you get won't be reproducible.

2) Count all the organisms you're interested in within the quadrat.

3) Repeat steps 1 and 2 lots of times. (The larger the sample size the better, see p.2.)

4) Work out the mean number of organisms per quadrat within the first sample area.

5) Repeat steps 1 to 4 in the second sample area.

6) Finally compare the two means. E.g. you might find 2 daisies per m² in the shade, and 22 daisies per m² (lots more) in an open field.

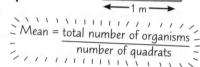

A quadrat

$$\text{Mean} = \frac{\text{total number of organisms}}{\text{number of quadrats}}$$

In the Exam You Might Have to Work Out Population Size

Ben liked looking after his quad-rats.

To work out the population size of an organism in one sample area:

1) Work out the mean number of organisms per m². (If your quadrat has an area of 1 m², this is the same as the mean number of organisms per quadrat, worked out above.)

2) Then multiply the mean by the total area (in m²) of the habitat.

3) E.g. if the area of an open field is 800 m², and there are 22 daisies per m², then the size of the daisy population is 22 × 800 = 17 600.

You can also find out how the distribution of an organism gradually changes across an area (e.g. from a hedge towards the middle of a field) using a belt transect:

1) Mark out a line in the area you want to study.

2) Put a quadrat down at the start of the line and count your organisms.

3) Then, instead of picking a second sample area at random, you take samples by moving your quadrat along the line, e.g. placing the quadrat at intervals of every 2 m.

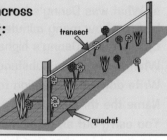

transect

quadrat

You Need to Know How to Measure Environmental Factors

If you find there's a difference in the distribution of organisms, you can investigate the environmental factors that might be causing it. E.g. if you found that daisies were more common in one area than the other, you could measure the light intensity in both places. You'd probably find that the light is much brighter in the area with more daisies. One explanation could be that there are more daisies because they get more sunlight for photosynthesis (see page 24). (Careful though, you'd have to do loads more investigations to prove this.)

Here's how you can measure some environmental factors:

1) Use a thermometer to measure the temperature in different places.

2) Use an electronic device called a light sensor to measure light intensity.

3) Measure soil pH using indicator liquid — a sample of the soil is mixed with an indicator liquid that changes colour depending on the pH. The colour is compared to a chart to find out the pH of the soil. Electronic pH monitors can also be used.

Drat, drat, and double drat — my favourite use of quadrats...

You must put your quadrat down in a random place before you start counting. Anything, even chucking the quadrat over your shoulder*, is better than plonking it down right on the first big patch of organisms that you see.

*Not an invitation to break equipment or maim fellow students etc.

Revision Summary for B2 Topic 2

Hurrah. The section is almost complete. Before you move on to Topic 3, try these revision questions. Do them all and check your answers. If you get any wrong, then learn those bits again, and do the questions again. Keep on going until you can get all the questions right. It's a hard slog, but you've got to do it. Otherwise all the useful facts you've just read will float away... and you'll be left with nothing but a vague mental image of an ant in a plant pot.

1) Which of the following statements are true? (You can pick more than one.)
   a) Respiration is breathing in and out.
   b) Carbon dioxide is a product of aerobic respiration.
   c) Respiration only happens in animals.
2) Write down the word equation for aerobic respiration.
3) What is diffusion?
4) Write down the word equation for anaerobic respiration.
5) Give one advantage and one disadvantage of anaerobic respiration.
6)* Danny measured his heart rate before, during and after exercise. He plotted a graph of the results. Look at the graph and then answer the three questions below.

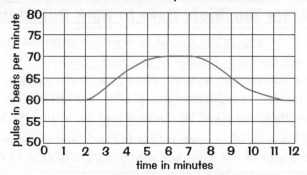

a) What was Danny's heart rate (in beats per minute) when he was at rest?
b) After how many minutes did Danny start exercising?
c) What was Danny's highest heart rate?
7) What is the green substance in leaves that absorbs energy from sunlight?
8) Write down the equation for photosynthesis.
9) Name the three factors that can limit photosynthesis.
10) You carry out an experiment where you change the light intensity experienced by a piece of Canadian pondweed by changing the distance between the pondweed and a lamp supplying it with light. Write down three things which must be kept constant for this experiment to be a fair test.
11) Explain why it's important that a plant doesn't get too hot.
12) What is osmosis?
13) A solution of pure water is separated from a concentrated sugar solution by a partially permeable membrane. In which direction will molecules flow, and what substance will these molecules be?
14) An osmosis experiment involves placing pieces of potato into sugar solutions of various concentrations and measuring their lengths before and after. What is:
   a) the independent variable,
   b) the dependent variable?
15) What is the advantage to a plant of having root hairs?
16) What is transpiration?
17) Describe how you collect insects using a pooter.
18) Describe how you would investigate the distribution of organisms using a quadrat.
19) How do you measure soil pH?

*Answer to this question is given on p.107.

Evidence for Evolution

The <u>theory of evolution</u> states that more than <u>3 billion years ago</u>, life on Earth began as <u>simple organisms</u> from which all the more <u>complex organisms evolved</u> (rather than just popping into existence).

Fossils *Provide Lots of* Evidence *for* Evolution

1) A fossil is <u>any trace</u> of an animal or plant that lived long ago.

2) Fossils can be <u>formed</u> in three ways:

- From <u>gradual replacement</u> by minerals — things like <u>teeth</u>, <u>shells</u> and <u>bones</u> don't <u>decay</u> easily so can last ages when <u>buried</u>. They're eventually replaced by <u>minerals</u>, forming a <u>rock-like</u> substance shaped like the original hard part. The fossil stays <u>distinct</u> inside rock, and is eventually <u>dug up</u>.
- From <u>casts</u> and <u>impressions</u> — fossils can form when an organism's buried in a <u>soft material</u> like <u>clay</u>. The clay hardens around it and the organism decays, leaving a <u>cast</u> of itself. Things like <u>footprints</u> can be pressed into these materials when soft, leaving an <u>impression</u> when it hardens.
- From <u>preservation</u> in places where <u>no decay happens</u> — this is because the conditions aren't suitable for microbes to work, e.g. in <u>glaciers</u> (too cold), in <u>peat bogs</u> (too acidic) and in <u>amber</u> (no oxygen or moisture).

3) Fossils found in <u>rock layers</u> tell us <u>three things</u>:
- What the creatures and plants <u>looked like</u>.
- How <u>long ago</u> they existed. Generally, the <u>deeper</u> the rock, the <u>older</u> the fossil.
- How they've <u>evolved</u>. From studying the <u>similarities</u> and <u>differences</u> between fossils in differently aged rocks, we can see how species have <u>changed</u> and <u>developed</u> over <u>billions of years</u>. E.g. if you look at the <u>fossilised bones</u> of a <u>horse</u>, you can put together a family tree — showing how modern horse have <u>evolved</u>.

Suggested evolution of the horse	
Body	Forefeet

4) The fossil record is <u>incomplete</u> (there are 'missing links'). This is because:
- <u>Very few</u> dead plants or animals actually turn into fossils. Most just <u>decay away</u>.
- Some body parts, like <u>soft tissue</u>, tend to decay away <u>completely</u>.
- There are fossils yet to be <u>discovered</u> that might help complete the picture.

The Pentadactyl Limb *Provides* Evidence *for* Evolution

1) A <u>pentadactyl limb</u> is a limb with <u>five digits</u>.

2) You can see the pentadactyl limb in <u>many species</u>, e.g. mammals, reptiles, amphibians.

3) In each of these species the pentadactyl limb has a <u>similar bone structure</u>, but usually a <u>different function</u>. For example, a <u>human's hand</u> and a <u>bat's wing</u> are both pentadactyl limbs — and they look pretty alike...

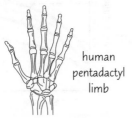

human pentadactyl limb

bat pentadactyl limb

© Untitled X-Ray / Nick Veasey /Getty Images

...but we can't use ours to <u>fly</u>. D'oh.

4) The <u>similarity</u> in bone structure provides <u>evidence</u> that species with a pentadactyl limb have all <u>evolved</u> from a <u>common ancestor</u> (that had a pentadactyl limb). If they'd all evolved from different ancestors, it'd be <u>highly unlikely</u> that they'd share a similar bone structure.

My brother's cleaning habits don't provide ANY evidence for evolution...

... but luckily, <u>fossils</u> do. So, you need to learn exactly how fossils and the <u>pentadactyl limb</u> provide evidence for evolution. Then, just before your brain is about to <u>overflow</u> with all that stuff, go and make yourself a cuppa.

Growth and Development

Growth — it happens to us all. You need to know how to <u>measure</u> it and the <u>processes</u> involved in both <u>animal</u> and <u>plant</u> growth. Then, just for you, there's a beauty of a <u>graph</u> at the bottom of the page. Enjoy.

Growth *is an Increase in Size or Mass*

You can <u>measure</u> the <u>growth</u> of an organism in these three ways:

1) **Size** — You can measure its <u>height</u>, <u>length</u>, <u>width</u> or <u>circumference</u>.

2) **Wet mass** — Organisms <u>contain</u> a lot of <u>water</u>. The mass of the organism depends on how much water it has gained or lost (e.g. through drinking or sweating). The <u>wet mass</u> of the organism is its mass <u>including all the water</u> in its body — it can vary a lot from <u>one day to the next</u>.

3) **Dry mass** — The <u>dry mass</u> is the mass of an organism with <u>no water in its body</u>. This doesn't vary in the same way as wet mass, but you can only measure it once the organism's dead. The dead organism is <u>dried out</u> by leaving it in a hot oven overnight — then what's left is weighed.

Growth *Involves Cell Differentiation, Division and Elongation*

1) Plants and animals <u>grow</u> and <u>develop</u> due to these processes:
   - <u>CELL DIFFERENTIATION</u> — the process by which a cell <u>changes</u> to become <u>specialised</u> for its <u>job</u>.
   - <u>CELL DIVISION</u> — by <u>mitosis</u> (see page 17).
   - <u>CELL ELONGATION</u> — where a plant cell <u>expands</u>, making the cell <u>bigger</u> and so making the plant <u>grow</u>. It happens only in <u>plants</u>.

2) Plants and animals <u>grow differently</u>.

3) Growth in <u>animals</u> happens by <u>cell division</u>. Animals tend to grow while they're <u>young</u>, and then they reach <u>full growth</u> and <u>stop</u> growing. So when you're young, cells divide at a <u>fast rate</u> but once you're an adult, most cell division is for <u>repair</u> — the cells divide to <u>replace</u> old or damaged cells. This also means, in most animals, <u>cell differentiation</u> is <u>lost</u> at an <u>early stage</u>.

4) <u>Plants</u> often grow <u>continuously</u> — even really old trees will keep putting out <u>new branches</u>. So, plants continue to <u>differentiate</u> to <u>develop new parts</u>, e.g. leaves, roots. Growth in <u>height</u> is mainly due to cell <u>elongation</u> — cell <u>division</u> usually just happens in the <u>tips</u> of the <u>roots</u> and <u>shoots</u>.

You Need to be Able to *Interpret Percentile Charts for Growth Data*

1) <u>Growth charts</u> are used to assess a child's growth over time, so that an <u>overall pattern in development</u> can be seen and any <u>problems highlighted</u> (e.g. obesity, malnutrition, dwarfism, etc.).

2) For example, a baby's growth is regularly <u>monitored</u> after birth to make sure it's growing <u>normally</u>. Three measurements are taken — <u>length</u>, <u>mass</u> and <u>head circumference</u>.

3) These results are plotted on <u>average growth charts</u>, like this...

4) The chart shows a number of 'percentiles'. E.g. the <u>50th percentile</u> shows the mass that <u>50%</u> of babies will have reached at a certain age.

5) Babies <u>vary</u> in size, so doctors aren't usually concerned unless a baby's size is above the <u>98th</u> percentile or below the <u>2nd</u> percentile, or if there's an <u>inconsistent pattern</u> (e.g. a small baby with a very large head).

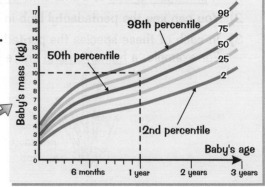

E.g. a one-year-old who weighs 10 kg is in the 75th percentile — 75% of one-year-olds are lighter and 25% are heavier. The baby is within the normal range — below the 98th percentile and above the 2nd percentile.

I'm growing rather sick of this topic...

Growth is pretty <u>important</u>. Obviously. Without it, you wouldn't be able to reach anything on the top shelf, look down your nose at someone or command respect from small children. So, now you appreciate just <u>how</u> important it is, it's time to get learning all of this stuff — yep, it's cover the page and scribble time...

Cell Organisation and the Circulatory System

Cells in <u>multicellular organisms</u> are organised. This involves a <u>to-do list</u>, a <u>diary</u> and a nice big <u>spreadsheet</u>...

Cells Make Up Tissues, Organs and Systems

Cells differentiate (see page 20) and become <u>specialised</u>. These <u>specialised cells</u> form <u>tissues</u>, which form <u>organs</u>, which form <u>organ systems</u> (see below). <u>Large multicellular organisms</u> have different <u>systems</u> inside them for <u>exchanging</u> and <u>transporting</u> materials.

TISSUES

A <u>tissue</u> (e.g. muscle tissue) is a <u>group</u> of <u>similar cells</u> that work together to carry out a particular <u>function</u>.

ORGANS

An <u>organ</u> (e.g. the heart) is a group of <u>different tissues</u> that work together to perform a particular <u>function</u>.

ORGAN SYSTEMS

An <u>organ system</u> (e.g. the circulatory system) is a <u>group of organs</u> working together to perform a particular <u>function</u>.

These tissues have a very particular function...

The Heart is Part of the Circulatory System

You need to learn this diagram of the heart with all its blummin' labels...

1)   The heart has <u>four chambers</u> and <u>four major blood vessels</u> (labelled in green on the diagram).

2)   The <u>right atrium</u> of the heart receives <u>deoxygenated</u> blood from the <u>body</u> (through the <u>vena cava</u>).
     (The plural of atrium is atria.)

3)   The deoxygenated blood moves through to the <u>right ventricle</u>, which pumps it to the <u>lungs</u> (via the <u>pulmonary artery</u>).

4)   The <u>left atrium</u> receives <u>oxygenated</u> blood from the <u>lungs</u> (through the <u>pulmonary vein</u>).

5)   The oxygenated blood then moves through to the <u>left ventricle</u>, which pumps it out round the <u>whole body</u> (via the <u>aorta</u>).

6)   The <u>left</u> ventricle has a much <u>thicker wall</u> than the <u>right</u> ventricle. It needs more <u>muscle</u> because it has to pump blood around the <u>whole body</u>, whereas the right ventricle only has to pump it to the <u>lungs</u>.

7)   <u>Valves</u> prevent the <u>backflow</u> of blood.

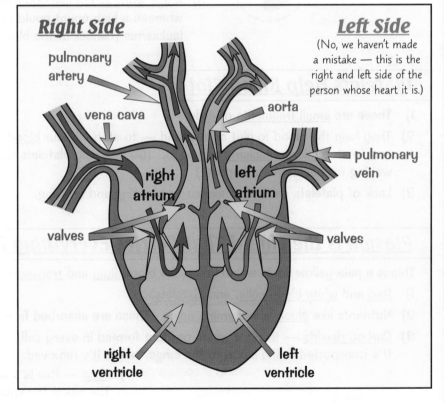

Right Side

Left Side
(No, we haven't made a mistake — this is the right and left side of the person whose heart it is.)

pulmonary artery

vena cava

aorta

pulmonary vein

right atrium

left atrium

valves

valves

right ventricle

left ventricle

Soft and quilted — the best kind of tissues...

OK, so <u>similar cells</u> are grouped together to make a <u>tissue</u>, and different tissues work together as an <u>organ</u>. Organs have a <u>particular job</u> to do in the body — e.g. the <u>heart</u> circulates blood. Groups of organs working together make up an <u>organ system</u>, like the <u>circulatory system</u>. And finally, groups of organs and organ systems working together make up a full <u>organism</u> like you or me. Phew, it's pretty complicated, this life business...

The Circulatory System — The Blood

The heart's a bit obsessed with pumping <u>blood</u> — it must be important stuff. Blood contains <u>four main things</u>...

Red **Blood Cells** Carry Oxygen

1) The job of red blood cells is to carry <u>oxygen</u> from the lungs to all the cells in the body.

2) They have a doughnut shape (or '<u>biconcave disc</u>' shape if you're being picky) to give a <u>large surface area</u> for absorbing <u>oxygen</u>.

3) They contain a substance called <u>haemoglobin</u>. <u>Haemoglobin</u> contains a lot of iron.

4) In the <u>lungs</u>, haemoglobin combines with <u>oxygen</u> to become <u>oxyhaemoglobin</u>. In body tissues the reverse happens to release oxygen to the <u>cells</u>.

The more red blood cells you've got, the more oxygen can get to your cells. At high altitudes there's less oxygen in the air — so people who live there produce more red blood cells to compensate.

5) Red blood cells <u>don't</u> have a nucleus — this allows more room for haemoglobin.

6) A <u>lack of iron</u> in the diet can lead to a type of <u>anaemia</u>, where the blood can't carry enough oxygen.

White **Blood Cells** Defend Against Disease

1) They can change shape to gobble up unwelcome <u>microorganisms</u>.

2) They produce <u>antibodies</u> to fight microorganisms, as well as <u>antitoxins</u> to neutralise any toxins produced by the microorganisms.

3) A <u>low white blood cell count</u> could increase the <u>risk of infection</u>, whereas a high count could mean you have an infection, or even leukaemia (cancer of the blood).

Platelets **Help Blood** Clot

1) These are <u>small fragments</u> of <u>cells</u>.

2) They help the blood to <u>clot</u> at a wound — to stop all your <u>blood pouring out</u> and to stop <u>microorganisms</u> getting in. (So basically platelets just float about waiting for accidents to happen.)

3) Lack of platelets can cause excessive bleeding and bruising.

Plasma **is the Liquid That** Carries Everything **in Blood**

This is a pale yellow liquid which keeps the blood <u>fluid</u> and <u>transports just about everything</u>:

1) <u>Red</u> and <u>white blood cells</u>, and <u>platelets</u>.

2) Nutrients like <u>glucose</u> and <u>amino acids</u>. These are absorbed from the gut and taken to body cells.

3) <u>Carbon dioxide</u> — this is a waste product formed in every cell. It's transported in the blood to the lungs, where it's removed.

4) <u>Urea</u> — this is a waste product formed in the liver. The blood transports it to the kidneys, where it's removed.

5) <u>Hormones</u> — transported from glands to target organs.

6) <u>Antibodies</u> and <u>antitoxins</u> produced by the white blood cells.

Platelets — ideal for small dinners...

When you're <u>ill</u> the doctor often takes a <u>blood sample</u> for analysis. Blood tests can be used to diagnose loads of things — <u>not</u> just disorders of the blood. This is because the blood transports <u>so many chemicals</u> produced by <u>so many organs</u>... and it's easier to take blood than, say, a piece of muscle.

The Circulatory System — Blood Vessels

The circulatory system needs <u>blood vessels</u> to <u>transport</u> the blood. It all gets a bit messy otherwise.

Blood Vessels <u>are</u> Designed <u>for Their</u> Function

There are <u>three</u> different types of <u>blood vessel</u>:

> 1) <u>ARTERIES</u> — these carry the blood <u>away</u> from the heart.
> 2) <u>CAPILLARIES</u> — these are involved in the <u>exchange of materials</u> with the tissues.
> 3) <u>VEINS</u> — these carry the blood <u>to</u> the heart.

Arteries <u>Carry Blood Under</u> Pressure

1) The heart pumps the blood out at <u>high pressure</u> so the artery walls are <u>strong</u> and <u>elastic</u>.

2) The walls are <u>thick</u> compared to the size of the hole down the middle (the "<u>lumen</u>"). They contain thick layers of <u>muscle</u> to make them <u>strong</u>.

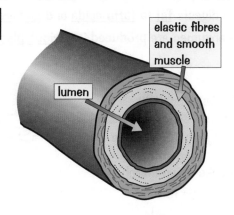

elastic fibres and smooth muscle

lumen

Capillaries <u>are Really</u> Small

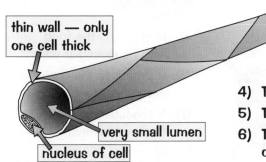

thin wall — only one cell thick

very small lumen

nucleus of cell

1) Arteries branch into <u>capillaries</u>.

2) Capillaries are really <u>tiny</u> — too small to see.

3) They carry the blood <u>really close</u> to <u>every cell</u> in the body to <u>exchange substances</u> with them.

4) They have <u>permeable</u> walls, so substances can <u>diffuse</u> in and out.

5) They supply <u>food</u> and <u>oxygen</u>, and take away <u>wastes</u> like CO_2.

6) Their walls are usually <u>only one cell thick</u>. This <u>increases</u> the rate of diffusion by <u>decreasing</u> the <u>distance</u> over which it occurs.

Veins <u>Take Blood Back</u> to the Heart

1) Capillaries eventually <u>join up</u> to form <u>veins</u>.

2) The blood is at <u>lower pressure</u> in the veins so the walls don't need to be as <u>thick</u> as artery walls.

3) They have a <u>bigger lumen</u> than arteries to help the blood <u>flow</u> despite the lower pressure.

4) They also have <u>valves</u> to help keep the blood flowing in the <u>right direction</u>.

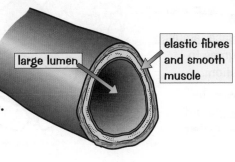

large lumen

elastic fibres and smooth muscle

Learn this page — don't struggle in vein...

Here's an interesting fact for you — your body contains about <u>60 000 miles</u> of blood vessels. That's about <u>six times</u> the distance from <u>London</u> to <u>Sydney</u> in Australia. Of course, capillaries are really tiny, which is how there can be such a big length — they can only be seen with a <u>microscope</u>.

The Digestive System and Enzymes

Digestion is the breakdown of food into soluble products, which are then absorbed into the body. It happens in the digestive system. Here, food is broken down mechanically (by chewing) and by digestive enzymes.

The Breakdown of Food is Catalysed by Enzymes

1) Starch, proteins and fats are BIG molecules — too big to pass through the walls of the digestive system.

2) Sugars, amino acids, glycerol and fatty acids are much smaller molecules — they can pass easily through the walls of the digestive system.

3) The digestive enzymes break down the BIG molecules into the smaller ones:
   - Carbohydrases (e.g. amylase) digest starch to sugars.
   - Proteases (e.g. pepsin) digest proteins to amino acids.
   - Lipase digests fat to fatty acids and glycerol.

4) Digestive enzymes are produced in various places in your digestive system...

Big molecules like starch are insoluble (don't dissolve in water). They're broken down into smaller molecules like sugars, which are soluble (do dissolve in water).

MOUTH

1) Food is moistened with saliva from the salivary glands.
2) The salivary glands produce amylase enzyme in the saliva, which breaks down starch.
3) Food is chewed to form a ball of food (bolus), before being swallowed.

Tongue

OESOPHAGUS

A tube that takes food from the mouth to the stomach. It's lined with muscles that contract to help the ball of food move along, by peristalsis (see page 38).

LIVER

Where bile is produced. Bile neutralises stomach acid and emulsifies fats (see page 38).

GALL BLADDER

Where bile is stored, before it's released into the small intestine.

STOMACH

1) It pummels the food with its muscular walls.
2) It produces the protease enzyme, pepsin.
3) It produces hydrochloric acid for two reasons:
   a) To kill bacteria
   b) To give the right pH for the protease enzyme to work (pH 2 — acidic).

PANCREAS

Produces protease, amylase and lipase enzymes. It releases these into the small intestine.

SMALL INTESTINE

1) Produces protease, amylase and lipase enzymes to complete digestion.
2) This is also where the "food" is absorbed out of the digestive system into the body.

LARGE INTESTINE

Where excess water is absorbed from the food.

Mmmm — so who's for a chocolate digestive...

Your digestive system gets loads of food piled into it. Sometimes though, I manage to miss my mouth and the food falls on my shirt. Luckily, some clever clogs thought of using enzymes in washing powder. They break down the big, insoluble molecules to smaller, soluble ones — so the mess on my shirt is washed away in water. Genius.

Investigating Digestive Enzymes

You can investigate the effect of <u>different concentrations</u> of a digestive enzyme on its substrate. E.g. you can look at the effect of <u>amylase</u> concentrations on the digestion of <u>starch</u>. You do it like this...

Use *Visking Tubing* to Model the *Gut*

1) Visking tubing is a <u>good model</u> for the gut because, like the gut, it only lets <u>small molecules</u> through and not <u>big molecules</u>. It's also a lot <u>cheaper</u>, <u>easier</u> and <u>less yukky</u> than using an animal's gut.

2) However, visking tubing <u>isn't</u> exactly the <u>same</u> as your gut. For example, your gut's a lot <u>longer</u> and has a <u>massive surface area</u> — so the speed of digestion and absorption will be slightly <u>different</u>.

3) So visking tubing is not an <u>exact</u> model, but it's <u>good enough</u> to see how digestive enzymes work.

Use *Iodine* to Test for *Starch* and *Benedict's* to Test for *Sugar*

So let the fun (and the experiment) begin...

1) Add the <u>same volume</u> of <u>starch suspension</u> and <u>0.25% amylase solution</u> to the visking tubing, then <u>rinse</u> the outside of the tubing under a tap.

2) Put the visking tubing into a <u>boiling tube</u> with <u>distilled water</u> in it.

3) <u>Straight away</u> test a drop of <u>water</u> from around the visking tubing with <u>iodine solution</u> (see p.13), and take 5 drops to test with <u>Benedict's reagent</u> (see below). Record the <u>colour</u> each time.

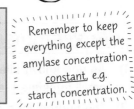

distilled water

boiling tube

take a drop of water

visking tubing containing amylase and starch solution

> **USING BENEDICT'S REAGENT:** Add 5 drops of water into a test tube. Add a drop of Benedict's reagent and put the test tube into a beaker of boiling water. Record the colour after 2-3 minutes.
>
> blue → green → yellow → orange → brick-red
>
> Benedict's reagent starts off blue and will change colour if there's any sugar present. The more sugar there is, the further the colour change goes towards brick-red.

Remember to keep everything except the amylase concentration <u>constant</u>, *e.g. starch concentration.*

4) Leave the boiling tube for <u>15 minutes</u>.

5) Then test the water again with <u>iodine solution</u> and <u>Benedict's reagent</u>. Record the <u>colour</u> each time.

6) <u>Repeat</u> the experiment using <u>other concentrations</u> of the amylase solution, e.g. 0.5%, 1.0%, 1.5%, 2.0%.

Enzyme Concentration *Affects the Rate of Reaction* Up to a Point

You might get <u>results</u> a bit like this...

Amylase concentration	Colour of iodine solution		Colour of Benedict's reagent	
	start of experiment	end of experiment	start of experiment	end of experiment
0.25%	orangey-brown	orangey-brown	blue	yellow
0.5%	orangey-brown	orangey-brown	blue	orange
1%	orangey-brown	orangey-brown	blue	brick-red

1) The <u>orangey-brown</u> colour of iodine shows that <u>no starch</u> is ever present in the water. This is because the starch molecules are <u>too big</u> to pass through the visking tubing into the water.

2) The colour change of the Benedict's reagent <u>from blue</u> shows that <u>sugar</u> is present in the water. This is because <u>starch</u> has been <u>broken down</u> by <u>amylase</u> to <u>sugar</u> in the visking tubing, and the sugar molecules are <u>small enough</u> to pass through the membrane into the water.

3) The <u>higher</u> the concentration of <u>amylase</u>, the <u>further</u> the Benedict's reagent has changed colour. This means lots <u>more starch</u> has been broken down to sugar. This is because at a <u>higher concentration</u> of amylase there are <u>more active sites</u> available to break down the starch into sugar, so the starch is broken down at a <u>faster rate</u>. But above a <u>certain amylase concentration</u> the reaction <u>won't</u> get any faster because there are already <u>enough active sites</u> to deal with all the starch. This is shown on the graph:

steady increase as more active sites on enzymes are available

increase in enzyme concentration has no further effect

Rate of reaction

Enzyme concentration

I think MY concentration has reached its maximum amount...

This is a fairly <u>grim</u> experiment, but at least you get some <u>pretty colours</u>. Learn all of this page in all its glory.

More on Digestion

Some parts of the digestive system are rather specialised. Check out these three lovely features...

Peristalsis Involves Longitudinal and Circular Muscles

1) There's muscular tissue all the way down the digestive system — there are:
   - longitudinal muscles down the length of the gut, and
   - circular muscles running in circles around the gut.
2) The job of these muscles is to squeeze the food along. This squeezing action is called peristalsis.
3) Waves of circular muscle contractions push the food along the gut.
4) Waves of longitudinal muscle contractions run slightly ahead to help keep the food in a ball.

The gut is also called the alimentary canal.

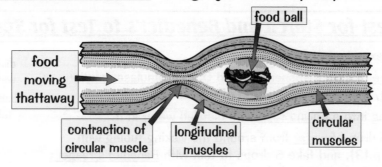

food moving thattaway

food ball

contraction of circular muscle

longitudinal muscles

circular muscles

Bile Neutralises the Stomach Acid and Emulsifies Fats

1) As you know, bile is produced in the liver and stored in the gall bladder before it's released into the small intestine (see page 36).
2) The hydrochloric acid in the stomach makes the pH too acidic for enzymes in the small intestine to work properly. Bile is alkaline — it neutralises the acid and makes conditions alkaline. The enzymes in the small intestine work best in these alkaline conditions.
3) It emulsifies fats. In other words it breaks the fat into tiny droplets. This gives a much bigger surface area of fat for the enzyme lipase to work on — which makes its digestion faster.

Villi Provide a Really Really Big Surface Area

The inside of the small intestine is covered in millions and millions of these tiny little projections called villi. Villi have three features that make absorbing digested food into the bloodstream really efficient:

1) They have a big surface area so that digested food is absorbed much more quickly into the blood.
2) They have a single layer of surface cells so that digested food diffuses quickly over a short distance.
3) They have a very good blood supply via a capillary network to assist quick absorption of digested food.

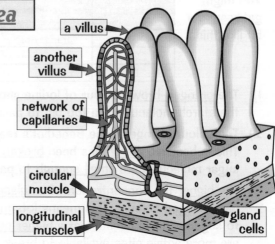

a villus

another villus

network of capillaries

circular muscle

longitudinal muscle

gland cells

You don't have to bust a gut to revise this page...

Living organisms are really well adapted for getting the substances they need to their cells. It makes sense — if they couldn't do this well, they'd die out. A large surface area is a key way that organisms' exchange surfaces are made more effective — molecules can only diffuse through a membrane when they're right next to it, and a large surface area means loads more molecules are close to the membrane. Brilliant.

Functional Foods

Welcome to the page where I say, "Don't worry, not all bacteria are bad" — yep, there are even some good ones out there (well, in there really — your gut). Some people say they're friendly, but I wouldn't go that far. It's not like they offer you a cup of tea or anything. They just help you out with a bit of digestion, that's all.

Functional Foods are Marketed as Having Health Benefits

A functional food is one that has some kind of health benefit beyond basic nutrition. For example, it might prevent some kind of disease, or it might (as the marketing folk may put it) 'promote your well-being'. You need to know about the following three foods.

Probiotics Contain 'Good' Bacteria

1) Probiotics are live bacteria, such as *Bifidobacteria* and *Lactobacillus* (a lactic acid bacterium). These 'good bacteria' are similar to those that are found naturally in your gut.
2) Probiotics are added to foods like yogurt, soya milk and dietary supplements (e.g. capsules). The bacteria may have already been there or they're added by the manufacturer.
3) It's thought that they may help to keep your digestive system healthy, e.g. by replacing gut bacteria that are lost during antibiotic treatment.

Prebiotics Promote the Growth of 'Good' Bacteria

1) Prebiotics are carbohydrates that we can't digest, e.g. oligosaccharides.
2) They occur naturally in foods like leeks, onions and oats, but you can't get enough of them in a normal diet to cause a significant effect. So some people take supplements containing prebiotics.
3) Prebiotics are a food supply for 'good' bacteria that are already in your digestive system. It's thought that taking prebiotics can help promote the growth of the 'good' bacteria in the gut, which in turn could improve the health of your digestive system and may also help to strengthen your immune system.

Plant Stanol Esters Reduce Cholesterol

1) Plant stanol esters are chemicals that can lower blood cholesterol and reduce the risk of heart disease.
2) Stanols occur naturally in plants, but in very small quantities. Stanols are produced commercially by using bacteria to convert sterols (types of fat found in plants like the soya bean) into stanols.
3) Some food manufacturers add them to spreads and some dairy products. People who are worried about their blood cholesterol levels may choose these spreads over normal spreads.

Not All Health Claims are Scientifically Proven

As you now know, functional foods claim they have certain health benefits. But how do you know they work... Well, when looking at evidence, it's a good idea to watch out for these things:

- Is the report a scientific study, published in a reputable journal?
- Was it written by a qualified person (not connected with the people selling it)?
- Was the sample of people asked/tested large enough to give reliable results?
- Have there been other studies which found similar results?

A "yes" to one or more of these is a good sign.

E.g. A study published in The New England Journal of Medicine provided evidence that plant stanols lower blood cholesterol. The study was in reputable journal and there have been other studies that have found similar results. Both of these things increase the reliability of the study.

While you're in there, make yourself useful...

Don't get functional foods mixed up — probiotics are bacteria you eat to 'top up' the bacteria in your gut. Prebiotics are non-digestable carbohydrates that feed the 'good' bacteria. And stanols are all about cholesterol.

Revision Summary for B2 Topic 3

And where do you think you're going? It's no use just reading through and thinking you've got it all — this stuff will only stick in your head if you've learnt it properly. And that's what these questions are for.

I won't pretend they'll be easy — they're not meant to be, but all the information's in the section somewhere. Have a go at all the questions, then if there are any you can't answer, go back, look stuff up and try again. Enjoy...

1) What is a fossil?

2) Explain how the pentadactyl limb provides evidence for evolution.

3) Give three ways that the growth of an organism can be measured.

4) What is cell differentiation?

5) What is a tissue? What about an organ?

6) Name one organ system found in the human body.

7) Name the blood vessel that takes blood from the right ventricle of the heart. Where does it take the blood?

8) Why does the left ventricle have a thicker wall than the right ventricle?

9) What do you call the stuff in red blood cells that makes them red and carries oxygen?

10) List three things that white blood cells do to help defend our bodies against disease.

11) What are the cell fragments called that help blood to clot? Why is it important that blood can clot?

12) What substances get carried around the body in plasma?

13) Why do arteries need very muscular, elastic walls?

14) Explain how capillaries are adapted to their function.

15) What does amylase do?

16) What two products does lipase break down fat into?

17) Describe three functions of the stomach.

18) What is the main function of the small intestine?

19) In a digestive enzyme experiment, what could you use to model the gut?

20) Describe how you can you test if starch is present in a solution.

21) Sketch a graph to show how enzyme concentration affects the rate of a reaction.

22) Give two functions of bile.

23) How does the structure of a villus make it good at its job?

24) Name two types of bacteria that a probiotic food might contain.

25) What are prebiotics? Why might some people choose to take them as a supplement?

26) Why are plant stanol esters added to spreads?

27) Give four things you should look out for when deciding whether a health claim about a functional food is true or not.

Atoms

Hello, good evening and welcome. This page covers lots of essential gory details — about atoms, their innards, and what they get up to with each other when no one's looking. This is not that hard, but you need to make sure you know it before you go any further.

Structure of the Atom — There's Nothing to It

The structure of atoms is quite simple. Just learn and enjoy, my friend.

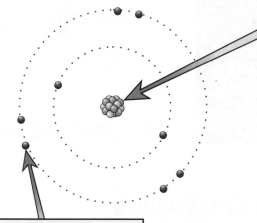

The Nucleus

1) It's in the middle of the atom.
2) It contains protons and neutrons.
3) The nucleus has an overall positive charge because protons are positively charged and neutrons have no charge.
4) Almost the whole mass of the atom is concentrated in the nucleus.
5) But size-wise it's tiny compared to the atom as a whole.

The Electrons

1) They move around the nucleus.
2) They have a negative charge (electrons and protons have equal but opposite charges).
3) They're tiny compared to the nucleus, but as they move around they cover a lot of space.
4) The size of their orbits determines how big the atom is.
5) They have virtually no mass.
6) They occupy shells (energy levels) around the nucleus.

Number of Protons Equals Number of Electrons

1) Neutral atoms have no charge overall.
2) The charge on the electrons is the same size as the charge on the protons, but opposite.
3) This means the number of protons always equals the number of electrons in an atom.
4) The number of neutrons isn't fixed but is usually about the same as the number of protons.

Know Your Particles...

1) Protons are heavy and positively charged.
2) Neutrons are heavy and neutral (no charge).
3) Electrons are tiny and negatively charged.

PARTICLE	RELATIVE MASS	RELATIVE CHARGE
Proton	1	+1
Neutron	1	0
Electron	$\frac{1}{2000}$	−1

Basic atom facts — they don't take up much space...

Atoms are tiny. But the atom's nucleus is REALLY tiny. An atom might measure 0.1 nanometres across — that's 0.000 000 000 1 metres, or a hundred-millionth of a centimetre. But THEN, if you imagine a whole atom as the size of a stadium, its nucleus would only be the size of a marble. Wow. That's little.

Electron Shells

The fact that electrons occupy "shells" around the nucleus is what causes the whole of chemistry.
Remember that, and watch how it applies to each bit of it. It's ace.

Electron Shell Rules:

1) Electrons always occupy shells
   (sometimes called energy levels).

2) The lowest energy levels are always filled first —
   these are the ones closest to the nucleus.

3) Only a certain number of electrons are allowed in each shell:
   1st shell: 2   2nd shell: 8   3rd shell: 8

4) Atoms are much happier when they have full electron shells.

5) In most atoms the outer shell is not full
   and this makes the atom want to react.

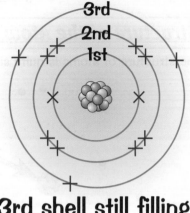

3rd
2nd
1st

3rd shell still filling

Follow the Rules to Work Out Electronic Configurations

You need to know the electronic configurations for the first 20 elements (things get a bit more complicated after that). But they're not hard to work out. For a quick example, take nitrogen. Follow the steps...

1) Nitrogen has seven protons... so it must have seven electrons.

2) Follow the 'Electron Shell Rules' above. The first shell can only take 2 electrons and the second shell can take a maximum of 8 electrons.

The first 20 elements means the first 20 in the periodic table (see page 46).

3) So the electronic configuration for nitrogen must be 2.5. Easy peasy.

4) Now you try it for argon.

The periodic table has a big gap here where the transition metals fit in on row four.

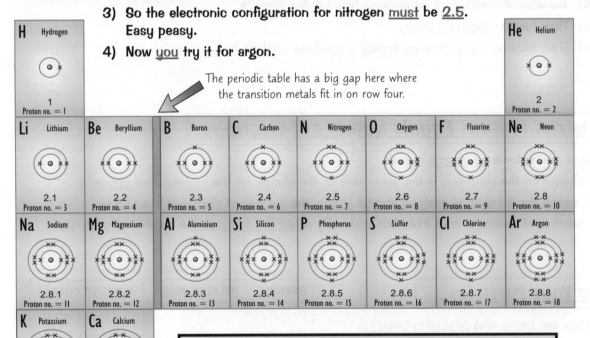

Answer... To calculate the electronic configuration of argon, follow the rules. It's got 18 protons, so it must have 18 electrons. The first shell must have 2 electrons, the second shell must have 8, and so the third shell must have 8 as well. It's as easy as 2.8.8.

One little duck and two fat ladies — 2.8.8...

You need to know enough about electron shells to draw out that whole diagram at the bottom of the page without looking at it. Obviously, you don't have to learn each element separately, just learn the pattern.

Elements

In times gone by, <u>alchemists</u> spent ages trying to turn ordinary bog-standard metals into <u>gold</u> — but they never had any joy. That's because an element is made up of one <u>type of atom</u>, and you can't convert one element into another using chemical reactions.

Elements Consist of One Type of Atom Only

Quite a lot of everyday substances are <u>elements</u>:

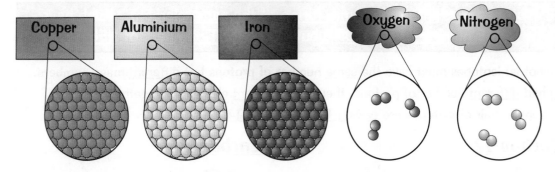

Each Element has a Different Number of Protons

It's the <u>number of protons</u> in an atom that decides what element it is.
For example, any atom of the element <u>helium</u> will have <u>2 protons</u> —
and any atom with <u>2 protons</u> will be a <u>helium</u> atom.

Each Element has an Atomic Number and a Mass Number

1) The <u>atomic number</u> says how many <u>protons</u> there are in an atom.

2) The <u>atomic number</u> is unique to that element, because no two elements have the same number of protons (e.g. only oxygen has the atomic number 8).

3) The atomic number <u>also</u> tells you how many <u>electrons</u> there are, because an atom has the same number of electrons as protons.

4) The <u>mass number</u> is the total number of <u>protons and neutrons</u> in the atom.
So if you want to find the number of <u>neutrons</u> in an atom, just <u>subtract</u> the <u>atomic number</u> from the <u>mass number</u> (e.g. there are 8 neutrons in an oxygen nucleus because 16 – 8 = 8).

5) The <u>mass number</u> is usually <u>roughly double</u> the <u>atomic</u> number, because there's <u>about the same</u> number of neutrons as protons in any nucleus.

> **Example: Oxygen**
>
> MASS NUMBER
> This tells you the total number of protons and neutrons in the atom. → **16**
>
> ATOMIC NUMBER
> This tells you the number of protons in the atom (and so the number of electrons too). → **8** **O**

Mass number 1 — 4:00 am daily in the monastery chapel...

There are some <u>really important things</u> to learn on this page that'll make the rest of the section make sense. Basically you need to know that the <u>atomic number</u> tells you how many <u>protons</u> (and electrons) are in the atom, and the <u>mass number</u> gives you the total number of <u>protons and neutrons</u> put together.

Isotopes and Relative Atomic Mass

Some elements have more than one isotope.

Isotopes are the Same Except for an Extra Neutron or Two

A favourite trick exam question: "Explain what is meant by the term isotope".
The trick is that it's impossible to explain what one isotope is. Nice of them that, isn't it!
You have to outsmart them and always start your answer "Isotopes are...". LEARN the definition:

> Isotopes are: different atomic forms of the same element, which have
> the SAME number of PROTONS but DIFFERENT numbers of NEUTRONS.

1) The upshot is: isotopes must have the same number of protons but different mass numbers.

2) If they had different number of protons, they'd be different elements altogether.

3) A very popular pair of isotopes are carbon-12 and carbon-14.

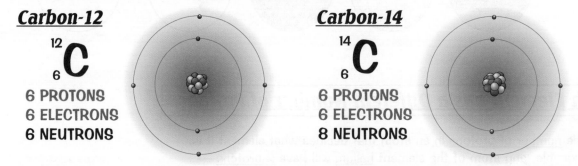

Carbon-12
$^{12}_{6}C$

6 PROTONS
6 ELECTRONS
6 NEUTRONS

Carbon-14
$^{14}_{6}C$

6 PROTONS
6 ELECTRONS
8 NEUTRONS

Relative Atomic Mass Takes Isotopes into Account

1) Relative atomic mass (A_r) uses the average mass of the isotopes of an element.
It has to allow for the relative mass of each isotope and its relative abundance.

2) Relative abundance just means how much there is of each isotope compared to the total amount
of the element in the world. This can be a ratio, a fraction or a percentage.

EXAMPLE: Work out the relative atomic mass of chlorine.

element	relative mass of isotope	relative abundance
chlorine	35	3
	37	1

ANSWER:
This means that there are 2 isotopes of
chlorine. One has a relative mass of 35
(^{35}Cl) and the other 37 (^{37}Cl).

The relative abundances show that there
are 3 atoms of ^{35}Cl to every 1 of ^{37}Cl.

- First, multiply the mass of each isotope by its relative abundance.
- Add those together.
- Divide by the sum of the relative abundances.

$$A_r = \frac{(35 \times 3) + (37 \times 1)}{3 + 1} = \underline{35.5}$$

3) Relative atomic masses don't usually come out as whole
numbers or easy decimals, but they're often rounded to
the nearest 0.5 in periodic tables (see page 46).

Will this be in your exam? — isotope so...

... because obviously you'll know it as well as you know not to eat yellow snow. Calculating the relative atomic
mass of an element from the relative masses and abundances of its isotopes could well be exam fodder.

A Brief History of the Periodic Table

In the 1800s chemists were keen to try and find <u>patterns</u> in the elements they knew about —
and the <u>more</u> elements that were identified, the <u>clearer</u> the patterns became...

They put the Elements in Order of their Atomic Mass

1) In the 1800s scientists had <u>no idea</u> about the <u>structure of atoms</u>, but they could measure the <u>relative atomic mass</u> of each element.

2) When all the elements were put <u>in order</u> of their relative atomic mass, scientists began to notice <u>periodic patterns</u> in the <u>properties</u> of the elements...

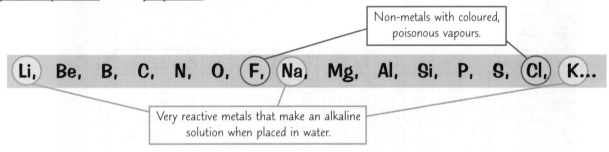

Non-metals with coloured, poisonous vapours.

Li, Be, B, C, N, O, F, Na, Mg, Al, Si, P, S, Cl, K...

Very reactive metals that make an alkaline solution when placed in water.

Dmitri Mendeleev Arranged the Elements in Groups

1) In <u>1869</u>, a Russian scientist called <u>Dmitri Mendeleev</u> arranged 50 or so known elements according to their <u>properties</u> and the properties of their <u>compounds</u> to make a Table of Elements.

2) Mendeleev's table placed elements with <u>similar chemical properties</u> in the same <u>vertical groups</u> — but he found that he had to leave <u>gaps</u> in his table to make this work.

Mendeleev's Table of the Elements

```
H
Li Be                                    B  C  N  O  F
Na Mg                                    Al Si P  S  Cl
K  Ca *  Ti V  Cr Mn Fe Co Ni Cu Zn *  *  As Se Br
Rb Sr Y  Zr Nb Mo *  Ru Rh Pd Ag Cd In Sn Sb Te I
Cs Ba *  *  Ta W  *  Os Ir Pt Au Hg Tl Pb Bi
```

Mendeleev's Table Predicted New Elements

1) The <u>gaps</u> in Mendeleev's table of elements were really clever because they <u>predicted</u> the properties of <u>undiscovered elements</u>.

2) Since then <u>new elements</u> have been found which <u>fit into the gaps</u> left in Mendeleev's table (e.g. scandium, gallium and germanium).

3) In fact, a whole <u>new group</u> of elements has been discovered and added to the table. This group includes <u>helium</u>, <u>neon</u> and <u>argon</u>. These are <u>colourless gases</u> that <u>don't react</u> with much at all (which is why no one knew about them in Mendeleev's day).

4) Over the last hundred years or so the table has been <u>refined</u> to produce the <u>periodic table</u> we know and love today (see <u>next page</u> for more on this)...

Elementary my dear Mendeleev...

The important thing to understand on this page is that a <u>scientific observation</u> (such as "elements can be grouped in a table according to their properties") can be used to <u>make predictions</u> (such as "there are gaps in the table so there must be some undiscovered elements to fill those gaps").

The Periodic Table

There are about 100 known elements. The modern periodic table is a refined version of Mendeleev's Table of Elements (see previous page) but the difference is that it shows the elements in order of atomic number (see page 43). Carry on reading to see it in all its glory...

Metals and Non-metals are on Opposite Sides of the Periodic Table

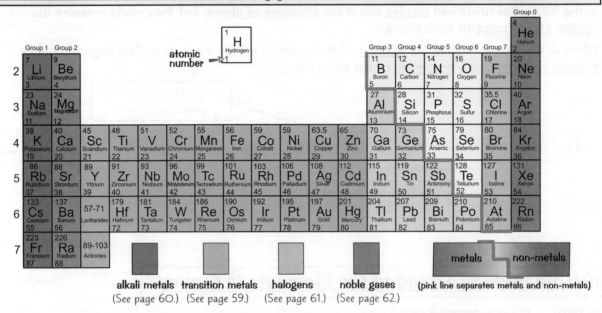

alkali metals   transition metals   halogens   noble gases   (pink line separates metals and non-metals)
(See page 60.)   (See page 59.)   (See page 61.)   (See page 62.)

The Periodic Table is Arranged in Periods and Groups

Periods

1) The rows of the periodic table are called periods.

2) The elements are arranged in order of increasing atomic number along each row. E.g. the atomic numbers of the Period 2 elements increase from 3 for Li to 10 for Ne.

3) The period number is the same as the number of electron shells. E.g. the Period 3 elements have 3 electron shells.

4) The properties of elements change as you go along a period (sometimes quite dramatically).

Period 1
Period 2
Period 3
Period 4
Period 5
Period 6
Period 7

Groups

1) The columns of the periodic table are called groups.

2) Elements in the same group have similar properties. This is because they have the same number of electrons in their outer shell (learn this).

3) The group number is always equal to the number of electrons in the outer shell. E.g. the Group 2 elements all have two electrons in their outer shell. The Group 0 elements are the exception to this — they all have 8 electrons in their outer shell.

4) The properties of elements (such as reactivity) often gradually change as you go down a group (as the atomic number increases).

Group 1
Group 2
Group 3
Group 4
Group 5
Group 6
Group 7
Group 0

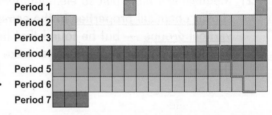

I've got a periodic table — Queen Anne legs and everything...

The periodic table is jam-packed with useful information. I like to think of it as a library and a crystal ball all rolled into one. For example, you can find out at a glance whether an element is a metal or a non-metal, and you can predict some of its properties too. Clever. Make sure you know your groups from your periods.

Ionic Bonding

Atoms of different elements can form <u>chemical bonds</u> and join together to create <u>new compounds</u>.
Very useful. One way they can do this is by <u>ionic bonding</u>. Read on to find out more...

Ionic Bonding — Transfer of Electrons

In <u>ionic bonding</u>, atoms <u>transfer</u> (lose or gain) <u>electrons</u> to form positively or negatively <u>charged atoms</u>
(or groups of atoms) called <u>ions</u>. Because of the attraction of opposite charges, + and –, the ions are
then <u>strongly attracted</u> to one another.

A Shell with Just One Electron is Well Keen to Get Rid...

<u>All</u> the atoms over at the <u>left-hand side</u> of the periodic table, e.g. <u>sodium, potassium, calcium</u> etc., have
just <u>one or two electrons</u> in their outer shell. And they're <u>pretty keen to get shot of them</u>, because then
they'll only have <u>full shells</u> left, which is how they <u>like</u> it. So given half a chance they do get rid, and that
leaves the atom as an <u>ion</u> instead. Now ions aren't the kind of things that sit around quietly watching the
world go by. They tend to <u>leap</u> at the first passing ion with an <u>opposite charge</u> and stick to it like glue.

A Nearly Full Shell is Well Keen to Get That Extra Electron...

On the <u>other side</u> of the periodic table, the elements in <u>Group 6</u> and <u>Group 7</u>, such as <u>oxygen</u> and
<u>chlorine</u>, have outer shells which are <u>nearly full</u>. They're obviously pretty keen to <u>gain</u> that <u>extra one or</u>
<u>two electrons</u> to fill the shell up. When they do of course they become <u>ions</u> (you know, not the kind of
things to sit around) and before you know it, <u>pop</u>, they've latched onto the atom (ion) that gave up the
electron a moment earlier. The reaction of sodium and chlorine is a <u>classic case</u>:

The <u>sodium</u> atom <u>gives up</u> its <u>outer</u>
<u>electron</u> and becomes an Na$^+$ ion.

The <u>chlorine</u> atom <u>picks up</u> the <u>spare</u>
<u>electron</u> and becomes a Cl$^-$ ion.

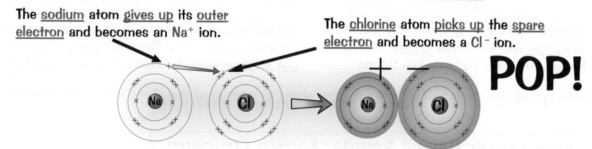

Groups 1 & 2 and 6 & 7 are the Most Likely to Form Ions

1) The elements that most readily form ions are those in Groups 1, 2, 6 and 7.
2) <u>Group 1 and 2 elements</u> are <u>metals</u> and they <u>lose</u> electrons to form <u>+ve ions</u> or <u>cations</u>.
3) <u>Group 6 and 7 elements</u> are <u>non-metals</u>. They <u>gain</u> electrons to form <u>–ve ions</u> or <u>anions</u>.
4) Make sure you know these easy ones:

Cations		Anions	
Group 1	Group 2	Group 6	Group 7
Li$^+$	Be^{2+}	O^{2-}	F$^-$
Na$^+$	Mg^{2+}		Cl$^-$
K$^+$	Ca^{2+}		

5) When any of these cations <u>join</u> with the anions, they form <u>ionic bonds</u>.

6) Only elements at <u>opposite sides</u> of the periodic table will form ionic bonds, e.g. Na and Cl, where one of them becomes a <u>cation</u> (+ve) and one becomes an <u>anion</u> (–ve).

Any old ion, any old ion — any, any, any old ion...

Remember, the + and – charges only appear when an element <u>reacts</u> with something. So, don't be fooling
yourself, sodium isn't always a flashy Na$^+$ ion — when he's being sodium metal he's just made up of boring
old <u>neutral sodium atoms, Na</u>. But wave some chlorine at him and he gets positively charged.

Ionic Compounds

Make sure you've really got your head around the idea of ionic bonding before you start on this page.

Ionic Compounds All Form in a Similar Way

'Dot and cross' diagrams show what happens to the electrons in ionic bonds:

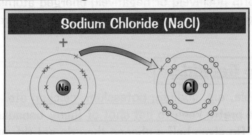

Sodium Chloride (NaCl)

The <u>sodium</u> atom gives up its outer electron, becoming an Na+ ion. The <u>chlorine</u> atom picks up the electron, becoming a Cl- (<u>chloride</u>) ion.

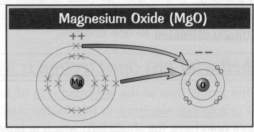

Magnesium Oxide (MgO)

The <u>magnesium</u> atom gives up its <u>two</u> outer electrons, becoming an Mg^{2+} ion. The <u>oxygen</u> atom picks up the electrons, becoming an O^{2-} (<u>oxide</u>) ion.

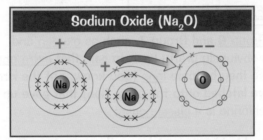

Sodium Oxide (Na₂O)

Two <u>sodium</u> atoms give up their outer electrons, becoming <u>two</u> Na+ ions. The <u>oxygen</u> atom picks up the <u>two</u> electrons, becoming an O^{2-} ion.

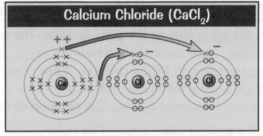

Calcium Chloride (CaCl₂)

The <u>calcium</u> atom gives up its <u>two</u> outer electrons, becoming a Ca^{2+} ion. The two <u>chlorine</u> atoms pick up <u>one electron each</u>, becoming <u>two</u> Cl- (chloride) ions.

Notice that <u>all</u> the atoms end up with <u>full outer shells</u> as a result of this giving and taking of electrons.

Ionic Compounds Have A Regular Lattice Structure

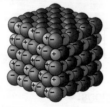

1) <u>Ionic bonds</u> always produce compounds with similar structures.

2) The ions form a <u>closely packed</u> regular lattice arrangement.

3) This is because ionic bonds are very strong <u>electrostatic forces of attraction</u> between <u>oppositely charged</u> ions.

4) Ionic compounds, like <u>sodium chloride</u> and <u>magnesium oxide</u>, all have <u>similar properties</u> caused by their <u>structure</u>...

1) They Have High Melting Points and Boiling Points

This is due to the <u>very strong</u> bonds between <u>the ions</u>. It takes a lot of <u>energy</u> to break these bonds.

2) They Conduct Electricity When Aqueous Or Molten

1) When in <u>aqueous solution</u> (dissolved), the ions <u>separate</u> and are all <u>free to move</u>, so they'll <u>carry electric current</u>.

2) The same happens when they <u>melt</u> — the ions are <u>free to move</u> and they'll carry electric current.

Ions are held rigidly in solids and so they aren't free to move and conduct electricity.

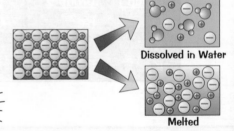

Dissolved in Water

Melted

Ionic lattices — all over your chips...

You need to be able to apply the <u>principle of ionic bonding</u> to any of the elements in Groups 1, 2, 6 and 7. This isn't too tricky because it always works the same way — just learn the patterns and it'll all be hunkydory.

Naming Compounds and Finding Formulas

Don't worry, this page doesn't contain a long list of baby names, but naming compounds is pretty important.
You can't just go around calling hydrochloric acid 'water' — things could get a wee bit nasty.
And in chemistry it's not just a chemical's name you need to get right, it's the formula too.

Naming Compounds — Two Simple Rules

RULE 1:   When two different elements combine the compound's name is 'something -IDE'.

> E.g. if sodium and chlorine combine, you get a compound called sodium chloride.
> If magnesium and oxygen combine, you get a compound called magnesium oxide.

RULE 2:   When three or more different elements combine and one of them is oxygen, the compound's name is often 'something -ATE'.

> E.g. copper, sulfur and oxygen combine to make copper sulfate.
> Sodium, nitrogen and oxygen combine to make sodium nitrate.

Look at Charges to Work Out the Formula of an Ionic Compound

To work out what formula you get when things react, you can look at what ions they form.

Positive Ions		Negative Ions	
1^+ ions	2^+ ions	2^- ions	1^- ions
All Group 1 metals, including:	All Group 2 metals, including:	Carbonate CO_3^{2-} Sulfate SO_4^{2-}	Hydroxide OH^- Nitrate NO_3^-
Lithium Li^+ Sodium Na^+ Potassium K^+	Magnesium Mg^{2+} Calcium Ca^{2+}	All Group 6 elements, including: Oxide O^{2-} Sulfide S^{2-}	All Group 7 elements, including: Fluoride F^- Chloride Cl^- Bromide Br^- Iodide I^-

The charges of the ions in a compound have to balance. For example...

> You need 1 hydroxide ion (OH^-) to balance the charge of 1 sodium ion (Na^+), so the formula for sodium hydroxide would be NaOH.

> You need 2 chloride ions (Cl^-) to balance the charge of 1 magnesium ion (Mg^{2+}), so the formula for magnesium chloride would be $MgCl_2$.

> You need 1 oxide ion (O^{2-}) to balance the charge of 1 calcium ion (Ca^{2+}), so the formula for calcium oxide would be CaO.

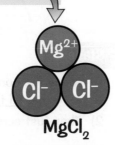

$MgCl_2$

Me sulfate — you sulfide...

OK, so you've read the page and you've got it nailed — compounds with two elements are -ides and compounds with three are -ates as long as oxygen's involved. To work out a compound's formula, you look at the charges of the ions involved and make sure that overall the charge is neutral — ions are charged, compounds aren't.

Preparing Insoluble Salts

Some salts are soluble and some are insoluble — it's just the way the cookie crumbles.

The Rules of Solubility

This table is a pretty fail-safe way of working out whether a substance is soluble in water or not.

Substance	Soluble or Insoluble?
common salts of sodium, potassium and ammonium	soluble
nitrates	soluble
common chlorides	soluble (except silver chloride and lead chloride)
common sulfates	soluble (except lead, barium and calcium sulfate)
common carbonates and hydroxides	insoluble (except for sodium, potassium and ammonium ones)

Making Insoluble Salts — Precipitation Reactions

1) To make a pure, dry sample of an insoluble salt, you can use a precipitation reaction. You just need to pick the right two soluble salts, they react and you get your insoluble salt.

2) E.g. to make lead chloride (insoluble), mix lead nitrate and sodium chloride (both soluble).

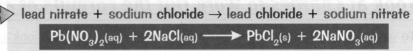

lead nitrate + sodium chloride → lead chloride + sodium nitrate

$$Pb(NO_3)_2{}_{(aq)} + 2NaCl_{(aq)} \longrightarrow PbCl_2{}_{(s)} + 2NaNO_3{}_{(aq)}$$

Method

Stage 1

1) Add 1 spatula of lead nitrate to a test tube, and fill it with distilled water. Shake it thoroughly to ensure that all the lead nitrate has dissolved. Then do the same with 1 spatula of sodium chloride. (Use distilled water to make sure there are no other ions about.)

2) Tip the two solutions into a small beaker, and give it a good stir to make sure it's all mixed together. The lead chloride should precipitate out.

precipitate

filter paper

filter funnel

Stage 2

1) Put a folded piece of filter paper into a filter funnel, and stick the funnel into a conical flask.

2) Pour the contents of the beaker into the middle of the filter paper. (Make sure that the solution doesn't go above the filter paper — otherwise some of the solid could dribble down the side.)

3) Swill out the beaker with more distilled water, and tip this into the filter paper — to make sure you get all the product from the beaker.

Stage 3

1) Rinse the contents of the filter paper with distilled water to make sure that all the soluble sodium nitrate has been washed away.

2) Then just scrape the lead chloride onto fresh filter paper and leave to dry.

lead chloride

If you aren't part of the solution, you're part of the precipitate...

In the exam, you could be asked to use the solubility rules to predict whether a precipitate will be formed when two given solutions are mixed together — and if it is, you might have to name it. So, unless you've got a crystal ball handy, I'd get learning the solubility rules or your 'prediction' might end up being a wild guess.

Barium Meals and Flame Tests

This page is a bit of a mish mash. It's about drinking <u>barium sulfate</u> (eurghh) but it's also about pretty <u>coloured flames</u> (ooo... ahh). You've gotta take the good with the bad though — it all needs learning.

Barium Sulfate is an Example of an Insoluble Salt

In fact it's the kind of <u>insoluble salt</u> you might get asked about in the exam (see previous page)...

<u>Example question:</u>

Describe how you would make a <u>pure, dry sample</u> of <u>barium sulfate</u> ($BaSO_4$), an insoluble salt.
You can use any of the following: barium iodide, barium nitrate, potassium chloride, potassium sulfate.

Answer:

1) Mix solutions of <u>barium nitrate</u> and <u>potassium sulfate</u>. ← So you want a soluble salt of <u>barium "something"</u>, and a soluble salt of <u>"something" sulfate</u>. Barium nitrate is soluble, and potassium sulfate is soluble. OK so far.

2) <u>Filter out</u> the <u>precipitate</u> of <u>barium sulfate</u>.

3) <u>Wash</u> it with <u>distilled water</u>. The question asks for a <u>pure, dry sample</u>, so you need to <u>wash</u> impurities off the precipitate, and then <u>dry</u> it.

4) <u>Dry</u> it on filter paper.

Barium Sulfate Can Be Used for X-Rays

<u>Barium sulfate</u> is pretty handy stuff...

1) Normally only <u>bones</u> show up when you have an <u>X-ray</u>.

2) However, barium sulfate is <u>opaque</u> to <u>X-rays</u>.
When <u>drunk</u> it shows up the <u>gut</u> so that any <u>problems</u> (e.g. blockages) can be seen.

3) Barium salts are <u>toxic</u>, but barium sulfate can be <u>safely drunk</u> because it's <u>insoluble</u>.
This means it isn't absorbed into the <u>bloodstream</u> — it just passes through the body.

4) When a patient <u>drinks</u> barium sulfate before an X-ray this is known as a <u>barium meal</u>.

Flame Tests — Spot the Colour

1) Some metals give a <u>flame</u> with a <u>characteristic colour</u>, as you see every November 5th when a <u>firework explodes</u>. So, remember, remember...

> (i) <u>Sodium</u> ions (Na^+) give a yellow/orange flame.
> (ii) <u>Potassium</u> ions (K^+) give a lilac flame.
> (iii) <u>Calcium</u> ions (Ca^{2+}) give a brick-red flame.
> (iv) <u>Copper</u> ions (Cu^{2+}) give a blue-green flame.

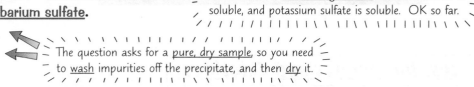

2) So if you stick a bit of <u>copper wire</u> in a Bunsen flame, you'll see a <u>blue-green flame</u>.

3) Flame tests don't just work when you've got a sample of a <u>pure element</u> — they also work with a <u>compound</u> that contains that element. So if you stick a sample of, say, <u>copper sulfate</u> in a Bunsen flame, you'll also see a <u>blue-green flame</u> because of the Cu^{2+} <u>ions</u> present.

4) To flame-test a compound in the lab, dip a <u>clean wire loop</u> into a sample of the compound, and put the wire loop in the clear blue part of the Bunsen flame (the hottest bit). First make sure the wire loop is really clean by dipping it into <u>hydrochloric acid</u> and rinsing it with <u>distilled water</u>.

5) You can use this method to test for sodium, potassium, calcium or copper <u>ions</u> in a <u>solid</u> or a <u>solution</u>. If you're using a <u>powdered solid</u>, you can dip the wire in the <u>hydrochloric acid</u> again to <u>moisten</u> it before dipping it in the solid, so that some of the solid <u>sticks</u> to the wire.

Testing metals is flaming useful...

Learning how to make <u>insoluble salts</u> might seem like a pain but barium meals go to show they have their uses. So, make sure you learn both halves of this page, don't just skip down to the cool <u>fireworks</u> bit.

Testing for Negative Ions and Spectroscopy

As if those flame tests on the previous page weren't exciting enough, there are more ways you can test for ions. And if you're really going for it today, there's always <u>spectroscopy</u> to learn about too...

Testing for Carbonates — Check for CO$_2$

First things first — the test for carbon dioxide (CO$_2$).

1) You can test to see if a gas is <u>carbon dioxide</u> by bubbling it through <u>limewater</u>. If it is <u>carbon dioxide</u>, the <u>limewater turns milky</u>:

2) You can use this to test for <u>carbonate</u> ions (CO$_3^{2-}$), since carbonates react with <u>dilute acids</u> to form <u>carbon dioxide</u>.

> acid + carbonate → salt + water + carbon dioxide

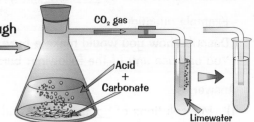

CO$_2$ gas

Acid + Carbonate

Limewater

Test for Sulfates and Chlorides

You can test for certain ions by seeing if a <u>precipitate</u> is formed after these reactions...

Sulfate Ions, SO$_4^{2-}$

1) To test for a <u>sulfate</u> ion (SO$_4^{2-}$), <u>add dilute HCl</u>, followed by <u>barium chloride solution</u>, BaCl$_2$.

2) A <u>white</u> precipitate of <u>barium sulfate</u> means the original compound was a sulfate.

$$Ba^{2+}(aq) + SO_4^{2-}(aq) \longrightarrow BaSO_4(s)$$

Chloride Ions, Cl$^-$

1) To test for <u>chloride</u> ions add <u>dilute nitric acid</u> (HNO$_3$), followed by <u>silver nitrate solution</u> (AgNO$_3$).

2) A <u>chloride</u> gives a <u>white</u> precipitate of <u>silver chloride</u>.

$$Ag^+(aq) + Cl^-(aq) \longrightarrow AgCl(s)$$

Spectroscopy Can Be Used to Identify Elements

1) Elements in a sample can be <u>identified</u> using <u>spectroscopy</u>. It's a little bit like a flame test (see previous page) — the patterns of light <u>emitted</u> by the elements in a heated sample are analysed.

2) Each element present in the sample produces a <u>different</u> pattern.

3) Spectroscopy is <u>fast</u> and <u>reliable</u> and it can be used to detect even very <u>small amounts</u> of elements in a sample.

4) Spectroscopy has also allowed scientists to discover <u>new elements</u>. For example, <u>rubidium</u> and <u>caesium</u> were both discovered because they produced <u>patterns</u> of light which had not been seen before.

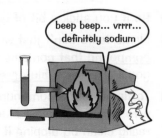

beep beep... vrrrr... definitely sodium

Just let me get my spectracles on to identify this ion...

It seems as though the <u>spectroscopy</u> machine has got it covered when it comes to identifying ions. But I'm afraid that life is not so peachy after all — you still need to know the tests for <u>carbonate</u>, <u>sulfate</u> and <u>chloride</u> ions. So, it's time to cover the page and scribble them down... it's the same old drill.

Covalent Bonding

Not all atoms form ionic bonds (see page 47). Luckily, there's another option — covalent bonding...

Covalent **Bonds** — **Sharing** Electrons

1) Sometimes atoms prefer to make covalent bonds by sharing a pair of electrons between two atoms.

2) This way both atoms feel that they have a full outer shell, and that makes them happy.

3) Each covalent bond provides one extra shared electron for each atom.

4) Each atom involved has to make enough covalent bonds to fill up its outer shell.

5) When atoms make covalent bonds with one or more other atoms, they form a molecule.

6) Learn these six important examples:

You only have to draw the outer shell of electrons.

1) Hydrogen, H_2

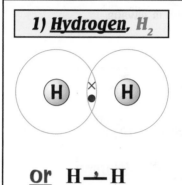

Hydrogen atoms have just one electron. They only need one more to complete the first shell so they often form single covalent bonds to achieve this.

Or H — H

2) Hydrogen Chloride, HCl

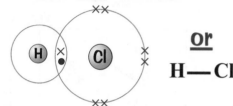

or

H — Cl

This is very similar to H_2. Again, both atoms only need one more electron to complete their outer shells.

3) Methane, CH_4

Carbon has four outer electrons, which is half a full shell.

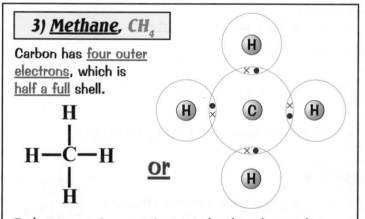

or

To become a 4+ or a 4− ion is hard work so it forms four covalent bonds to make up its outer shell.

4) Oxygen, O_2

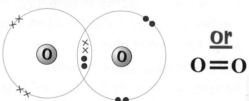

or

O = O

Oxygen atoms have six outer electrons. They sometimes form ionic bonds by takin... two electrons to complete their outer she...

However they'll also cheerfully form covalent bonds and share a pair of electrons instead.

5) Water, H_2O

In water molecules, the oxygen shares electrons with the H atoms.

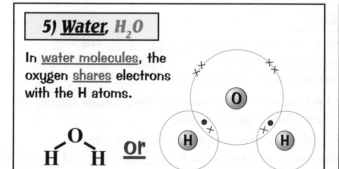

or

6) Carbon Dioxide, CO_2

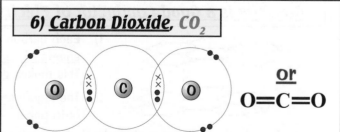

or

O = C = O

In carbon dioxide, two oxygen atoms share electrons with a carbon atom.

Covalent bonding — it's good to share...

Make sure you learn these six really basic examples and why they work. Every atom wants a full outer shell, and they can get that either by becoming an ion (see page 47) or by sharing electrons.

Covalent Substances — Two Kinds

There are two kinds of covalent substance: simple molecular and giant molecular.

Simple Molecular Covalent Substances

1) The atoms in these substances make very strong covalent bonds to form small molecules of two or more atoms.

2) By contrast, the forces of attraction between these molecules are very weak.

3) The result of these feeble inter-molecular forces is that the melting and boiling points are very low, because the molecules are easily parted from each other.

4) Most molecular substances are gases or liquids at room temperature.

5) Molecular substances don't conduct electricity, simply because there are no ions.

6) You can usually tell a molecular substance just from its physical state, which is always kinda 'mushy' — i.e. liquid or gas or an easily-melted solid.

Very weak inter-molecular forces

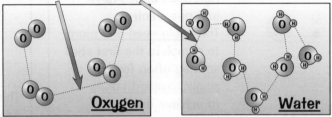

Hydrogen   Oxygen   Water

Giant Molecular Covalent Substances

1) These are similar to ionic lattices (see p. 48) except that there are no charged ions.

2) All the atoms are bonded to each other by strong covalent bonds.

3) They have very high melting and boiling points.

4) Except for graphite, they don't conduct electricity — not even when molten.

5) They're usually insoluble in water.

6) The main examples are diamond and graphite, which are both made only from carbon atoms.

Diamond is the Hardest Natural Substance

1) Each carbon atom forms four covalent bonds in a very rigid giant covalent structure, which makes diamond really hard. This makes diamonds great as cutting tools.

2) It doesn't conduct electricity because there are no free electrons.

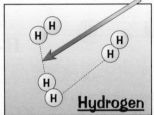

Graphite is a Good Conductor of Electricity

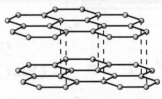

1) Each carbon atom only forms three covalent bonds, creating sheets of carbon atoms which are free to slide over each other. This makes graphite useful as a lubricant.

2) The layers are held together so loosely that they can be rubbed off onto paper — that's how a pencil works.

3) As only three out of each carbon's four outer electrons are used in bonds, there are lots of spare (delocalised) electrons. These electrons can move, so graphite is a good conductor of electricity. This means that graphite can be used in electrodes.

Carbon is a girl's best friend...

Remember — graphite and diamond are both giant covalent structures made of carbon, but they still have different properties and uses. Then there are simple molecular substances, like hydrogen, which are different again.

Classifying Elements and Compounds

Don your tweed jacket and spectacles — it's time for a bit of <u>detective work</u>...

Identifying the Bonding in a Substance by its Properties

If you've learnt the properties of the <u>three types</u> of substance properly, together with their <u>names</u> of course, then you should be able to easily <u>identify</u> the structure of most substances just by the way they <u>behave</u> as either:

That's the guy.

- <u>ionic lattice</u> (see page 48 if you can't remember these),
- <u>giant molecular</u>,
- <u>simple molecular</u>.

The way they're likely to test you in the Exam is by describing the <u>physical properties</u> of a substance and asking you to decide <u>which type of bonding</u> it has and therefore what type of material it is.

If you know your onions you'll have no trouble at all.
If not, you're gonna struggle. Try this one:

Example: Seven substances were tested for melting point, boiling point and electrical conductivity. Here are the results:

> Some of the substances don't have melting or boiling points. This is because the molecules decompose (break up) instead. E.g. if something decomposes before it boils, then it won't have a boiling point.

Substance	Melting point (°C)	Boiling point (°C)	Good electrical conductor when solid?	Good electrical conductor when in solution?
sodium chloride	801	1413	no	yes
magnesium sulfate	1124	decomposes	no	yes
hexane	−95	69	no	no (insoluble)
liquid paraffin	4	224	no	no (insoluble)
silicon(IV) oxide	1650	2230	no	no (insoluble)
copper sulfate	decomposes	none — already decomposed	no	yes
sucrose (sugar)	186	decomposes	no	soluble but doesn't conduct

Identify the type of bonding in each substance.

Answer:

- <u>Sodium chloride</u>, <u>magnesium sulfate</u> and <u>copper sulfate</u> all <u>conduct</u> electricity when <u>dissolved</u>, but not when solid. So, they must be <u>ionic lattices</u>.

- <u>Hexane</u> and <u>liquid paraffin don't conduct</u> electricity at all and have <u>low</u> melting and boiling points. So, they must be <u>simple molecular</u> covalent substances.

- <u>Silicon(IV) oxide doesn't conduct</u> electricity and has <u>high</u> melting and boiling points, so it must be a <u>giant molecular</u> substance.

- <u>Sucrose</u> doesn't conduct electricity even in solution so it <u>can't be an ionic lattice</u>. It has a <u>low</u> melting point and is <u>soluble</u> in water, so it must be a <u>simple molecular</u> substance.

Simple molecules? — not so sure about that...

You have to be able to identify the bonding in a substance based on its properties — and explain <u>why</u>. So if it's not immediately obvious to you what the mystery substance is, then use a process of <u>elimination</u>. Work out what it definitely can't be and see what you're left with — that should be your guy.

Separation Techniques

It's pretty easy to create a <u>mixture of liquids</u> — you just pour one into the other and, hey presto, that's it. It's <u>separating</u> them out again that can be a bit trickier. Not to worry though, this page has the answers...

Some Liquid Mixtures are Immiscible and Some are Miscible

1) Some liquids will <u>mix</u> with each other — and some <u>won't</u>.

2) For example, when you put a splash of milk in your tea the milk <u>mixes</u> with the tea — it doesn't float on top no matter how much you put in. In fact, you've created a <u>miscible</u> mixture of liquids.

3) On the other hand, if you tried to put oil in your tea it <u>wouldn't mix</u> properly and the oil would float on the top — the liquids are <u>immiscible</u>.

4) There are different ways of <u>separating</u> mixtures of liquids depending on whether they're miscible or immiscible... and you need to know 'em.

Use a Separating Funnel to Separate Immiscible Liquids

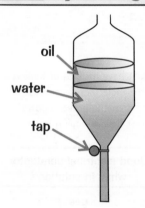
oil
water
tap

1) If two <u>immiscible</u> liquids are <u>shaken</u> together, when they are allowed to <u>stand</u> they will <u>separate</u> out into layers.

2) The <u>denser</u> liquid <u>sinks</u> to the bottom and the <u>less dense</u> one forms a layer on the <u>top</u>.

3) These layers can be separated using a <u>separating funnel</u> with a <u>tap</u>. The tap can be opened to <u>drain</u> off the denser liquid into a beaker.

4) For example, a mixture of <u>oil</u> and <u>water</u> can be separated in this way.

Fractional Distillation Separates Out Miscible Liquids

1) Mixtures of <u>miscible liquids</u> can be separated by <u>fractional distillation</u>.

2) The different liquids must have <u>different boiling points</u> though. If the mixture is <u>heated</u>, the different liquids will <u>condense at different temperatures</u> and can be collected separately.

3) For example, we can <u>fractionally distil liquid air</u> to get a variety of products (e.g. nitrogen and oxygen) for use in <u>industry</u>:

1) Air is <u>filtered</u> to remove dust.

2) It's then <u>cooled</u> to around <u>-200 °C</u> and becomes a <u>miscible</u> mixture of liquids.

3) During cooling <u>water vapour</u> condenses and is removed.

4) <u>Carbon dioxide</u> freezes and is removed.

5) The liquefied air then enters the fractionating column and is <u>heated</u> slowly.

6) The remaining gases are separated by <u>fractional distillation</u>. Oxygen and argon come out together so <u>another</u> column is used to separate them.

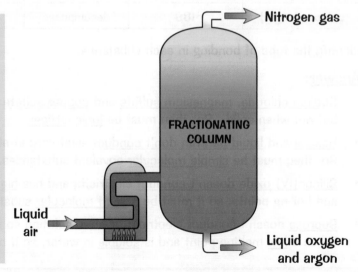
Nitrogen gas
FRACTIONATING COLUMN
Liquid air
Liquid oxygen and argon

Enter the fractionating column — it's an air-raising experience...

So, there's two techniques used to separate mixtures of liquids — <u>funnels</u> for <u>immiscible</u> liquids and <u>fractional distillation</u> for <u>miscible</u> liquids. Don't be put off by the weird words for liquids that mix and liquids that don't.

Chromatography

Paper chromatography is a pretty darn <u>useful chemical technique</u>. It's also pretty straightforward to carry out — which is good, because you've got to be able to describe the process...

Chromatography *Can Be Used to* Identify Substances

You can use <u>paper chromatography</u> to <u>identify</u> different <u>substances</u> in a mixture.
It uses the fact that different <u>substances</u> wash through <u>wet filter paper</u> at different <u>rates</u>.

Here's what to do...

1) Put <u>spots</u> of each mixture being tested on a <u>pencil baseline</u> on <u>filter paper</u>.

2) Roll up the paper and put it in a <u>beaker</u> containing a <u>solvent</u>, such as ethanol or water. The baseline must be kept <u>above</u> the level of the solvent.

3) The solvent <u>seeps</u> up the paper, taking the samples with it.

4) The different chemicals in the sample form <u>separate spots</u> on the paper.

5) The result of chromatography analysis is called a <u>chromatogram</u>. A chromatogram with <u>four spots</u> means there are <u>at least four</u> different substances in the sample mixture.

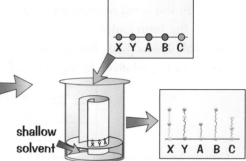

shallow solvent

INTERPRETING A CHROMATOGRAM

One use for chromatography is to separate out the mixture of <u>colouring agents</u> in <u>food</u>.
To <u>identify</u> which agents are present, run samples of <u>known mixtures</u> alongside the unknown mixture and <u>compare</u> where the spots end up.

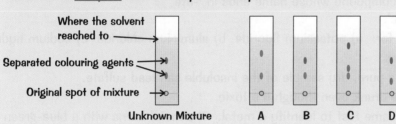

Where the solvent reached to

Separated colouring agents

Original spot of mixture

Unknown Mixture   A   B   C   D

You can see from the position of the spots on the filter paper that the <u>unknown mixture</u> has the <u>same composition</u> as <u>mixture B</u>.

You can Calculate the R_f Value for Each Chemical

1) You need to know how to work out the R_f values for <u>spots</u> on a chromatogram.

An R_f value is the <u>ratio</u> between the distance travelled by the dissolved substance and the distance travelled by the solvent. You can find them using the formula:

$$R_f = \frac{\text{distance travelled by substance}}{\text{distance travelled by solvent}}$$

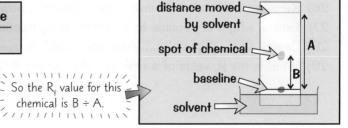

distance moved by solvent

spot of chemical

baseline

solvent

2) R_f values are used in the <u>food industry</u> and in <u>forensic science</u>. Scientists keep tables of these values and refer to them to <u>identify</u> substances like <u>food additives</u> and <u>drugs</u>.

So the R_f value for this chemical is B ÷ A.

Comb-atography — identifies mysterious things in your hair...

Always draw your baseline and write any labels in <u>pencil</u> not pen — the ink from the pen will dissolve in the solvent and <u>confuse</u> your results. Useful little tip that. Excellent.

Revision Summary for C2a Topics 1, 2 & 3

Ooo another revision summary — is it really that time again? Well, they do say that time flies when you're having fun. So, why stop now? You might as well have a go at these and find out which sections you need to read again.

1) Name the three types of particle in an oxygen atom. State the relative mass and charge of each particle.

2) The element boron has 5 protons. How many electrons does a boron atom have in its outer shell?

3) Describe how you would work out the electron configuration of an atom, given its atomic number. Find the electronic configuration of potassium (using the periodic table at the front of the book).

4) Is it the number of protons or the number of neutrons that defines each element?

5) What do the mass number and atomic number represent?

6) Define the term isotope.

7)* The table below gives the masses and relative abundances of the isotopes of neon: Calculate the relative atomic mass of neon. Give your answer to 2 decimal places.

relative mass of isotope	relative abundance
20	91%
22	9%

8) Explain how Mendeleev arranged known elements in a table. How did he predict new elements?

9) What feature of atoms determines the order of the modern periodic table?

10) What are groups in the periodic table? Explain their significance in terms of electrons.

11) Describe the process of ionic bonding.

12) Are cations positive or negative ions?

13) List the main properties of ionic compounds.

14) Explain the difference between a compound whose name ends in '-ate' and one whose name ends in '-ide'.

15)* Write down the chemical formula for: a) potassium fluoride b) aluminium chloride c) sodium hydroxide

16) Name two insoluble metal chlorides.

17) Describe how you would prepare a pure, dry sample of the insoluble salt lead sulfate.

18) Explain why barium sulfate can be drunk even though it's toxic.

19) A forensic scientist carries out a flame test to identify a metal. The metal burns with a blue-green flame. Which metal does this result indicate?

20) What tests could you use to distinguish between a solution of sodium chloride and magnesium sulfate?

21) Give two elements that were discovered by spectroscopy.

22) What is covalent bonding?

23) What are the two types of covalent substance? Give two examples of each.

24) Industrial diamonds are used in drill tips and precision cutting tools. What property of diamond makes it suitable for this use? Explain how the bonding in diamond causes its physical properties.

25)*Substance X conducts electricity only when in solution. What type of structure does Substance X have?

26) Kerosene and water are immiscible. Describe how you could separate a mixture of these two liquids.

27) Explain why it is possible to separate air by fractional distillation.

28) Describe how paper chromatography could be used to analyse colouring agents in food.

29)*What is the R_f value of a chemical that moves 4.5 cm when the solvent moves 12 cm?

* Answers on page 107.

C2a Topic 3 — Covalent Compounds and Separation Techniques

Properties of Metals

Metals — yes, they're strong and useful for conducting electricity but some have hidden talents too. Those transition metals are great for making things brightly coloured — I kid you not.

Metals **are on the** Left **and** Middle **of the** Periodic Table

1) Most of the elements are metals — so they cover most of the periodic table.

2) In fact, only the elements on the far right are non-metals.

3) The transition metals are found in the centre block of the periodic table. Many of the metals in everyday use are transition metals — such as titanium, iron and nickel.

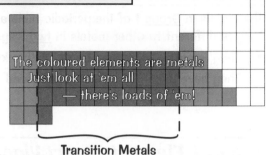

The coloured elements are metals Just look at 'em all — there's loads of 'em!

Transition Metals

Metals **are** Bendy **and They're** Great Conductors

All metals have some fairly similar typical properties.

1) They conduct electricity well. This makes them great for making electrical wires.

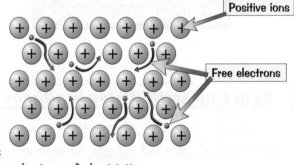

2) They're malleable — this means they can be bent or hammered into different shapes. This makes them handy for making into things like bridges and car bodies.

Transition Metals have Similar Properties

Most metals are transition metals. As well as having all the typical properties of metals they also:

1) have high melting points (e.g. iron melts at 1538 °C, copper melts at 1085 °C).

2) form very colourful compounds (e.g. potassium chromate(VI) is yellow, potassium manganate(VII) is purple, copper(II) sulfate is blue). Transition metals are responsible for hair dyes, the colours in gemstones (like blue sapphires and green emeralds) and the colours in pottery glazes.

It's the Structure of Metals **That Gives Them Their** Properties

1) All metals have the same basic properties. These are due to the special type of bonding in metals.

2) Metals consist of a regular arrangement of atoms held together with metallic bonds.

3) The metallic bonds give the metal a giant structure consisting of positive ions and free electrons. This is because metallic bonds allow the outer electron(s) of each atom to become delocalised (move freely).

Positive ions

Free electrons

4) This creates a "sea" of delocalised electrons throughout the metal, which is what gives rise to many of the properties of metals. For example, the ability of electrons to move freely through the structure makes metals good conductors of electricity.

5) The giant metallic structure and strong bonds mean that metals have extremely high melting points (and boiling points) and are insoluble.

6) They also allow the layers of atoms to slide over each other, allowing metals to be bent and shaped. This makes metals malleable.

Metals are also used by orchestras — they're great conductors...

Ah, now I see why a transition metal is the material of choice for aliens or robots trying to take over the world. Unlike the rubbish witch from the Wizard of Oz, you can't dissolve them and they won't melt easily either. Still, you can use them to form pretty coloured compounds. That will help me sleep easy tonight.

Group 1 — The Alkali Metals

Alkali metals all have <u>one electron</u> in their outermost shell. The atoms are keen to <u>get rid</u> of this extra electron, which makes them very <u>reactive</u>. <u>Lithium</u>, <u>sodium</u> and <u>potassium</u> are stars of the show here.

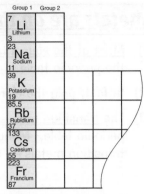

Alkali Metals are *Soft* and Have *Low Melting Points*

The metals in <u>Group 1</u> of the periodic table are known as the <u>alkali metals</u>. They're different to other metals in <u>two</u> ways.

- They're <u>soft</u> — they can be cut with a knife.
- They have <u>low melting points</u> compared with other metals.

Group 1 *Elements* React Vigorously *in* Water

1) When <u>lithium</u>, <u>sodium</u> or <u>potassium</u> are put in <u>water</u>, they react <u>vigorously</u> to form <u>hydroxides</u>.

2) The <u>reaction</u> makes an <u>alkaline</u> solution (which would change <u>universal indicator</u> to <u>blue</u> or <u>purple</u>) — this is why Group 1 metals are known as the <u>alkali metals</u>.

3) As you go <u>down</u> Group 1, the <u>lone electron</u> is in a shell that's <u>further from the nucleus</u>. As they're further apart, the <u>attraction</u> between the <u>positively</u> charged nucleus and the <u>negatively</u> charged electron <u>decreases</u>. This means the electron is <u>easier to get rid of</u>.

4) That makes the elements further down Group 1 <u>more reactive</u>.

5) You can see this in the time it takes the different elements to <u>react completely</u> with the water and disappear.

6) <u>Lithium</u> takes longer than sodium or potassium to react, so it's the <u>least reactive</u>. <u>Potassium</u> takes the shortest time to react of these three elements, so it's the <u>most reactive</u>.

REACTIONS WITH WATER

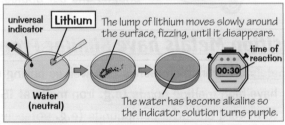

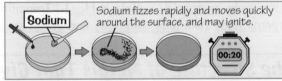

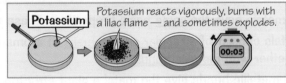

> The elements in <u>GROUP 1</u> get <u>MORE REACTIVE</u> as the <u>ATOMIC NUMBER INCREASES</u>.

Reaction with Water Produces *Hydrogen Gas*

1) The <u>reaction</u> of an alkali metal with water produces hydrogen — this is what you can see <u>fizzing</u>.

2) A <u>lighted splint</u> will <u>indicate</u> the hydrogen by making the notorious "<u>squeaky pop</u>" as the H_2 ignites.

3) These reactions can be written down as <u>chemical equations</u> — e.g. for <u>sodium</u> the equation is...

In words: sodium + water → sodium hydroxide + hydrogen

In symbols: $2Na_{(s)} + 2H_2O_{(l)} \rightarrow 2NaOH_{(aq)} + H_{2(g)}$

Notorious Squeaky Pop — a.k.a. the Justin Timberlake test...

Alkali metals are ace. They're <u>so reactive</u> you have to store them in <u>oil</u> — because otherwise they'd react with the air. AND they <u>fizz</u> in water and <u>burn</u> and <u>explode</u> and everything. <u>Cool</u>.

Group 7 — The Halogens

Next up is the halogens. Even though they sound like a sixties pop group they're pretty useful to chemists because they're really reactive. This is all because they only need one electron to fill their outer shells.

Group 7 Elements are Known as the 'Halogens'

The halogens all have 7 electrons in their outer shell
— so they've all got similar properties.

> At room temperature:
> • Chlorine is a fairly reactive, poisonous, dense green gas.
> • Bromine is a dense, poisonous, orange liquid.
> • Iodine is a dark grey crystalline solid.

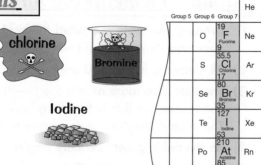

chlorine

Bromine

Iodine

	Group 5	Group 6	Group 7	Group 0
				He
	O	S	$\begin{array}{c}19\\ F\\ \text{Fluorine}\\ 9\end{array}$	Ne
			$\begin{array}{c}35.5\\ Cl\\ \text{Chlorine}\\ 17\end{array}$	Ar
	Se		$\begin{array}{c}80\\ Br\\ \text{Bromine}\\ 35\end{array}$	Kr
	Te		$\begin{array}{c}127\\ I\\ \text{Iodine}\\ 53\end{array}$	Xe
	Po		$\begin{array}{c}210\\ At\\ \text{Astatine}\\ 85\end{array}$	Rn

The Halogens React with Metals to Form Metal Halides

Halogens react with most metals, including iron and aluminium, to form salts called metal halides.

$$2Al_{(s)} + 3Cl_{2(g)} \rightarrow 2AlCl_{3(s)} \text{ (Aluminium chloride)}$$
$$2Fe_{(s)} + 3Br_{2(g)} \rightarrow 2FeBr_{3(s)} \text{ (Iron(III) bromide)}$$

Halogens Can React With Hydrogen to Form Hydrogen Halides

1) Halogens react with hydrogen to form hydrogen halides.
   For example, chlorine reacts with hydrogen to form hydrogen chloride gas.

$$Cl_{2(g)} + H_{2(g)} \rightarrow 2HCl_{(g)}$$

2) Hydrogen halides are soluble — they dissolve in water to form acidic solutions.
   E.g. hydrogen chloride gas can be dissolved in water to make hydrochloric acid.

More Reactive Halogens will Displace Less Reactive Ones

1) The higher up Group 7 an element is, the more reactive it is. This is because the outer shell is nearer to the nucleus, so the pull from the positive nucleus is greater which attracts extra electrons more strongly.

2) When halides dissolve in water, the halide ions are free to react.

3) If a more reactive halogen reacts with a solution containing halide ions it will "push out" (displace) the less reactive halogen.

4) This is called a displacement reaction.

5) For example, chlorine is more reactive than iodine (it's higher up Group 7). Chlorine therefore reacts with potassium iodide to form potassium chloride and iodine.

Cl_2 gas

Solution of potassium iodide

Iodine forming in solution

$$Cl_{2(g)} + 2KI_{(aq)} \rightarrow I_{2(aq)} + 2KCl_{(aq)}$$
$$Cl_{2(g)} + 2KBr_{(aq)} \rightarrow Br_{2(aq)} + 2KCl_{(aq)}$$

These are the equations for chlorine displacing iodine and bromine. They might give you a different example in the exam, but the equations are all quite similar.

Halogens — one electron short of a full shell...

The halogens are another group from the periodic table, and just like the alkali metals (see p. 60), you've got to learn their trends and the reactions. Learn them, cover up the page, scribble, check. It's the only way it'll stick.

Group 0 — The Noble Gases

The noble gases — stuffed full of every honourable virtue. They don't react with very much and you can't even see them — making them, well, a bit dull really.

Group 0 Elements are All Inert, Colourless Gases

1) Group 0 elements are called the noble gases and include the elements helium, neon and argon (plus a few others).

2) All elements in Group 0 are colourless gases at room temperature.

3) They are also more or less inert — this means they don't react with much at all. The reason for this is that they have a full outer shell. This means they're not desperate to give up or gain electrons.

4) As the noble gases are inert they're non-flammable — they won't set on fire.

5) These properties make the gases hard to observe — it took a long time for them to be discovered.

6) The gases were found when chemists noticed that the density of nitrogen made in chemical reactions was different to the density of nitrogen taken from the air.

7) They hypothesised that the nitrogen obtained from air must have other gases mixed in with it.

8) Scientists gradually discovered the different noble gases through a series of experiments, including the fractional distillation of air (see page 56).

	Group 6	Group 7	Group 0
			4 He Helium 2
	O	F	20 Ne Neon 10
	S	Cl	40 Ar Argon 18
	Se	Br	84 Kr Krypton 36
	Te	I	131 Xe Xenon 54
	Po	At	222 Rn Radon 86

The Noble Gases have Many Everyday Uses...

Argon is used to provide an inert atmosphere in filament lamps (light bulbs). As the argon is non-flammable it stops the very hot filament from burning away. It can also be used to protect metals that are being welded. The inert atmosphere stops the hot metal reacting with oxygen.

Helium is used in airships and party balloons. Helium has a lower density than air — so it makes balloons float.

I love Helium

Helium is ace!

There are Patterns in the Properties of the Noble Gases

The boiling points and densities of the noble gases increase as you move down the group.

Noble Gas	Boiling Point (°C)	Density (g/cm³)
helium	-269	0.0002
neon	-246	0.0009
argon	-186	0.0018
krypton	-153	0.0037
xenon	-108	0.0059
radon	-62	0.0097

In the exam you may be given the boiling point or density of one noble gas and asked to estimate the value for another one. So, make sure you know the patterns, but don't worry about learning the numbers.

They don't react — that's Noble De use to us chemists...

Well, they don't react so there's a bit less to learn about the noble gases. Nevertheless, there's likely to be a question or two on them so make sure you learn everything on this page...

Energy Transfer in Reactions

In a chemical reaction, <u>energy</u> is usually <u>transferred</u> to or from the <u>surroundings</u>, and it's all about making and breaking bonds.

Energy Must Always be Supplied to Break Bonds

1) During a chemical reaction, <u>old bonds are broken</u> and <u>new bonds are formed</u>.

2) Energy must be <u>supplied</u> to break <u>existing bonds</u> — so bond breaking is an <u>endothermic</u> process.

3) Energy is <u>released</u> when new bonds are <u>formed</u> — so bond formation is an <u>exothermic</u> process.

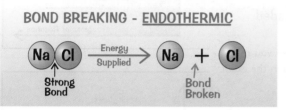

BOND BREAKING - <u>ENDOTHERMIC</u>

Na Cl → Energy Supplied → Na + Cl

Strong Bond

Bond Broken

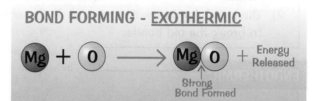

BOND FORMING - <u>EXOTHERMIC</u>

Mg + O → Mg O + Energy Released

Strong Bond Formed

In an Exothermic Reaction, Energy is Given Out

1) In an <u>EXOTHERMIC</u> reaction, the heat energy <u>released</u> in forming bonds in the products is <u>greater</u> than the energy used in <u>breaking</u> old bonds in the reactants.

> An <u>EXOTHERMIC reaction</u> is one which overall <u>GIVES OUT ENERGY</u> to the surroundings in the form of <u>heat</u>, shown by a <u>RISE IN TEMPERATURE</u>.

2) <u>Burning fuels</u> (<u>combustion</u>) gives out a lot of heat — it's very exothermic. That's because making new bonds in the products (water and carbon dioxide) gives out <u>much more energy</u> than it takes to break the bonds in the fuel.

3) <u>Explosions</u> are also exothermic — lots of heat energy is released.

In an Endothermic Reaction, Energy is Taken In

1) In an <u>ENDOTHERMIC</u> reaction, the energy <u>required</u> to break old bonds in the reactants is <u>greater</u> than the heat energy <u>released</u> when <u>new bonds</u> are formed in the products.

> An <u>ENDOTHERMIC reaction</u> is one which overall <u>TAKES IN ENERGY</u> from the surroundings in the form of <u>heat</u>, shown by a <u>FALL IN TEMPERATURE</u>.

2) Endothermic reactions are much <u>less common</u>.
Here are a couple of examples:

- <u>Photosynthesis</u> uses <u>light</u> energy from the <u>sun</u> to convert carbon dioxide and water into glucose and oxygen.

- As <u>ammonium nitrate dissolves</u> in water it <u>takes in heat</u> energy from its surroundings. This temperature change can be easily <u>measured</u> (see the next page).

Right, so burning gives out heat — really...

This whole energy transfer thing is a fairly simple idea — don't be put off by the long words. Remember, "<u>exo-</u>" = <u>exit</u>, "<u>-thermic</u>" = <u>heat</u>, so an exothermic reaction is one that <u>gives out</u> heat. And "<u>endo-</u>" = erm... the other one. Okay, so there's no easy way to remember that one. Sorry.

Energy Changes and Measuring Temperature

This is about <u>measuring</u> the stuff that you learned about on the previous page.

Energy Level Diagrams _Show if it's_ Exothermic _or_ Endothermic

EXOTHERMIC

1) This shows an <u>exothermic reaction</u> — the products are at a <u>lower energy</u> than the reactants. The difference in <u>height</u> represents the energy <u>given out</u> in the reaction.

2) The <u>initial rise</u> in the line represents the energy needed to <u>break</u> the old bonds.

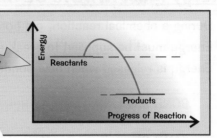

Learn these graphs — you may be asked to draw them in the exam.

ENDOTHERMIC

1) This shows an <u>endothermic reaction</u> because the products are at a <u>higher energy</u> than the reactants.

2) The <u>difference in height</u> represents the <u>energy taken in</u> during the reaction.

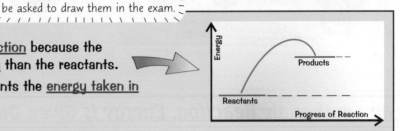

Temperature Change _can be_ Measured

1) In your exam you may be asked how you would <u>measure</u> the temperature <u>changes</u> during any of these four reactions:

- <u>dissolving salts</u> in water.
- <u>neutralisation</u> reactions (where an <u>acid</u> and <u>base</u> react together).
- <u>displacement</u> reactions (where a <u>more reactive</u> element takes the place of a <u>less reactive</u> element).
- <u>precipitation</u> reactions (where <u>two solutions</u> react to produce an <u>insoluble precipitate</u>).

2) You can measure the amount of <u>energy produced</u> by a <u>chemical reaction</u> in solution by taking the <u>temperature of the reactants</u> (making sure they're the same), <u>mixing</u> them in a <u>polystyrene cup</u> and measuring the <u>temperature of the solution</u> at the <u>end</u> of the reaction. Easy.

3) The biggest <u>problem</u> with temperature measurements is the amount of heat <u>lost to the surroundings</u>.

4) You can reduce it a bit by putting the polystyrene cup into a <u>beaker of cotton wool</u> to give <u>more insulation</u>, and putting a <u>lid</u> on the cup to reduce energy lost by <u>evaporation</u>.

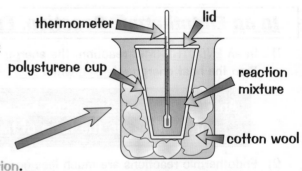

<u>Example — neutralising hydrochloric acid with sodium hydroxide:</u>

1) Add 25 cm³ of dilute hydrochloric acid to a polystyrene cup, and record the temperature of the acid.
2) Put 25 cm³ of dilute sodium hydroxide in a measuring cylinder and record its temperature.
3) Making sure they're the same temperature, add the alkali to the acid and stir.
4) Take the temperature of the mixture every 30 seconds, and record the highest temperature it reaches.

Save energy — break fewer bonds...

You can get <u>cooling packs</u> that use an <u>endothermic</u> reaction to draw heat from an injury. The pack contains two compartments with different chemicals in. When you use it, you snap the partition and the chemicals <u>mix</u> and <u>react</u>, taking in <u>heat</u> — pretty cool, I reckon (no pun intended).

Rates of Reaction

Chemical reactions <u>aren't</u> all the same. There are <u>slow</u> ones (like a statue being eroded by acid rain) and <u>quick</u> ones (like a whopping great explosion). The <u>rate of reaction</u> tells you how quick a reaction will be...

Reactions Can Go at All Sorts of Different Rates

1) One of the <u>slowest</u> is the <u>rusting</u> of iron (it's not slow enough though — what about my little bike).

2) An example of a <u>moderate speed</u> reaction is a <u>metal</u> (like magnesium) reacting with <u>acid</u> to produce a gentle stream of <u>bubbles</u>.

3) A <u>really fast</u> reaction is an <u>explosion</u>, where it's all over in a <u>fraction</u> of a second.

The Rate of a Reaction Depends on Four Things:

1) <u>Temperature</u>
2) <u>Concentration</u> — (or <u>pressure</u> for gases)
3) <u>Catalyst</u>
4) <u>Surface area</u> of a solid — (or <u>size</u> of particles)

LEARN THEM!

Typical Graphs for Rate of Reaction

The plot below shows how the speed of a particular reaction varies under <u>different conditions</u>. The quickest reaction is shown by the line that becomes <u>flat</u> in the <u>least</u> time. The <u>quickest</u> reaction will also start with the <u>steepest slope</u>, and the <u>slowest</u> reaction with the <u>shallowest slope</u>.

1) <u>Graph 1</u> represents the original <u>fairly slow</u> reaction. The graph is not too steep.

2) <u>Graphs 2 and 3</u> represent the reaction taking place <u>quicker</u> but with the <u>same initial amounts</u> of reactants. The slope of the graphs gets steeper.

3) The <u>increased rate</u> could be due to <u>any</u> of these:

a) increase in <u>temperature</u>
b) increase in <u>concentration</u> (or pressure)
c) <u>catalyst</u> added
d) an increase in <u>surface area</u> (e.g. a solid reactant crushed up into smaller bits).

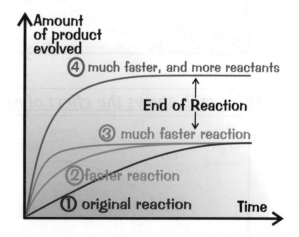

4) <u>Graph 4</u> shows <u>more product</u> as well as a <u>much faster reaction</u>. This can <u>only</u> happen if <u>more reactant(s)</u> are added at the start. <u>Graphs 1, 2 and 3</u> all converge at the same level, showing that they all produce the same amount of product, although they take <u>different</u> times to get there.

How to get a fast, furious reaction — crack a wee joke...

<u>Industrial</u> reactions generally use a <u>catalyst</u> and are done at <u>high temperature and pressure</u>. Time is money, so the faster an industrial reaction goes the better... but only <u>up to a point</u>. Chemical plants are quite expensive to rebuild if they get blown into lots and lots of teeny tiny pieces.

Rates of Reaction Experiments

Remember: Any reaction can be used to investigate any of the factors that affect the rate. Here's an important reaction which is great for investigating the effect of surface area and concentration on the rate of reaction. But you could just as easily use it to test the effect of temperature as well.

Reaction of Hydrochloric Acid and Marble Chips

This experiment is often used to demonstrate the effect of increasing the surface area of a solid.

1) Measure the volume of gas evolved with a gas syringe and take readings at regular intervals.

2) Make a table of readings and plot a graph with time on the x-axis and volume on the y-axis.

3) Repeat the experiment with exactly the same volume of acid, and exactly the same mass of marble chips, but with the marble more crunched up (so it has a bigger surface area).

4) Then repeat with the same mass of powdered marble instead of marble chips.

5) The experiment can also be used to test how the concentration of acid affects the rate of reaction. The concentration of the HCl is changed each time whilst the other factors remain the same.

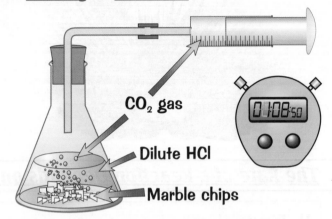

CO$_2$ gas

Dilute HCl

Marble chips

You can also find rate of reaction by measuring the decrease in the total mass of the flask during the reaction.

This graph shows the effect of using finer particles of solid

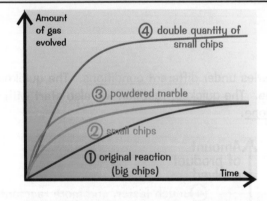

Amount of gas evolved

④ double quantity of small chips

③ powdered marble

② small chips

① original reaction (big chips)

Time

1) An increase in surface area causes more collisions, so the rate of reaction is faster.

2) Line 4 shows the reaction if a greater mass of small marble chips is added. The extra surface area gives a quicker reaction and there is also more gas evolved overall.

This graph shows the effect of using more concentrated acid solutions

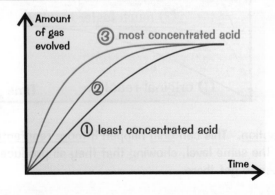

Amount of gas evolved

③ most concentrated acid

②

① least concentrated acid

Time

1) Plot a graph of the volume of gas evolved at regular time intervals.

2) Repeat with more concentrated acid solutions, but always with the same size marble chips.

3) The volume of acid must always be kept the same too — only the concentration is increased.

4) The three graphs show the same old pattern — a higher concentration giving a steeper graph, with the reaction finishing much quicker.

I'll have a large marble chips with a sprinkling of HCl please...

So, an increase in surface area is great for making a reaction go quicker. It's the same if you use more concentrated reactants as well. Ah, but what about the effect of temperature on the rate of reaction, I hear your enthusiastic voice cry. Well, flip over the page and all shall become clear...

Rates of Reaction Experiments and Catalysts

Changing the <u>temperature</u> can affect the <u>rate</u> of a reaction. Here's how...

Sodium Thiosulfate and HCl Produce a Cloudy Precipitate

1) These two chemicals are both <u>clear solutions</u>.
2) They react together to form a <u>yellow precipitate</u> of <u>sulfur</u>.
3) The experiment involves watching a black mark <u>disappear</u> through the <u>cloudy sulfur</u> and <u>timing</u> how long it takes to go.

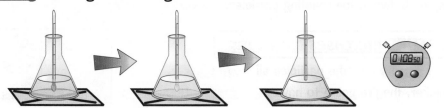

Remember you can also use the marble chip/acid reaction (see previous page) to test how temperature affects rate of reaction.

4) The reaction can be <u>repeated</u> for solutions at different <u>temperatures</u>. A <u>water bath</u> is used to heat both solutions to the right temperature <u>before you mix them</u>.
5) The <u>depth</u> of liquid must be kept the <u>same</u> each time, of course.
6) The results will of course show that the <u>higher</u> the temperature the <u>quicker</u> the reaction and therefore the <u>less time</u> it takes for the mark to <u>disappear</u>. These are typical results:

Temperature (°C)	20	25	30	35	40
Time taken for mark to disappear (s)	193	151	112	87	52

7) One sad thing about this reaction is it <u>doesn't</u> give a set of graphs. Well I think it's sad. All you get is a set of <u>readings</u> of how long it took till the mark disappeared for each temperature. Boring.

Catalysts Speed Up the Rate of Reaction

A <u>catalyst</u> is a substance which <u>changes</u> the speed of a reaction, without being <u>used up</u> in the reaction.

1) A catalyst works by <u>lowering the energy</u> required by the reactants to react.
2) This makes it easier for the reaction to happen and <u>increases</u> the rate of reaction.
3) This means that a <u>lower temperature</u> can be used, <u>without</u> the rate of reaction <u>dropping</u>.

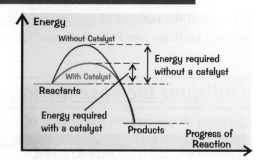

Catalytic Converters are Used in Vehicle Exhausts

1) One use of catalysts is in <u>catalytic converters</u>. These are found in <u>motor vehicles</u>.
2) <u>Vehicle exhausts</u> can give off <u>poisonous</u> gases like carbon monoxide if petrol doesn't burn properly.
3) So a <u>catalytic converter</u> is used in the exhaust pipe. It increases the rate at which <u>carbon monoxide</u> and unburnt fuel in exhaust gases react with <u>oxygen</u> in the air to produce <u>carbon dioxide</u> and <u>water</u>.
4) The catalyst has a <u>large surface area</u> and works best at <u>high temperatures</u> to <u>increase</u> the rate of reaction.

Catalysts — also useful for organising felines...

Pretty useful things these catalysts. Not only do they speed up loads of useful reactions but they <u>don't</u> get used up themselves at the end of a reaction so they can be used <u>over and over</u> again. Brilliant.

Collision Theory

Reaction rates are explained perfectly by collision theory. It's really simple. It just says that the rate of a reaction simply depends on how often and how hard the reacting particles collide with each other. The basic idea is that particles have to collide in order to react, and they have to collide hard enough (with enough energy).

More Collisions Increases the Rate of Reaction

All four methods of increasing the rate of reactions can be explained in terms of increasing the number of successful collisions between the reacting particles:

1) HIGHER TEMPERATURE increases collisions

1) When the temperature is increased the particles all move quicker.
2) If they're moving quicker, they're going to have more frequent collisions.

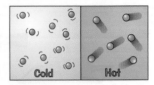
Cold   Hot

2) HIGHER CONCENTRATION (or PRESSURE) increases collisions

1) If a solution is made more concentrated it means there are more particles of reactant knocking about between the water molecules.
2) This makes collisions between the particles more likely.
3) In a gas, increasing the pressure means the particles are more squashed up together so there are going to be more frequent collisions.

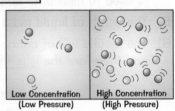
Low Concentration (Low Pressure)   High Concentration (High Pressure)

3) LARGER SURFACE AREA increases collisions

1) If one of the reactants is a solid then breaking it up into smaller pieces will increase its surface area.
2) This means the particles around it in the solution will have a larger area to react with, so there'll be more frequent collisions.

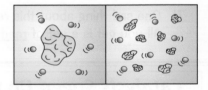

4) CATALYSTS increase the number of SUCCESSFUL collisions

1) A solid catalyst works by giving the reacting particles a surface to stick to.
2) They increase the number of successful collisions by lowering the energy particles need to start reacting with each other.

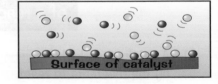
Surface of catalyst

Faster Collisions Increase the Rate of Reaction

Higher temperature also increases the energy of the collisions, because it makes all the particles move faster.

Faster collisions are ONLY caused by increasing the temperature.

1) Reactions only happen if the particles collide with enough energy.
2) This is because there's a minimum energy needed to break the initial bonds.
3) At a higher temperature there will be more particles colliding with enough energy to make the reaction happen.

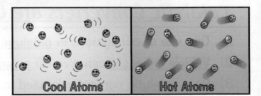
Cool Atoms   Hot Atoms

Collision theory — that lamppost ran into me...

Once you've learnt everything off this page, the rates of reaction stuff should start making a lot more sense to you. The concept's fairly straightforward — the more often particles bump into each other, and the harder they hit when they do, the faster the reaction happens. Hopefully nothing too tricky to get your head around.

Relative Formula Mass

The biggest trouble with _relative atomic mass_ and _relative formula mass_ is that they _sound_ so blood-curdling. Take a few deep breaths, and just enjoy, as the mists slowly clear...

Relative Atomic Mass, A_r — Easy Peasy

1) You'll probably remember about _relative atomic mass_ A_r from page 44.

2) The A_r for each element is the _same_ as its _mass number_ (see page 43).

3) So, you can find it easily by looking at the _periodic table_ — the _bigger number_ for each element is the _relative atomic mass_. For example:

Relative atomic mass

$$^4_2He \qquad\qquad ^{12}_6C$$

Relative Formula Mass, M_r — Also Easy Peasy

1) If you have a compound like $MgCl_2$ then it has a _relative formula mass_, M_r, which is just all the relative atomic masses _added together_.

2) For $MgCl_2$ it would be:

$$MgCl_2$$

$$24 \quad + \quad (35.5 \times 2) \quad = \quad 95$$

> So the M_r for $MgCl_2$ is simply **95**.

3) Although you can get the A_r for any element from the periodic table (see inside front cover), in the _exam_ you'll probably be given them in the question.

4) I'll tell you what, since it's nearly Christmas I'll run through another example for you:

> Question: Find the relative formula mass for the alcohol $C_2H_4(OH)_2$, using the given data:
> A_r for C = 12 A_r for H = 1 A_r for O = 16

ANSWER:

$$C_2H_4(OH)_2$$

$$(12 \times 2) + (1 \times 4) + [(16 + 1) \times 2] = 62$$

> So the M_r for $C_2H_4(OH)_2$ is **62**.

5) And that's all it is. A big fancy name like _relative formula mass_ and all it means is "_add up all the mass numbers_". What a swizz, eh? You'd have thought it'd be something a bit juicier than that, wouldn't you. Still, that's life — it's all a big disappointment in the end. Sigh.

Numbers? — and you thought you were doing chemistry...

So relative formula mass — hopefully not as bad as you thought it was going to be. You'll be given all the numbers in the exam so you just have to remember to _add them up_ and the job's a good'un. Be careful of more _complicated_ molecules like $C_2H_4(OH)_2$ — you need to make sure you know how many of each type of atom there are before you do any adding. Anyway, for a bit of _practice_, try this question:
Find the relative formula mass of these compounds: $NaOH$, Fe_2O_3, C_6H_{14}, $Mg(NO_3)_2$ _Answers on page 107._

Two Formula Mass Calculations

Although relative atomic mass and relative formula mass are easy enough, it can get just a tad trickier when you start getting into other calculations which use them. It depends on how good your maths is basically, because it's all to do with ratios and percentages.

Calculating % Composition by Mass of Elements in a Compound

This is actually dead easy — so long as you've learnt this formula:

$$\text{Percentage mass OF AN ELEMENT IN A COMPOUND} = \frac{A_r \times \text{No. of atoms (of that element)}}{M_r \text{ (of whole compound)}} \times 100$$

If you don't learn the formula then you'd better be pretty smart — or you'll struggle.

EXAMPLE: Find the percentage mass of sodium in sodium carbonate, Na_2CO_3.

ANSWER:

A_r of sodium = 23, A_r of carbon = 12, A_r of oxygen = 16

M_r of $Na_2CO_3 = (2 \times 23) + 12 + (3 \times 16) = 106$

Now use the formula:

$$\underline{\text{Percentage mass}} = \frac{A_r \times n}{M_r} \times 100 = \frac{23 \times 2}{106} \times 100 = 43.4\%$$

And there you have it. Sodium makes up 43.4% of the mass of sodium carbonate. By using the same method you can work out the percentage of carbon and oxygen in sodium carbonate as well.

Finding the Empirical Formula (from Masses)

This also sounds a lot worse than it really is. Try this for an easy peasy stepwise method:

1) List all the elements in the compound (there's usually only two or three!)
2) Underneath them, write their experimental masses.
3) Divide each mass by the A_r for that particular element.
4) Turn the numbers you get into a nice simple ratio by multiplying and/or dividing them by well-chosen numbers.
5) When the ratio is in its simplest form, this tells you the empirical formula of the compound.

Example: Find the empirical formula of the magnesium oxide produced when 9.6 g of magnesium react with 6.4 g of oxygen. (A_r for magnesium = 24, A_r for oxygen = 16)

Method:

1) List the two elements:	Mg	O
2) Write in the experimental masses:	9.6	6.4
3) Divide by the A_r for each element:	$9.6/24 = 0.4$	$6.4/16 = 0.4$
4) Multiply by 10...	4 :	4
5) ...then divide by 4	1 :	1

6) So the simplest formula is 1 atom of Mg to 1 atom of O, i.e. MgO. And that's it done.

> You need to realise (for the exam) that this empirical method (i.e. based on experiment) is the only way of finding out the formula of a compound. Rust is iron oxide, sure, but is it FeO, or Fe_2O_3? Only an experiment to determine the empirical formula will tell you for certain.

With this empirical formula I can rule the world! — mwa ha ha...

Make sure you learn the formula and the five rules in the red box. Then try these: Answers on page 107.
1) Find the percentage mass of oxygen in each of these: a) Fe_2O_3 b) H_2O.
2) Find the empirical formula of the compound formed from 2.4 g of carbon and 0.8 g of hydrogen.

Calculating Masses In Reactions

These can be kinda scary too, but chill out, little trembling one — just relax and enjoy.

The Three Important Steps — Not to be Missed...

(Miss one out and it'll all go horribly wrong, believe me.)

1) Write out the balanced equation.

2) Work out M_r — just for the two bits you want.

3) Apply the rule: Divide to get one, then multiply to get all.
(But you have to apply this first to the substance they give information about, and then the other one!)

Don't worry — these steps should all make sense when you look at the example below.

Example: What mass of magnesium oxide is produced when 60 g of magnesium is burned in air?

Answer:

1) Write out the balanced equation:

$$2Mg + O_2 \rightarrow 2MgO$$

2) Work out the relative formula masses:

(don't do the oxygen — you don't need it)

$$2 \times 24 \rightarrow 2 \times (24 + 16)$$
$$48 \rightarrow 80$$

3) Apply the rule: Divide to get one, then multiply to get all.
The two numbers, 48 and 80, tell us that 48 g of Mg react to give 80 g of MgO.
Here's the tricky bit. You've now got to be able to write this down:

48 g of Mg ......reacts to give.....80 g of MgO
1 g of Mg ......reacts to give.....
60 g of Mg .....reacts to give......

The big clue is that in the question they've said that "60 g of magnesium" is burnt, i.e. they've told us how much magnesium to have, and that's how you know to fill in the left-hand side of the box first, because:

We'll first need to ÷ by 48 to get 1 g of Mg
and then need to × by 60 to get 60 g of Mg.

Then you can work out the numbers on the other side (shown in red below) by realising that you must divide both sides by 48 and then multiply both sides by 60. It's tricky.

÷48 { 48 g of Mg .... 80 g of MgO } ÷48
     { 1 g of Mg .... 1.67 g of MgO }
×60 { 60 g of Mg .... 100 g of MgO } ×60

The mass of product is called the yield of a reaction. Masses you calculate in this way are called THEORETICAL YIELDS. In practice you never get 100% of the yield, so the amount of product will be less than calculated (see p. 72).

This finally tells us that 60 g of magnesium will produce 100 g of magnesium oxide.

If the question had said, "Find how much magnesium gives 500 g of magnesium oxide", you'd fill in the MgO side first instead, because that's the one you'd have the information about. Got it? Good-O!

Reaction mass calculations — no worries, matey...

Answers on page 107

The only way to get good at these is to practise. So make sure you can do the example, then try these:
1) Find the mass of calcium which gives 30 g of calcium oxide (CaO) when burnt in air.
2) What mass of fluorine fully reacts with potassium to make 116 g of potassium fluoride (KF)?

Percentage Yield

Percentage yield tells you about the <u>overall success</u> of an experiment. It compares what you think you should get (<u>theoretical yield</u>) with what you get in practice (<u>actual yield</u>).

Percentage *Yield Compares Actual and Theoretical Yield*

1) The <u>yield</u> of a reaction is the <u>mass</u> of <u>product</u> it produces.

2) The more reactants you start with, the higher the <u>actual yield</u> will be — that's pretty obvious.

3) You can work out the <u>theoretical (predicted) yield</u> of a reaction from the <u>balanced reaction equation</u>.

4) The <u>percentage yield</u> compares the actual yield with the theoretical yield. It <u>doesn't</u> depend on the amount of reactants you started with — it's a <u>percentage</u>.

5) Percentage yield is given by the <u>formula</u>:

$$\text{percentage yield} = \frac{\text{actual yield (grams)}}{\text{theoretical yield (grams)}} \times 100$$

6) Percentage yield is <u>always</u> somewhere between 0 and 100%.

7) A 100% yield means that you got <u>all</u> the product you expected to get.

8) A 0% yield means that <u>no</u> reactants were converted into product, i.e. no product at all was <u>made</u>.

Yields are Always *Less Than 100%*

In real life, you <u>never</u> get a 100% yield. Some product or reactant <u>always</u> gets lost along the way — and that goes for big <u>industrial processes</u> as well as school lab experiments. There are a number of ways this may happen, and there are <u>three</u> you need to learn:

1) <u>Incomplete reactions</u> — if not all of the <u>reactants</u> are <u>converted</u> to product, the reaction is incomplete and the yield will be lower than expected.

2) <u>Practical losses during preparation</u> — you always lose a bit when you transfer chemicals from one container to another. Think about transferring a <u>liquid</u> to a new container — some of it always gets left behind on the <u>inside surface</u> of the old container.

3) <u>Unwanted reactions</u> — things don't always go exactly to plan. Sometimes you get unexpected reactions happening, so the yield of the <u>intended product</u> goes down. These can be caused by <u>impurities</u> in the reactants, but sometimes just changing the <u>reaction conditions</u> affects what products you make.

Waste *in Reactions Costs Money*

1) Pretty obviously, if you're making <u>lots of waste</u>, that's a <u>problem</u>. Reactions that make lots of waste aren't usually <u>profitable</u>. This is because waste products usually <u>aren't commercially useful</u> (they can't be sold to make money).

2) If a waste product is <u>harmful</u>, it can pose a threat to <u>people</u> and the <u>environment</u>. Disposing of harmful waste products <u>safely</u> can be <u>very expensive</u>.

3) Chemists in industry are always looking for ways to produce products in a way that safely makes the <u>most profit</u>. They work to find reactions with these characteristics:

    a) They give a <u>high percentage yield</u> — so lots of product is made from the expensive raw materials.

    b) <u>All</u> of the products are <u>commercially useful</u> so there isn't any waste.

    c) They are a <u>suitable speed</u> — so the products are made <u>quickly</u> and <u>safely</u>.

You can't always get what you want...

A high percentage yield means there's <u>not much waste</u> — which is good for <u>preserving resources</u>, and keeping production <u>costs down</u>. If a reaction's going to be worth doing commercially, it generally has to have a high percentage yield or recyclable reactants. Yep, it's all about making money.

P24 Topic 1 — Static and Current Electricity

Revision Summary for C2b Topics 4, 5 & 6

I don't know about you but I'm pretty glad to see the back of this section. There were a few bits in there that looked really complicated but hopefully once you got your teeth into them they weren't too much of a problem. Because I like to just keep giving I have filled this page with some lovely questions for you to have a go at. Don't just ignore them and keep going — doing them until you get them right is the only way you know for sure you've got this stuff nailed.

1) Give two typical properties of metals.
2) Name two additional properties shared by transition metals.
3) Describe how the structure of a metal allows it to conduct electricity.
4) Is the following statement true or false? "Alkali metals have high melting points."
5) Potassium ($^{39}_{19}$K) is a Group 1 element. When placed in water, a lump of potassium violently explodes.
   a) Name the gas that is produced by this reaction.
   b) Describe how the pH of the water changes during the experiment.
   c) The experiment is repeated with the same sized lump of sodium ($^{23}_{11}$Na). How would it be different?
6) What is the physical state of bromine at room temperature?
7) Do hydrogen halides dissolve in water to form acidic or alkaline solutions?
8) Explain why the halogens become less reactive as their atomic number increases.
9) What is a displacement reaction?
10) Name a halogen that would displace chlorine from a solution of a chloride.
11) Explain why the noble gases are inert.
12) Name two noble gases and state a use for each.
13) What is an exothermic reaction? Give two examples.
14) Give two examples of an endothermic reaction.
15) a) Draw graphs showing energy change in endothermic and exothermic reactions.
    b) Explain how bond breaking and bond forming relate to these graphs.
16) How would you measure the temperature change during a neutralisation reaction?
17) What are the four factors that affect the rate of a reaction?
18)* A student carries out an experiment to measure the effect of surface area on the reaction between marble and hydrochloric acid. He measures the amount of gas given off at regular intervals. He uses four samples for his experiment:
    Sample A – 10 g of powdered marble   Sample B – 10 g of small marble chips
    Sample C – 10 g of large marble chips   Sample D – 5 g of powdered marble
    Sketch a typical set of graphs for this experiment.
19) What is the definition of a catalyst?
20) What is the role of a catalytic converter in car exhausts?
21) Excluding catalysts, explain how each of the three other factors which affect reaction rates increase the frequency of collisions between particles.
22)*Find M_r for each of these (use the periodic table inside the front cover):
    a) CO_2 b) $MgCO_3$ c) $Al(OH)_3$ d) ZnO e) Na_2CO_3
23)*Calculate the percentage by mass of nitrogen in $NaNO_3$.
24)*Using the periodic table, find the empirical formula of the compound formed when 227 g of calcium reacts with 216 g of fluorine.
25)*a) What mass of magnesium oxide is produced when 112.1 g of magnesium burns in air?
    b) What mass of sodium is needed to produce 108.2 g of sodium oxide?
26) a) What is the formula for percentage yield?
    b) How does percentage yield differ from actual yield?
27) Outline two factors that may prevent the percentage yield of a reaction being 100%.
28) Why may a chemical company wish to avoid using a reaction that produces harmful products?

* Answers on page 107.

Static Electricity

Static electricity is all about charges which are <u>not</u> free to move. This causes them to build up in one place and it often ends with a <u>spark</u> or a <u>shock</u> when they do finally move. But before we get to all that, we first need to look at the <u>structure</u> of the atom...

Atoms *Have a* Central Nucleus *with* Electrons Moving Round It

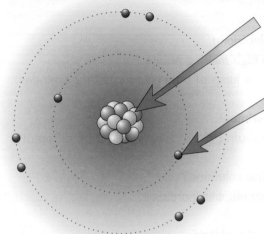

The <u>nucleus</u> is <u>tiny</u> but it makes up most of the <u>mass</u> of the atom. It contains <u>protons</u> (which are <u>positively charged</u>) and <u>neutrons</u> (which are <u>neutral</u>) — which gives it an overall positive charge.

The rest of the atom is mostly <u>empty space</u>. The <u>negative electrons</u> whizz round the outside of the nucleus really fast. They give the atom its <u>overall size</u>. But they have virtually <u>no</u> mass.

Learn the relative charges and masses of each particle:

PARTICLE	MASS	CHARGE
Proton	1	+1
Neutron	1	0
Electron	$\frac{1}{2000}$	-1

Build-up of Static *is Caused by* Friction

1) When two <u>insulating</u> materials are <u>rubbed</u> together, electrons will be <u>scraped off</u> <u>one</u> and <u>dumped</u> on the other.

2) This'll leave a <u>positive</u> static charge on one and a <u>negative</u> static charge on the other.

3) <u>Only</u> electrons can move, <u>not protons</u>. <u>Which way</u> the electrons are transferred <u>depends</u> on the <u>two materials</u> involved.

4) The classic examples are <u>polythene</u> and <u>acetate</u> rods being rubbed with a <u>cloth</u> <u>duster</u>, as shown in the diagrams.

With the <u>polythene rod</u>, electrons move <u>from the duster</u> to the rod. The <u>rod</u> becomes <u>negatively charged</u> and the <u>duster</u> is left with an <u>equal positive charge</u>.

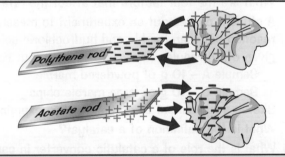

With the <u>acetate rod</u>, electrons move <u>from the rod</u> to the duster. The <u>duster</u> becomes <u>negatively charged</u> and the <u>rod</u> is left with an <u>equal positive charge</u>.

Like *Charges Repel,* Unlike *Charges Attract*

This is <u>easy</u> and, I'd have thought, <u>kind of obvious</u>.
Two things with <u>opposite</u> electric charges are <u>attracted</u> to each other.
Two things with the <u>same</u> electric charge will <u>repel</u> each other.
These forces get <u>weaker</u> the <u>further apart</u> the two things are.

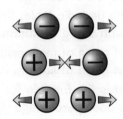

Static caravans — where electrons go on holiday...

<u>Bad hair days</u> are caused by static — it builds up on your hair, so your strands of hair repel each other. Boo static electricity. But before I start a revolution against it, let's have a recap... Insulators can be charged by friction, through the transfer of electrons — leaving one material negatively charged and t'other positively charged.

Static Electricity

You might not realise it, but we often experience some common electrostatic phenomena in our everyday lives. It's shocking stuff...

Static Electricity can Cause Little Sparks or Shocks

1) Clothing Crackles

When synthetic clothes are dragged over each other (like in a tumble drier) or over your head, electrons get scraped off, leaving static charges on both parts. That leads to the inevitable — attraction (they stick together) and little sparks as the charges rearrange themselves.

2) Car Shocks

Static charge can also build up between your clothes and a synthetic car seat — the friction between the two causes electrons to be scraped off. Then, when you get out of the car and touch the metal door, the charge flows and it can give you a real 'buzz'. Some cars have conducting strips which hang down behind the car. This gives a safe discharge to earth (p.76).

3) Shocks From Door Handles

If you walk on a nylon carpet wearing shoes with insulating soles, there will be a transfer of electrons from the carpet to you and charge will build up on your body. Then if you touch a metal door handle, the charge flows to the conductor and you get a little shock.

Some Electrically Charged Objects can Attract Other Objects

1) Balloons can Stick to Walls

Rubbing a balloon against your hair or clothes causes electrons to be transferred to the balloon, leaving it with a negative charge. If you then hold it up against a wall it will stick, even though the wall isn't charged. That's because the charges on the surface of the wall can move a little — the negative charges on the balloon repel the negative charges on the surface of the wall. This leaves a positive charge on the surface, which attracts the negatively charged balloon — this attraction holds the balloon on the wall.

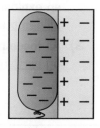

This method of using a charged object to force charges in an uncharged object to move is called induction. And it isn't just balloons and walls where we can see it happen...

2) A Charged Comb can Pick Up Small Pieces of Paper

If you run a comb through your hair, electrons will be transferred to the comb and it will become negatively charged. It can then be used to pick up little pieces of paper, even though they have no charge — holding it near the little pieces of paper causes induction in the paper, which means they stick to the comb.

Lightning is also Caused by a Build-Up of Static Charge

Rain drops and ice bump together inside storm clouds, knocking off electrons and leaving the top of the cloud positively charged and the bottom of the cloud negative. This creates a huge voltage and a big spark.

I know, I know — yet another shocking joke...

Lightning always chooses the easiest path to get to the ground — even if that means going through tall buildings and trees. That's why you should never put up an umbrella or fly a kite in a thunderstorm.

Uses and Dangers of Static Electricity

Static electricity can be a bit of a <u>nuisance</u> sometimes, but it also has some <u>good uses</u>, e.g. in industry. But don't get too happy clappy about how wonderful static electricity is — it can be pretty <u>dangerous</u> too.

Paint Sprayers Use Electrostatic Charges to get an Even Coat

1) Bikes and cars are painted using <u>electrostatic paint sprayers</u>.

2) The spray gun is <u>charged</u>, which charges up the small drops of paint. Each paint drop <u>repels</u> all the others, since they've all got the <u>same charge</u>, so you get a very <u>fine spray</u>.

3) The object to be painted is given an <u>opposite charge</u> to the gun. This <u>attracts</u> the fine spray of paint.

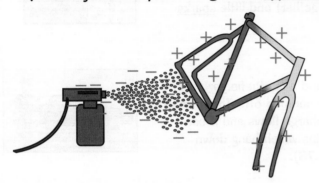

4) This method gives an <u>even coat</u> and hardly any paint is <u>wasted</u>. In addition, parts of the bicycle or car pointing <u>away</u> from the spray gun <u>still receive paint</u>, i.e. there are no paint <u>shadows</u>.

5) Many other electrostatic sprayers work in exactly the <u>same way</u>, e.g. <u>insecticide sprayers</u>.

Just Say No To Electrostatic Sprayers

Electrostatic Charges can Cause a Fuel Filling Nightmare

1) As <u>fuel</u> flows out of a <u>filler pipe</u>, e.g. into an <u>aircraft</u> or <u>tanker</u>, then <u>static can build up</u>.

2) This can easily lead to a <u>spark</u> which might cause an explosion in <u>dusty</u> or <u>fumey</u> places — like when <u>filling up</u> a car with fuel at a <u>petrol station</u>.

3) All these problems with <u>sparks</u> can be solved by <u>earthing charged objects</u> (see below).

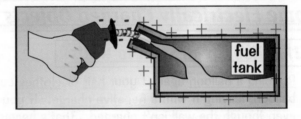

fuel tank

Objects Can be Earthed to Stop Electrostatic Charge Building Up

1) Dangerous <u>sparks</u> can be prevented by connecting a charged object to the <u>ground</u> using a <u>conductor</u> (e.g. a copper wire) — this is called <u>earthing</u>.

2) <u>Earthing</u> provides an <u>easy route</u> for the static charges to travel into the ground. This means <u>no charge</u> can <u>build up</u> to give you a shock or make a spark.

3) The <u>electrons</u> flow <u>down</u> the conductor to the ground if the charge is <u>negative</u> and flow <u>up</u> the conductor from the ground if the charge is <u>positive</u>.

4) <u>Fuel tankers</u> must be <u>earthed</u> to prevent any sparks that might cause the fuel to <u>explode</u>.

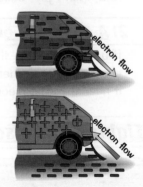

That page really brought me back down to Earth...

As useful as static electricity can be, you've got to be aware of its dangers too. And more importantly how to <u>prevent</u> these dangers. Remember that <u>earthing</u> stops lots of charge building up in once place so there aren't any sparks — which is really important for fuelling aircraft etc. Hmm, let's hope the next page is a bit more cheery.

Charge and Current

This page is all about charges <u>moving</u> in an <u>electrical circuit</u>. And if you're worried that reading this might damage your street cred, then let me assure you that it's all <u>current</u>. Chortle, chortle.

An <u>Electric Current</u> <u>is</u> the <u>Rate</u> <u>of</u> <u>Flow</u> <u>of</u> <u>Charge</u>

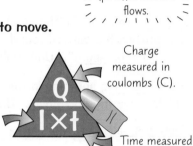

When you earth a charged conductor (p.76), a current flows.

1) Current is the <u>rate of flow of charge</u> around a circuit.

2) In the <u>metal wires</u> of a circuit, this charge is carried by <u>electrons</u>. Metals are <u>good conductors</u> as they have <u>free electrons</u> which are able to move.

3) When <u>current</u> flows past a point in a circuit for a length of <u>time</u> then the <u>charge</u> that has passed is given by this formula:

Charge measured in coulombs (C).

> ## Charge = Current × Time

Current measured in amperes (A).

Time measured in seconds (s).

4) <u>More charge</u> passes around the circuit when a <u>bigger current</u> flows.

> **EXAMPLE:** A battery charger passes a current of 2.5 A through a cell over a period of 4 hours. How much charge does the charger transfer to the cell altogether?
>
> **ANSWER:** Q = I × t = 2.5 × (4 × 60 × 60) = 36 000 C (36 kC).

> **EXAMPLE:** A charge of 540 C passes through a bulb over 3 minutes. Calculate the current flowing through the bulb.
>
> **ANSWER:** First we need to rearrange the formula using the formula triangle:
>
> $$I = \frac{Q}{t} = \frac{540}{(3 \times 60)} = 3\ A.$$

<u>Cells</u> <u>and</u> <u>Batteries</u> <u>Supply</u> <u>Direct Current</u>

1) <u>Cells</u> and <u>batteries</u> can be used in an electrical circuit to supply <u>direct current</u> (d.c.).

2) Direct current is a current that keeps flowing in the <u>same direction</u>.

3) This means that the <u>charge</u> moves in <u>one direction</u> only.

4) We can look at a direct current trace on an <u>oscilloscope</u>. A direct current source is always at the <u>same voltage</u>, so you get a <u>straight line</u>.

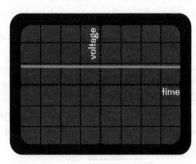

Mains electricity is an <u>alternating</u> current — it is constantly changing direction.

<u>Finding it hard to revise charge and current? Don't QIT it yet...</u>

Formulas, smormulas. They crop up everywhere. Make sure you know how to <u>rearrange</u> and use the one above. Don't forget that the symbol for current is <u>I</u> and the symbol for charge is <u>Q</u>. Barmy. Know all the definitions too, like electric current being the rate of flow of charge. And that direct current only flows in one direction. Good-o.

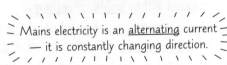

Electric Current and Potential Difference

Isn't electricity great. Mind you it's pretty bad news if the words don't mean anything to you. Ho hum.
Oh, but what's that? Why it's a shed-load of <u>definitions</u> for you to take a gander at...

1) <u>Current</u> is the rate of <u>flow</u> of charge round the circuit (p.77).
Current will <u>only flow</u> through a component if there is a
<u>voltage</u> across that component. Unit: ampere, A.

2) <u>Voltage</u> (potential difference) is the <u>driving force</u>
that pushes the current round.   Kind of like
"<u>electrical pressure</u>". Unit: volt, V.

3) <u>Resistance</u> is anything in the circuit
which <u>slows the flow down</u>. Unit: ohm, Ω.

4) <u>There's a balance</u>: the <u>voltage</u> is trying to <u>push</u> the current round
the circuit, and the <u>resistance</u> is <u>opposing</u> it — the <u>relative sizes</u>
of the voltage and resistance decide <u>how big</u> the current will be:

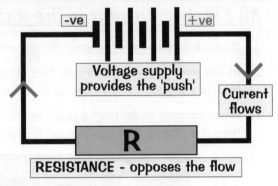

Voltage supply provides the 'push'

Current flows

R

RESISTANCE - opposes the flow

> If you <u>increase the voltage</u> — then <u>more current</u> will flow.
> If you <u>increase the resistance</u> — then <u>less current</u> will flow
> (or <u>more voltage</u> will be needed to keep the <u>same current</u> flowing).

Potential difference is just another name for <u>voltage</u> — they both mean the <u>same thing</u>.

Potential Difference *is the* <u>Energy</u> *Transferred per Unit* <u>Charge Passed</u>

1) When an electrical <u>charge</u> goes through a <u>change</u> in
<u>potential difference</u>, then <u>energy</u> is <u>transferred</u>.

2) Energy is <u>supplied</u> to the charge at the
<u>power source</u> to 'raise' it through a voltage.

3) The charge <u>gives up</u> this energy when it '<u>falls</u>' through
any <u>voltage drop</u> in <u>components</u> elsewhere in the circuit.

4) The <u>bigger</u> the <u>change</u> in voltage, the <u>more energy</u> is transferred
for a <u>given amount of charge</u> passing through the circuit.
<u>1 volt = 1 joule/coulomb</u>.

5) That means that a battery with a <u>bigger voltage</u> will supply <u>more energy</u> to the circuit for every <u>coulomb</u> of
charge which flows round it, because the charge is raised up "<u>higher</u>" at the start (see above diagram) —
and as the diagram shows, <u>more energy</u> will be <u>dissipated</u> in the circuit too.

Charges gaining energy at the battery

Charges releasing energy in resistors

+6V
+6V
+3V
0V
0V
Battery
R
R

Current *is Conserved* <u>at a Junction</u>

1) In a <u>parallel circuit</u>, each <u>component</u> is <u>separately</u>
connected to the +ve and –ve of the <u>supply</u>.

2) There are <u>junctions</u> where the
current either <u>splits</u> or <u>rejoins</u>.

3) Current <u>doesn't</u> get <u>used up</u> or <u>lost</u> in a circuit —
it is <u>conserved</u>. So, current at a <u>junction</u> is conserved.

4) The total current <u>entering</u> a junction is <u>equal</u>
to the <u>total current leaving</u> a junction.

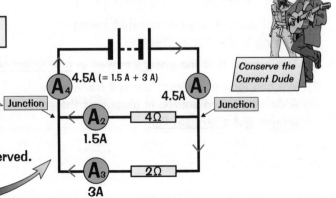

A₄ 4.5A (= 1.5 A + 3 A)
A₁ 4.5A
Junction
Junction
A₂ 1.5A 4Ω
A₃ 3A 2Ω

Conserve the Current Dude

I'm always conserved at road junctions...

...which means I'm often late for work. Maybe I should just take the bus. It's really important that you get the
definitions for <u>potential difference</u> and <u>current</u> clear in your head. They pop up lots on the next couple of pages.

Resistance and V = I × R

Ooh experiments, you've gotta love 'em. Here's a <u>simple experiment</u> for investigating resistance.

The Standard Test Circuit

This is without doubt the most totally bog-standard circuit the world has ever known. So know it.

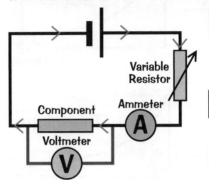

Variable Resistor

Component

Ammeter

Voltmeter

The Ammeter

1) Measures the <u>current</u> (in <u>amps</u>) flowing through the component.
2) Must be placed <u>in series</u> (connected in a line with the component).

The Voltmeter

1) Measures the <u>voltage</u> or <u>potential difference</u> (in <u>volts</u>) across the component.
2) Must be placed <u>in parallel</u> around the <u>component</u> under test — <u>NOT</u> around the variable resistor or the cell.

Investigating the Relationship Between Voltage, Current and Resistance

1) The circuit above is a <u>very basic</u> circuit used for testing <u>components</u>, and for getting <u>voltage-current graphs</u> (V-I graphs) for them (see below).
2) The <u>component</u>, the <u>ammeter</u> and the <u>variable resistor</u> are all in <u>series</u>, which means they can be put in <u>any order</u> in the main circuit. The <u>voltmeter</u>, on the other hand, can only be placed <u>in parallel</u> around the <u>component under test</u>, as shown. Anywhere else is a definite <u>no-no</u>.
3) As you <u>vary</u> the <u>variable resistor</u> it alters the <u>current</u> flowing through the circuit (see p.78).
4) This allows you to take several <u>pairs of readings</u> from the <u>ammeter</u> and <u>voltmeter</u>.
5) You can then <u>plot</u> these values for <u>current</u> and <u>voltage</u> on a <u>V-I graph</u>.

Three Hideously Important Voltage-Current Graphs to Learn

V-I graphs show how the current varies as you change the voltage. Learn these three real well:

Fixed Resistors
The current through a <u>resistor</u> (at constant temperature) is <u>proportional to voltage</u>. <u>Different resistors</u> have different <u>resistances</u>, hence the different <u>slopes</u>.

Filament Lamp
As the <u>temperature</u> of the filament <u>increases</u>, the <u>resistance</u> <u>increases</u>, hence the <u>curve</u>.

Diode
Current will only flow through a diode <u>in one direction</u>, as shown.

There's a Formula Linking V and I

You need to know how to use this formula and how to <u>rearrange</u> it:

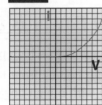

Potential Difference = Current × Resistance

EXAMPLE: A 4 Ω resistor in a circuit has a potential difference of 6 V across it. What is the current through the resistor?

ANSWER: Use the formula V = I × R. We need to find I, so the version we need is I = V/R.
The answer is then: 6/4 which is 1.5 A.

You can use this formula to work out the resistance from a V-I graph, by taking a pair of values (V, I) from the graph and sticking them in the formula R = V/I.

Measure gymnastics — use a vaultmeter...

Learn the experiment above and know what an ammeter and voltmeter are used for, and where they go in a circuit. Remember the shapes of the three example <u>voltage-current graphs</u> too — the examiners love them.

Devices and Resistance

Resistors come in all shapes and sizes. Some have fixed resistance, while others can change their resistance...

Light-Dependent Resistor or "LDR" to You

A light-dependent resistor or LDR is a special type of resistor that changes its resistance depending on how much light there is:

1) In bright light, the resistance falls.
2) In darkness, the resistance is highest.

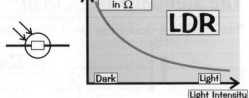

Thermistor (Temperature-Dependent Resistor)

A thermistor is like an LDR — but its resistance depends on temperature.

1) In hot conditions, the resistance drops.
2) In cool conditions, the resistance goes up.

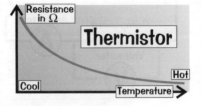

Resistors Get Hot When an Electric Current Passes Through Them

1) When there is an electric current in a resistor there is an energy transfer which heats the resistor.

2) This energy transfer is due to the electrons colliding with ions in the lattice that make up the resistor as they move through it.

3) These collisions give the ions in the lattice extra energy, which is emitted as heat. This heating effect increases the resistor's resistance — so less current will flow, or a greater voltage will be needed to produce the same current. If it gets too hot, no current will flow.

A lattice is just the way the ions are arranged.

4) This heating effect can make electrical circuits less efficient, as some energy is wasted as heat. It can also cause components in the circuit to melt — which means the circuit will stop working, or not work properly. Fuses use this effect to protect circuits — they melt and break the circuit if the current gets too high.

5) The heating effect of an electric current can have other advantages. For example, it's ace if you want to heat something. Toasters contain a coil of wire with a really high resistance. When a current passes through the coil, its temperature increases so much that it glows and gives off infrared (heat) radiation which cooks the bread. Light bulbs work in a similar way.

Electrical Power is the Rate at Which an Appliance Transfers Energy

1) An appliance with a high power rating transfers a lot of energy in a short time.

2) This energy comes from the current flowing through it. This means that an appliance with a high power rating will draw a large current from the supply.

3) Power is measured in watts (W). The formula for electrical power is:

$$\frac{P}{V \times I}$$

ELECTRICAL POWER = POTENTIAL DIFFERENCE × CURRENT

4) The energy transferred by an appliance depends on the current through it, the voltage supplied to it and how long it is on for (measured in seconds, s). The formula for energy transferred is:

ENERGY TRANSFERRED = CURRENT × POTENTIAL DIFFERENCE × TIME

$$\frac{E}{I \times V \times t}$$

EXAMPLE: The motor in an electric toothbrush is attached to a 3 V battery. If a current of 0.8 A flows through the motor for 3 minutes, calculate the energy transferred by the motor.

ANSWER: Use E = I × V × t = 0.8 × 3 × (3 × 60) = 432 J

Current = heat — so eat fruit cake when you're cold...

Crikey, that page was full to the brim with facts. Make sure you can explain why there is a heating effect when an electric current goes through a resistor. Know how to use those two formulas at the bottom too. Good stuff.

Velocity and Acceleration

Speed, velocity, acceleration... no doubt you've heard these words being bandied about during dinner parties. If you've ever felt out of your depth when talk turns to the <u>difference</u> between speed and velocity, then this is the page for you...

Speed <u>and</u> Velocity <u>are</u> Both: HOW FAST YOU'RE GOING

<u>Speed and velocity</u> are both measured in <u>m/s</u> (or km/h or mph). They both simply say <u>how fast</u> you're going, but there's <u>a subtle difference</u> between them which <u>you need to know</u>:

> <u>SPEED</u> is just <u>how fast</u> you're going (e.g. 30 mph or 20 m/s) with no regard to the direction.
>
> <u>VELOCITY</u> however must <u>also</u> have the <u>DIRECTION</u> specified, e.g. 30 mph north or 20 m/s, 060°. The distance in a particular direction is called the <u>DISPLACEMENT</u>.

Velocity and displacement are <u>vector quantities</u> — they have magnitude (size) <u>and</u> direction.

Speed, Distance and Time — the Formula:

You really ought to get <u>pretty</u> <u>slick</u> with this <u>very easy</u> <u>equation</u>, it pops up a lot...

$$\text{Speed} = \frac{\text{Distance}}{\text{Time}}$$

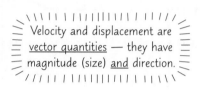

<u>EXAMPLE</u>: A cat skulks 20 m in 35 s. Find: a) its speed,   b) how long it takes to skulk 75 m.
<u>ANSWER</u>:   Using the formula triangle: a) s = d/t = 20/35 = <u>0.57 m/s</u>
                                        b) t = d/s = 75/0.57 = 132 s = <u>2 min 12 s</u>

A lot of the time we tend to use the words "speed" and "velocity" interchangeably. But if you're asked to calculate a velocity in the exam, don't forget to state a <u>direction</u>.

Acceleration is How Quickly Velocity is Changing

Acceleration is <u>definitely not</u> the same as <u>velocity</u> or <u>speed</u>.

1) Acceleration is <u>how quickly</u> the velocity is <u>changing</u>.

2) This change in velocity can be a <u>CHANGE IN SPEED</u> or a <u>CHANGE IN DIRECTION</u> or both. (You only have to worry about the change in speed bit for calculations.)

BUT, acceleration is a <u>vector quantity</u> like velocity — it has <u>magnitude</u> and <u>direction</u>.

Acceleration — The Formula:

$$\text{Acceleration} = \frac{\text{Change in Velocity}}{\text{Time taken}}$$

Here, u is the <u>initial</u> <u>velocity</u> of the object and v is its <u>final velocity</u>.

There are <u>two tricky things</u> with this equation. First there's the '(v – u)', which means working out the '<u>change in velocity</u>', as shown in the example below, rather than just putting a <u>simple value</u> for velocity or speed in.   Secondly there's the <u>unit</u> of acceleration, which is m/s^2. (Don't get confused with the units for <u>velocity</u>, m/s).

<u>EXAMPLE</u>: A skulking cat accelerates from 2 m/s to 6 m/s in 5.6 s. Find its acceleration.
<u>ANSWER</u>: Using the formula triangle: a = (v – u) / t = (6 – 2) / 5.6 = 4 ÷ 5.6 = <u>0.71 m/s²</u>

They say a change in velocity is as good as a rest...

Lots of facts to remember there, but it's all important stuff. Make sure you've learnt it all before you move on. Remember — displacement, velocity and acceleration are all <u>vector quantities</u> because they have <u>size</u> and <u>direction</u>.

D-T and V-T Graphs

Make sure you learn all these details real good. Make sure you can <u>distinguish</u> between the two graphs too.

Distance-Time Graphs

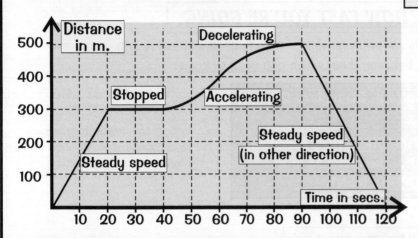

Very Important Notes:

1) <u>Gradient = speed</u>.
2) <u>Flat</u> sections are where it's <u>stopped</u>.
3) The <u>steeper</u> the graph, the <u>faster</u> it's going.
4) <u>Downhill</u> sections mean it's <u>going back</u> toward its starting point.
5) <u>Curves</u> represent <u>acceleration</u> or deceleration.
6) A <u>steepening</u> curve means it's <u>speeding up</u> (increasing gradient).
7) A <u>levelling off</u> curve means it's <u>slowing down</u> (decreasing gradient).

Calculating Speed from a Distance-Time Graph — It's Just the Gradient

For example, the <u>speed</u> of the <u>return</u> section of the graph is:

$$\underline{Speed} = \underline{gradient} = \frac{\text{vertical}}{\text{horizontal}} = \frac{500}{30} = \underline{16.7 \text{ m/s}}$$

This is just the speed equation (p.81).

Don't forget that you have to use the <u>scales</u> of the axes to work out the gradient. <u>Don't</u> measure in <u>cm</u>!

Velocity-Time Graphs

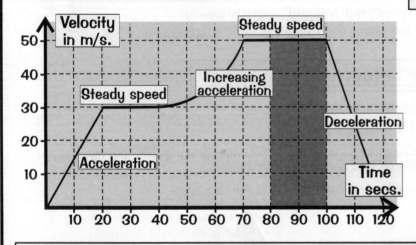

Very Important Notes:

1) <u>Gradient = acceleration</u>.
2) <u>Flat</u> sections represent <u>steady</u> speed.
3) The <u>steeper</u> the graph, the <u>greater</u> the <u>acceleration</u> or deceleration.
4) <u>Uphill</u> sections (/) are <u>acceleration</u>.
5) <u>Downhill</u> sections (\) are <u>deceleration</u>.
6) The <u>area</u> under any section of the graph (or all of it) is equal to the <u>distance</u> travelled in that <u>time</u> interval.
7) A <u>curve</u> means <u>changing acceleration</u>.

Calculating Acceleration and Distance from a Velocity-Time Graph

1) The <u>acceleration</u> represented by the <u>first section</u> of the graph is:

$$\underline{Acceleration} = \underline{gradient} = \frac{\text{vertical}}{\text{horizontal}} = \frac{30}{20} = \underline{1.5 \text{ m/s}^2}$$

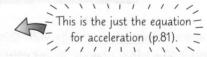 This is the just the equation for acceleration (p.81).

2) The <u>distance travelled</u> in any time interval is equal to the <u>area</u> under the graph. For example, the distance travelled between $t = 80$ s and $t = 100$ s is equal to the <u>shaded area</u> which is equal to <u>1000 m</u>. (But we can only use the method for <u>uniform</u> (constant or steady) <u>acceleration</u>).

Understanding motion graphs — it can be a real uphill struggle...

The tricky thing about these two types of graph is that they can look pretty much the same but represent totally different kinds of motion. Make sure you learn all the numbered points, and whenever you're reading a motion graph, <u>check the axis</u> labels carefully so you know which type of graph it is.

Forces

A <u>force</u> is simply a <u>push</u> or a <u>pull</u>. We can draw <u>force diagrams</u> to show the forces <u>acting on</u> an object.

Arrows _Show the Size_ and _Direction_ of Forces

In the exam, you might be given a <u>diagram</u> of an <u>object</u> and asked to <u>draw arrows</u> to show the <u>forces</u> <u>acting on it</u>, or be asked to <u>interpret</u> a force diagram. The three important things to remember are:

1) The <u>length</u> of the arrow shows the <u>size</u> of the force.

2) The <u>direction</u> of the arrow shows the <u>direction</u> of the force (didn't see that one coming, did you...).

3) If the arrows come in <u>opposite pairs</u>, and they're all the same <u>size</u>, then the <u>forces</u> are <u>balanced</u>.

And there are basically only <u>five different force diagrams</u>:

1) Stationary Object — All Forces in Balance

1) The force of <u>GRAVITY</u> (or weight) is acting <u>downwards</u> (see p.84).

2) This causes a <u>REACTION FORCE</u> from the surface <u>pushing</u> the object <u>back up</u>. This is the <u>only way</u> it can be in <u>BALANCE</u>.

3) On the diagram, this is shown by the <u>length</u> of the <u>reaction</u> and <u>weight</u> arrows being the <u>same size</u> and in <u>opposite</u> directions.

4) <u>Without</u> a reaction force, the object would <u>accelerate</u> <u>downwards</u> due to the pull of gravity.

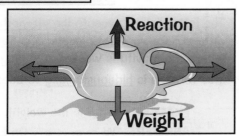

5) The two <u>HORIZONTAL</u> forces must be <u>equal and opposite</u> (or zero) otherwise the object will <u>accelerate</u> <u>sideways</u>. This is shown on the diagram by the two arrows being <u>equal</u> in <u>length</u> and in <u>opposite directions</u>.

2) Steady Horizontal Velocity — All Forces in Balance

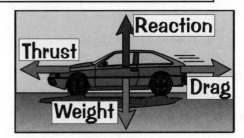

3) Steady Vertical Velocity — All Forces in Balance

This skydiver is free-falling at 'terminal velocity' — see next page.

<u>Take note</u> — to move with a <u>steady speed</u> the forces must be in <u>balance</u> (notice the length and direction of the arrows). If there is an <u>unbalanced force</u> then you get <u>acceleration</u>, not steady speed (see below).

4) Horizontal Acceleration — Unbalanced Forces

1) You only get <u>acceleration</u> with an overall <u>resultant</u> (unbalanced) <u>force</u> — this is shown on the diagrams by the length of one arrow being <u>longer</u> than the arrow in the <u>opposite</u> direction.

2) The <u>bigger</u> this <u>unbalanced</u> <u>force</u>, the <u>greater</u> the <u>acceleration</u> (see p.86).

Note that the forces in the <u>other (perpendicular)</u> <u>direction</u> are still <u>balanced</u>.

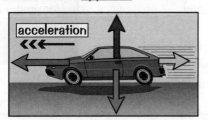

5) Vertical Acceleration — Unbalanced Forces

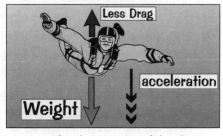

Just after dropping out of the plane, a skydiver accelerates — see next page.

I thought skydiving was cool — but it's all about forces...

So, things <u>only</u> accelerate in a particular direction if there's an <u>overall force</u> in that direction. Simple.

Weight and Terminal Velocity

On the last page, we looked at <u>forces</u> acting on objects. Here's a bit more on one of those forces — <u>weight</u>.

Weight and Mass are Not the Same

1) <u>Weight</u> is a <u>force</u> measured in <u>newtons</u> (N). Weight is caused by the <u>pull</u> of gravity.

2) <u>Mass</u> is <u>not</u> a force. It is just the <u>amount of 'stuff'</u> in an object. For any given object this will have the same value <u>anywhere</u> in the Universe. Mass is measured in <u>kilograms</u>.

3) An object has the <u>same</u> mass whether it's on <u>Earth</u> or on the <u>Moon</u> — but its <u>weight</u> will be <u>different</u>.

The Very Important Formula Relating Mass, Weight and Gravity

> Weight = mass × gravitational field strength

The letter "g" represents the <u>strength</u> of the gravity, and its value is <u>different</u> for <u>different planets</u>. On Earth g ≈ <u>10 N/kg</u>. On the Moon, where the gravity is weaker, g is only about <u>1.6 N/kg</u>.

This formula is <u>hideously easy</u> to use:

> <u>EXAMPLE:</u> What is the weight, in newtons, of a 5 kg mass, both on Earth and on the Moon?
> <u>ANSWER:</u> "W = m × g". On Earth: W = 5 × 10 = <u>50 N</u>   (The weight of the 5 kg mass is 50 N.)
>   On the Moon: W = 5 × 1.6 = <u>8 N</u>   (The weight of the 5 kg mass is 8 N.)

See what I mean. Hideously easy — as long as you've learnt what all the letters mean.

Falling Objects in a Vacuum Accelerate at the Same Rate

1) The <u>accelerating force</u> acting on <u>all falling objects</u> is <u>gravity</u>.

2) In a <u>vacuum</u>, e.g. in space, gravity makes <u>all</u> objects <u>accelerate</u> at exactly the <u>same rate</u>.

3) This means that on the <u>Moon</u>, hammers and feathers dropped simultaneously will hit the ground <u>together</u>. This happens because there is <u>no air</u> in a vacuum, so there is no <u>air resistance</u> to slow down the falling objects.

4) But here on <u>Earth</u>, where there <u>is</u> air resistance, things are a little different...

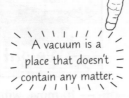

A vacuum is a place that doesn't contain any matter.

Objects Falling Through an Atmosphere Reach a Terminal Velocity

1) On Earth, when falling objects first <u>set off</u> they have <u>much more</u> force (weight) <u>accelerating</u> them than <u>resistance</u> slowing them down.

2) As the <u>speed</u> increases the <u>air resistance</u> increases too.

3) This gradually <u>reduces</u> the <u>acceleration</u> until eventually the <u>air resistance</u> is <u>equal</u> to the <u>weight</u> of the falling object.

4) When these two forces are <u>balanced</u>, the object then <u>won't accelerate</u> any more. It will have reached its maximum speed or <u>terminal velocity</u>.

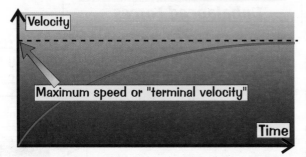

Velocity

Maximum speed or "terminal velocity"

Time

CGP health and safety tip #49 — beware of falling objects...

That sounded like a threat. It wasn't meant to be. Anyway, remember that all objects falling in a <u>vacuum</u> accelerate at the <u>same rate</u>. But that doesn't happen on Earth because of air resistance. Make sure you know how air resistance affects a falling object, and why it reaches a <u>terminal velocity</u>. Right, I'm off to buy a helmet.

Forces and Motion

The next couple of pages have some really important rules about <u>forces and motion</u>. They were worked out by a chap called Isaac Newton, but you <u>don't</u> need to know about him for the exam. Just this stuff...

When *Two Bodies Interact* They Exert a *Force* on *Each Other*

> If object A <u>exerts a force</u> on object B then object B exerts <u>the exact opposite force</u> on object A.

1) That means if you <u>push</u> something, say a shopping trolley, the trolley will <u>push back</u> against you, <u>just as hard</u>.

2) And as soon as you <u>stop</u> pushing, <u>so does the trolley</u>. Kinda clever really.

3) The force of you pushing the trolley is called the <u>action force</u>. The force of the trolley pushing back against you is called the <u>reaction force</u> (see p.83).

4) So far so good. The slightly tricky thing to get your head round is this — if the forces are always equal, <u>how does anything ever go anywhere</u>? The important thing to remember is that the two forces are acting on <u>different objects</u>. Think about a pair of ice skaters:

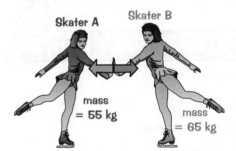

When skater A pushes on skater B (the <u>action</u> force), she feels an equal and opposite force from skater B's hand (the <u>reaction</u> force). Both skaters feel the <u>same sized force</u>, in <u>opposite directions</u>, and so accelerate away from each other. Skater A will be <u>accelerated</u> more than skater B, though, because she has a smaller mass (see p.86).

5) It's the same sort of thing when you go <u>swimming</u>. You <u>push</u> back against the <u>water</u> with your arms and legs, and the water pushes you forwards with an <u>equal-sized force</u> in the <u>opposite direction</u>.

No Resultant Force *Means* No Change *in Velocity*

> If there is a <u>zero resultant force</u> acting on a body (the forces are balanced) then the body will <u>remain at rest</u>, or else if it's already moving it'll just carry on at the <u>same velocity</u>.

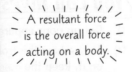
A resultant force is the overall force acting on a body.

1) When a train or car or bus or anything else is <u>moving</u> at a <u>constant velocity</u> then the <u>forces</u> on it must all be <u>balanced</u> — there is <u>no resultant force</u>.

2) Never let yourself entertain the <u>ridiculous idea</u> that things need a constant overall force to <u>keep</u> them moving — NO NO NO NO NO NO!

3) To keep going at a <u>steady speed</u>, there must be <u>zero resultant force</u> — and don't you forget it.

I have a reaction to forces — they bring me out in a rash...

Ooh the stuff on that page is a bit tricky. Remember, when two objects touch, they exert an <u>equal and opposite</u> force on each other. Know what is meant by <u>action</u> and <u>reaction</u> forces too. And don't forget that if the resultant force on an object is <u>zero</u>, the object will either <u>remain still</u> or keeping going at a <u>constant velocity</u>.

Force and Acceleration

A Resultant Force Means Acceleration

> If the resultant force acting on a body is not zero, it will accelerate in the direction of the resultant force.

1) An unbalanced force will always produce acceleration (or deceleration).
2) This "acceleration" can take five different forms:
   starting, stopping, speeding up, slowing down and changing direction.
3) On a force diagram, the arrows will be unequal.
4) Force is a vector quantity — it has magnitude and direction (see p.81).

Don't ever say: "If something's moving there must be an overall resultant force acting on it".
Not so. If there's an overall force it will always accelerate. You get steady speed from balanced forces.

> 1) The bigger the resultant force, the greater the acceleration or deceleration.
> 2) The bigger the mass of the object, the smaller the acceleration.
> 3) To get a big mass to accelerate as fast as a small mass it needs a bigger resultant force.

There is an Equation for Resultant Force

Any resultant force will produce acceleration, and this is the formula for it:

$$\text{Force} = \text{mass} \times \text{acceleration}$$

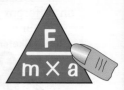

EXAMPLE: A car of mass of 1750 kg has an engine which provides a driving force of 5200 N.
At 70 mph the drag force acting on the car is 5150 N.
Find its acceleration a) when first setting off from rest, and b) at 70 mph.

ANSWER: 1) First draw a force diagram for both cases (no need to show the vertical forces):

2) Work out the resultant force in each case, and apply "F = ma" using the formula triangle:

Resultant force = 5200 N   Resultant force = 5200 – 5150 = 50 N
a = F/m = 5200 ÷ 1750 = 3.0 m/s²   a = F/m = 50 ÷ 1750 = 0.03 m/s²

You can Investigate F = ma Using a Trolley

To reduce the effects of friction make sure your runway's smooth.

1) Set up your apparatus like the diagram shown on the right.
2) To see how the trolley's acceleration is affected by the force acting on it, keep the mass of the trolley constant and vary the force.
3) Hold the trolley, add 100 g mass to the end of the string and then release the trolley. The 100 g mass pulls the trolley with a constant force (F = mg, where g is the acceleration due to gravity).
4) The light gate detects each piece of card as it passes through it and breaks a light beam.
5) Data logging software uses the width of the first piece of card (input into the computer) and the time it blocked the light beam to work out the 'initial' velocity of the trolley (using velocity = distance ÷ time). The same is done with the second piece of card to work out the trolley's 'final' velocity.
6) You can work out the trolley's acceleration using acceleration = (final velocity – initial velocity) ÷ time (see p.81). The time is the time it took for the whole trolley to pass through the light gate.
7) You should repeat the experiment several times and get an average value for the acceleration.
8) Repeat the whole thing again using different masses. You should find the greater the force, the greater the acceleration.
9) You can investigate the relationship between mass and acceleration by varying the trolley's mass and keeping the mass on the string the same (so the force is constant). You should find the greater the mass, the smaller the acceleration.

Investigating acceleration — you've gotta be off your trolley...

So, a resultant force makes an object accelerate. F = ma is bound to crop up in the exam — so learn it good.

Revision Summary for P2a Topics 1, 2 & 3

More jolly questions which I know you're going to really enjoy. You know what to do with the tricky questions — read over the relevant stuff again, then have another go at them. Keep at it 'til you can do every question.

1) Draw and label a sketch to show the structure of an atom.

2) Draw a table stating the relative mass and charge of protons, neutrons and electrons.

3) What causes the build-up of static electricity? Which particles move when static builds up?

4) Give three examples of how static electricity can be a nuisance.

5) Explain why a negatively charged comb is able to pick up little pieces of uncharged paper.

6) Describe how electrostatic paint sprayers use static electricity to get an even coat of paint.

7) Explain how you can reduce the danger of getting a static electric shock.

8) Give a definition for current.

9) * A charge of 900 C passes through a component over 10 minutes.
   Calculate the current flowing through the component.

10) What type of current do cells and batteries supply?

11) Explain what voltage and resistance are in an electric circuit. How does the current depend on them?

12) Explain what is meant by potential difference.

13) Sketch typical voltage-current graphs for: a) a fixed resistor, b) a filament lamp, c) a diode.
    Explain the shape of each graph.

14) * Calculate the resistance of a wire if the voltage across it is 12 V and the current through it is 2.5 A.

15) Describe how the resistance of an LDR varies with light intensity.

16) Explain why resistors get hot when an electric current passes through them.

17) * Calculate the current that flows through a toaster rated 230 V, 1100 W.

18) What's the difference between speed and velocity? Give an example of each.

19) * Write down the formula for working out speed. Find the speed of a partly chewed mouse which hobbles 3.2 m in 35 s. Find how far he would get in 25 minutes.

20) * A speed camera is set up in a 30 mph (13.4 m/s) zone. It takes two photographs 0.5 s apart.
    A car travels 6.3 m between the two photographs. Was the car breaking the speed limit?

21) What is acceleration? What is the unit used?

22) * Write down the formula for acceleration. What's the acceleration of a soggy pea flicked from rest to a speed of 14 m/s in 0.4 seconds?

23) Sketch a typical distance-time graph and point out all the important parts of it.

24) Explain how to calculate speed from a distance-time graph.

25) Sketch a typical velocity-time graph and point out all the important parts.

26) Explain how to find velocity, distance and acceleration from a velocity-time graph.

27) Sketch five standard force diagrams, showing the forces and the types of motion.

28) What's the formula for weight? Illustrate it with a worked example of your own.

29) What is "terminal velocity"?

30) Explain what a reaction force is and where it pops up.

31) If an object has zero resultant force on it, can it be moving? Can it be accelerating?

32) * Write down the formula relating resultant force and acceleration.
    A force of 30 N pushes a trolley of mass 4 kg. What will be its acceleration?

* Answers on page 107.

Stopping Distances

The stopping distance of a car is the distance covered in the time between the driver <u>first spotting</u> a hazard and the car coming to a <u>complete stop</u>. Examiners are pretty keen on this, so make sure you <u>learn it properly</u>.

Many Factors **Affect Your Total** Stopping Distance

The distance it takes to stop a car is made up of the <u>sum</u> of the <u>THINKING DISTANCE</u> and the <u>BRAKING DISTANCE</u>.

1) *Thinking Distance*

"The distance the car travels in the time between the driver noticing the hazard and applying the brakes."

It's affected by <u>TWO MAIN FACTORS</u>:

a) <u>Your REACTION time</u> — this is affected by <u>tiredness</u>, <u>drugs</u>, <u>alcohol</u>, <u>old age</u>, and a <u>careless</u> blasé attitude.

b) <u>How FAST you're going</u> — obviously. Whatever your reaction time, the <u>faster</u> you're going, the <u>further</u> you'll go.

> The figures below for typical stopping distances are from the Highway Code. It's frightening to see just how far it takes to stop when you're going at 70 mph.

2) *Braking Distance*

"The distance the car travels during its deceleration whilst the brakes are being applied."

It's affected by <u>FOUR MAIN FACTORS</u>:

a) <u>How FAST you're going</u> — the <u>faster</u> you're going, the <u>further</u> it takes to stop.

b) <u>The MASS of your vehicle</u> — with the <u>same</u> brakes, <u>a heavily laden</u> vehicle takes <u>longer to stop</u>. A car won't stop as quickly when it's full of people and luggage and towing a caravan.

c) <u>How good your BRAKES are</u> — all brakes must be checked and maintained <u>regularly</u>. Worn or faulty brakes will let you down <u>catastrophically</u> just when you need them the <u>most</u>, i.e. in an <u>emergency</u>.

d) <u>How good the GRIP is</u> — you need <u>friction</u> between your <u>tyres</u> and the <u>road surface</u> in order to be able to <u>stop</u>.
This depends on:
1) <u>road surface</u>, 2) <u>weather</u> conditions, 3) <u>tyres</u>.

30 mph	50 mph	70 mph
9 m	15 m	21 m
14 m		
6 car lengths	38 m	
	13 car lengths	75 m
	Thinking distance	
	Braking distance	24 car lengths

Leaves, diesel spills and muck on the road are <u>serious hazards</u> because they're <u>unexpected</u>. <u>Wet</u> or <u>icy roads</u> are always much more <u>slippy</u> than dry roads because there isn't much <u>friction</u> between the tyres and the road. A tyre <u>tread depth</u> of at least <u>1.6 mm</u> is essential for getting rid of the <u>water</u> in wet conditions. Without it, a tyre will simply <u>ride</u> on a <u>layer of water</u> and skid <u>very easily</u>. This is called "<u>aquaplaning</u>" and isn't nearly as cool as it sounds.

The *Amount You Slide* Depends on *Friction*

You can investigate how much <u>frictional force</u> different <u>surfaces</u> provide with a simple experiment:

1) Set up your <u>apparatus</u> as shown here:
2) Add <u>masses</u> one by one to the <u>mass holder</u> to provide a <u>force</u> on the block until it eventually <u>slides</u>.
3) The <u>amount</u> of force (the amount of mass) you need to slide the block will depend on the amount of <u>friction</u> between the <u>block</u> and the <u>surface</u>, just like the <u>tyres</u> of a vehicle driving on different <u>road surfaces</u>.
4) You can experiment with different surfaces — try foil, sandpaper, plastic covered in washing up liquid etc.
5) The <u>smaller</u> the frictional force between the block and the surface, the <u>smaller</u> the force you'll need to make the block slide.

Pulley | String | Heavy block | Mass holder | Bench | 'Road' surface

Stop right there — and learn this page...

Scary stuff. Makes you think doesn't it. Learn all the details and write yourself a <u>mini-essay</u> to see how much you really know. You might have to interpret charts of stopping distance in your exam.

Car Safety

A <u>large</u> lorry being driven very <u>fast</u> is going to be a lot harder to stop than a granny on a bicycle out for a Sunday afternoon ride — that's momentum for you.

Momentum = Mass × Velocity

1) The <u>greater</u> the <u>mass</u> of an object and the <u>greater</u> its <u>velocity</u>, the <u>more momentum</u> the object has.

2) Momentum is a <u>vector</u> quantity — it has size <u>and</u> direction (like <u>velocity</u>, but not speed, see p.81).

$$\frac{\text{momentum}}{\text{mass} \times \text{velocity}}$$

Momentum (kg m/s) = Mass (kg) × Velocity (m/s)

Momentum Before = Momentum After

<u>Momentum is conserved</u> when no external forces act, i.e. the total momentum <u>after</u> is the <u>same</u> as it was <u>before</u>. This is particularly obvious when you have a <u>linear system</u> — when the forces are working along the <u>same line</u>.

Example:

Two skaters approach each other, collide and move off together as shown. At what velocity do they move after the collision?

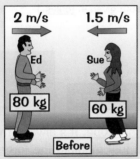

2 m/s   1.5 m/s   Velocity (v)=?

Ed   Sue

80 kg   60 kg   (80+60) kg

Before   **After**

1) Choose which direction is <u>positive</u>. I'll say "<u>positive</u>" means "<u>to the right</u>".

2) <u>Total momentum before</u> collision
   = momentum of Ed + momentum of Sue
   = {80 × 2} + {60 × (–1.5)} = <u>70 kg m/s</u>

3) <u>Total momentum after</u> collision
   = momentum of Ed and Sue together
   = <u>140 × v</u>

4) So 140v = 70, i.e. <u>v = 0.5 m/s to the right</u>.

Forces Cause Changes in Momentum

1) When a <u>force</u> acts on an object, it causes a <u>change</u> in momentum.

2) A <u>larger</u> force means a <u>faster</u> change of momentum (and so a greater <u>acceleration</u>, see p.86).

3) Likewise, if someone's momentum changes <u>very quickly</u> (like in a <u>car crash</u>), the <u>forces</u> on the body will be very <u>large</u>, and more likely to cause <u>injury</u>.

4) This is why <u>cars</u> are designed with <u>protective features</u> to slow people down over a <u>longer time</u> when they have a crash — the <u>longer</u> it takes for a <u>change in momentum</u>, the <u>smaller</u> the <u>force</u>.

$$\text{Force (N)} = \frac{\text{Change in momentum (kg m/s)}}{\text{Time (s)}}$$

$$F = \frac{mv - mu}{t}$$

Here, 'v' is the final velocity, 'u' is the initial velocity and m is the mass.

<u>CRUMPLE ZONES</u> crumple on impact, <u>increasing the time</u> taken for the car to stop.

<u>SEAT BELTS</u> stretch slightly, <u>increasing the time</u> taken for the wearer to stop. This <u>reduces the forces</u> acting on the chest.

<u>AIR BAGS</u> also slow you down more <u>gradually</u>.

5) <u>Bubble wrap</u> works in a similar way to crumple zones as it <u>increases</u> the <u>time</u> over which any knocks and bumps happen to the stuff inside it — so it <u>reduces the forces</u> on your precious bit of kit.

The effect of crumple zones can be <u>shown</u> using <u>eggs</u>. Drop an egg on a hard floor and the <u>force of the impact</u> will <u>shatter</u> it immediately. Drop it onto <u>cushions</u>, surround it in <u>foam</u> or build some more elaborate crumple zone out of <u>cardboard</u> and <u>bubble wrap</u> and you might be more lucky. All because the collision happens over a <u>longer time</u>, and so the force on the egg is <u>smaller</u>.

Learn this stuff — it'll only take a moment... um...

Momentum's a pretty <u>fundamental</u> bit of Physics — so make sure you learn it properly. <u>Bubble wrap</u> is a good demonstration of the relationship between force and momentum — the changes in momentum take <u>longer</u>, <u>reducing the force</u>. Who'd have thought bubble wrap could be so educational... And so darned satisfying to pop.

Work and Power

In Physics, "work done" means something special — it's got its own formula and everything.

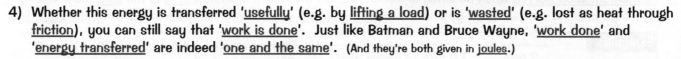

When a force moves an object, energy is transferred and work is done.

That statement sounds far more complicated than it needs to. Try this:

1) Whenever something moves, something else is providing some sort of 'effort' to move it.

2) The thing putting the effort in needs a supply of energy (like fuel or food or electricity etc.).

3) It then does 'work' by moving the object — and one way or another it transfers the energy it receives (as fuel etc.) into other forms.

4) Whether this energy is transferred 'usefully' (e.g. by lifting a load) or is 'wasted' (e.g. lost as heat through friction), you can still say that 'work is done'. Just like Batman and Bruce Wayne, 'work done' and 'energy transferred' are indeed 'one and the same'. (And they're both given in joules.)

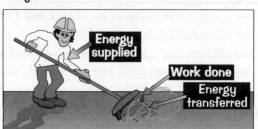

It's Just Another Trivial Formula:

Work Done = Force × Distance moved in the direction of the force

Whether the force is friction or weight or tension in a rope, it's always the same. To find how much energy has been transferred (in joules), you just multiply the force in N by the distance moved in the direction of the force, measured in metres. Easy as that. I'll show you...

__EXAMPLE:__ Some hooligan kids drag an old tractor tyre 5 m over rough ground. They pull with a total force of 340 N. Find the energy transferred.

__ANSWER:__ Energy transferred is work done, so:
$E = F \times d = 340 \times 5 = \underline{1700\ J}$. Phew — easy peasy isn't it?

Power is the "Rate of Doing Work" — i.e. How Much per Second

Power is not the same thing as force, nor energy. A powerful machine is not necessarily one which can exert a strong force (though it usually ends up that way). A powerful machine is one which transfers a lot of energy in a short space of time. This is the very easy formula for power:

$$Power = \frac{Work\ done}{Time\ taken}$$

__EXAMPLE:__ A motor transfers 4.8 kJ of useful energy in 2 minutes. Find its power output.

__ANSWER:__ $P = E / t = 4800/120 = 40\ W$ (or 40 J/s)
(Note that the kJ had to be turned into J, and the minutes into seconds.)

1 kJ = 1000 J

MOTOR

4.8 kJ of useful energy in 2 minutes

Power is Measured in Watts (or J/s)

The proper unit of power is the watt (W). One watt = 1 joule of energy transferred per second. Power means "how much energy per second", so watts are the same as "joules per second" (J/s). Don't ever say "watts per second" — it's nonsense.

Force yourself to do some work and learn this page...

Work done can sound like quite a wishy washy term, but the thing to remember is that it's just the energy transferred to something when you force it to move some distance. Like when you push a shopping trolley — you apply a force and cruise down the aisles as you bask in the glory of having transferred chemical energy to kinetic.

Kinetic and Potential Energy

Sat high on your stool in science class you have <u>gravitational potential energy</u> — there's always the potential to fall backwards off it and look a right numpty. So be careful to sit up straight, studying's a dangerous business...

Kinetic Energy is Energy of Movement

Anything that's <u>moving</u> has <u>kinetic energy</u>. There's a slightly <u>tricky formula</u> for it, so you have to concentrate a little bit <u>harder</u> for this one. But hey, that's life — it can be real tough sometimes:

$$\text{Kinetic Energy} = \tfrac{1}{2} \times \text{mass} \times \text{velocity}^2$$

EXAMPLE: A car of mass 2450 kg is travelling at 38 m/s.
Calculate its kinetic energy.
ANSWER: Plug the numbers into the formula — but watch the 'v²'!
K.E. = ½mv² = ½ × 2450 × 38² = <u>1 768 900 J</u>. (Joules because it's <u>energy</u>.)

Remember, the <u>kinetic energy</u> of something depends both on <u>mass</u> and <u>velocity</u>.
The <u>more it weighs</u> and the <u>faster it's going</u>, the <u>bigger</u> its kinetic energy will be.

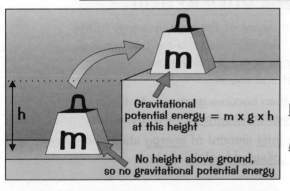

small mass, not fast low kinetic energy

big fast lorries Ltd

big mass, real fast high kinetic energy

Stopping Distances Increase Alarmingly with Extra Speed

To stop a car, the <u>kinetic energy</u>, ½mv², has to be <u>converted to heat energy</u> at the <u>brakes and tyres</u>:

$$\text{Initial Kinetic Energy} = \text{Work Done by Brakes to Stop Vehicle}$$
$$\tfrac{1}{2} \times m \times v^2 = F \times d$$

v = <u>velocity</u> of car   F = maximum <u>braking force</u>   d = <u>braking distance</u>

<u>Learn this real good</u>: if you <u>double the speed</u>, you double the value of <u>v</u>, but the <u>v²</u> means that the <u>K.E.</u> is then increased by a factor of <u>four</u>. However, 'F' is always the <u>maximum possible</u> braking force which <u>can't</u> be increased, so <u>d</u> must also increase by a factor of <u>four</u> to make the equation <u>balance</u>, i.e. if you go <u>twice as fast</u>, the <u>braking distance</u> 'd' (see p.88) must increase by a <u>factor of four</u> to dissipate the <u>extra K.E.</u>

Gravitational Potential Energy is Energy Due to Height

$$\text{Gravitational Potential Energy} = \text{mass} \times g \times \text{height}$$

The proper name for g is '<u>gravitational field strength</u>' and its units are <u>newtons per kilogram (N/kg)</u>. On <u>Earth</u>, g is approximately <u>10 N/kg</u>. On the Moon, its closer to 1.6 N/kg.

Gravitational potential energy = m x g x h at this height

No height above ground, so no gravitational potential energy

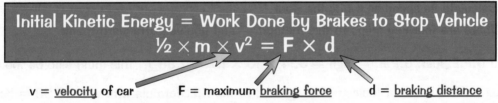

EXAMPLE: A sheep of mass 47 kg is slowly raised through 6.3 m. Find the gain in gravitational potential energy.
ANSWER: Just plug the numbers into the formula:
G.P.E. = mgh = 47 × 10 × 6.3 = <u>2961 J</u>.
(Joules because it's <u>energy</u>.)

Shopping distance — I can carry on for miles...

The stopping distance of a vehicle depends on the <u>initial velocity squared</u>. And the 'squared' makes all the difference — if you're going three times as fast, it will take you nine times as long to stop. A good reason to drive safely then.

Conservation of Energy

What goes up must come down — that's the principle of the <u>conservation of energy</u> in action. It's a really fundamental concept behind pretty much everything in physics. A good one to get your head around then.

The Principle of the Conservation of Energy Can be Stated Thus:

> Energy can never be <u>created nor destroyed</u>
> — only <u>transferred</u> from one form to another.

Another <u>important principle</u> which you need to <u>learn</u> is this one:

> Energy is <u>only useful</u> when it's <u>transferred</u> from one form to another.

Calculating the Speed of Falling Objects

When something falls, its <u>gravitational potential energy</u> (p.91) is <u>converted</u> into <u>kinetic energy</u> (principle of conservation of energy). Hence the <u>further</u> it falls, the <u>faster</u> it goes. In practice, some of the G.P.E. will be <u>dissipated</u> (spread out) as <u>heat</u> due to <u>air resistance</u> (p.84), but most of the time you can ignore that and learn this simple equation instead:

> Kinetic energy <u>gained</u> = Gravitational potential energy <u>lost</u>

<u>EXAMPLE:</u> A mouldy tomato of mass 140 g is dropped from a height of 1.7 m. Calculate its speed as it hits the floor.

<u>ANSWER:</u> There are four key steps to this method — and you've gotta learn them:

Step 1) Find G.P.E. lost: G.P.E. = mgh = $0.14 \times 10 \times 1.7$ = <u>2.38 J</u>. This must also be the K.E. gained.

Step 2) Equate the number of joules of K.E. gained to the K.E. formula with v in: $2.38 = \frac{1}{2}mv^2$

Step 3) Stick the numbers in: $2.38 = \frac{1}{2} \times 0.14 \times v^2$ or $2.38 = 0.07 \times v^2$
$2.38 \div 0.07 = v^2$ so $v^2 = 34$

Step 4) Square root: $v = \sqrt{34}$ = <u>5.83 m/s</u>

Easy peasy? Not really, no, but if you practise using the four steps you'll find it's not too bad.

Most Energy Transfers Involve Some Losses, Often as Heat

1) Every time energy is <u>transferred</u> from one form to another, some of the energy is <u>lost</u> to the surroundings — often as <u>heat</u>, and sometimes as <u>sound</u>. For example, in a car you want all the <u>chemical energy</u> of the fuel to be transferred into <u>kinetic energy</u>, but the car <u>warms up</u> and makes a <u>load of noise</u>, so some energy is lost as heat and sound.

2) Heat energy is <u>transferred</u> to <u>cooler</u> surroundings, which then become <u>warmer</u>. As the heat is <u>transferred</u> to cooler surroundings, the <u>energy</u> becomes <u>less concentrated</u> — it dissipates.

3) According to the <u>Principle of Conservation of Energy</u>, the <u>total</u> amount of <u>energy</u> stays the <u>same</u>. So the energy is still there, but it <u>can't be easily used</u> or <u>collected back in</u> again.

Conserve your energy — you'll need it for the next page...

<u>Rollercoasters</u> are a good example of the conversion of <u>gravitational potential energy</u> into <u>kinetic energy</u> — and one that pops up in exams time and time again. Just remember that some of the energy will be <u>wasted as heat</u>.

Radioactivity

Not every atom of an element is stable — and unstable atoms give out radiation. But we'll get onto that towards the end of the page. First up, a nifty way to write the number of protons and neutrons in an atom...

Elements **can be** Described **Using** Atomic **and** Mass Numbers

We can describe how many protons and neutrons there are in the nucleus of an atom of a particular element using this handy form...

EXAMPLE: OXYGEN

THE MASS (NUCLEON) NUMBER — total of protons and neutrons $\longrightarrow$ ^{16}

THE ATOMIC (PROTON) NUMBER — number of protons $\longrightarrow$ $_{8}$O

O is the chemical symbol for oxygen.

Isotopes **are** Different Forms **of the** Same Element

1) Isotopes are atoms with the same number of protons in their nucleus, but a different number of neutrons.

2) Hence they have the same atomic number, but different mass numbers.

3) Carbon-12 and carbon-14 are good examples:

4) Most elements have different isotopes, but there's usually only one or two stable ones (like carbon-12).

5) The other isotopes tend to be radioactive (like carbon-14) which means they decay into other elements and give out radiation. This is where all radioactivity comes from — unstable radioactive isotopes undergoing nuclear decay and spitting out high-energy particles or waves.

$^{12}_{6}$C — Mass number / Atomic number — 6 protons and 6 neutrons so it's carbon-12

$^{14}_{6}$C — 6 protons and 8 neutrons so it's carbon-14

Radioactivity **is a** Totally Random Process

1) Unstable nuclei will decay and in the process give out ionising radiation (see below).

2) This process is entirely random. This means that if you have 1000 unstable nuclei, you can't say when any one of them is going to decay, nor can you do anything at all to make a decay happen.

3) When the nucleus does decay it will spit out one or more of three types of radiation — alpha, beta or gamma (see next page). In the process, the nucleus will often change into a new element.

Alpha, Beta **and** Gamma Radiation can Cause Ionisation

1) Atoms can gain or lose electrons. When an atom (with no overall charge) loses or gains an electron it is turned into an ion (which is charged). This is known as ionisation.

2) Alpha, beta and gamma are all types of ionising radiation — they can cause ionisation of atoms.

3) Alpha particles have a large positive charge. When an alpha particle passes close to an atom, it can pull a negatively-charged electron out of orbit.

4) Beta particles (which are negatively charged) cause ionisation in a similar way to alpha particles. But instead of pulling an electron out of orbit, they push it out (as like charges repel each other, see p.74).

5) Gamma rays can interact with the electrons orbiting an atom and transfer energy to them. If the electron gets enough energy, it can break free from the atom.

I'm free!

See the next page for info on how well alpha, beta and gamma ionise.

Completely random — just like your revision shouldn't be...

It's the number of protons which decides what element something is, then the number of neutrons decides what isotope of that element it is. And it's unstable isotopes which undergo radioactive decay and give out radiation — alpha, beta or gamma. There's lots more to know about those three — the next page is packed full of fun facts.

Radioactivity

What's that? You'd love to hear more about the properties of alpha, beta and gamma radiation? Well, since you asked so nicely...

Alpha, Beta and Gamma Radiation Have Different Properties

You need to remember three things about each type of radiation:

1) What it actually is.
2) How strongly it ionises a material (i.e. removes electrons from atoms — see page 93).
3) How well it penetrates materials.

There's a pattern: the more ionising the radiation is, the less penetrating it is. Strongly ionising radiation gives up its energy quickly as it creates ions — so they don't penetrate far into materials.

Alpha Particles are Helium Nuclei ^4_2He

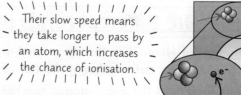

1) They're made up of two protons and two neutrons.
2) They are relatively big and heavy and slow-moving.
3) They have a strong positive charge.
4) Their big mass and charge make them strongly ionising. This just means they are able to remove electrons from lots of atoms, creating lots of ions. So they don't penetrate far into materials, but are stopped quickly.

Their slow speed means they take longer to pass by an atom, which increases the chance of ionisation.

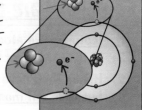

Beta Particles are Electrons Emitted from a Nucleus $^0_{-1}e$

1) These are in between alpha and gamma in terms of their properties.
2) They move quite fast and they are quite small (they're electrons).
3) They have a negative charge.
4) They are moderately ionising and penetrate moderately far into materials (further than alpha particles) before being stopped.
5) For every beta-particle emitted, a neutron turns to a proton in the nucleus.

Gamma Rays are a Type of Electromagnetic Radiation

1) They are the opposite of alpha particles in a way.
2) They are weakly ionising and can penetrate a long way into materials before eventually interacting with an atom.

Remember What Blocks the Three Types of Radiation...

Alpha particles are blocked by paper and cardboard.
Beta particles are blocked by thin aluminium.
Gamma rays are blocked by thick lead.

Of course anything equivalent will also block them, e.g. skin will stop alpha, but not the others; a thin sheet of any metal will stop beta; and very thick concrete will stop gamma just like lead does.

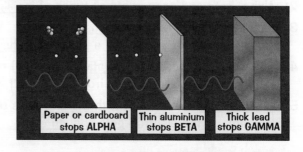

Paper or cardboard stops ALPHA | Thin aluminium stops BETA | Thick lead stops GAMMA

Don't let alpha particles upset you — be a bit more thick-skinned...

So, three things to learn about each type of ionising radiation — what it is, how ionising it is and how well it penetrates materials. Nothing too taxing on the brain, I reckon. It's the different properties of these types of radiation that make them suitable for different purposes — but you'll find out more about that later on...

Nuclear Fission

It's amazing how much <u>energy</u> there is <u>trapped</u> in a little atom. This energy is released by <u>nuclear fission</u>.

Nuclear Fission — The Splitting Up of Uranium Atoms

<u>Nuclear fission</u> is a type of <u>nuclear reaction</u> that is used to <u>release energy</u> from uranium (or plutonium) atoms, e.g. in a nuclear reactor. <u>Huge amounts</u> of energy can be released this way by using a <u>chain reaction</u>...

The Chain Reaction:

1) A <u>slow-moving neutron</u> is fired at an isotope of uranium — uranium-235. The neutron is <u>absorbed</u> by the nucleus — this makes the atom unstable and causes it to split.

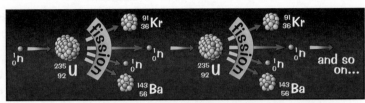

2) When the U-235 atom splits it forms <u>two new lighter</u> elements ('<u>daughter nuclei</u>') and <u>thermal</u> (heat) <u>energy</u> is released.

A neutron is <u>absorbed</u> by the nucleus because it has <u>no charge</u> — i.e. it's not <u>repelled</u> by the positive charge of the nucleus.

3) There are lots of different pairs of atoms that uranium can split into, e.g. krypton-91 and barium-143, but all these new nuclei are <u>radioactive</u> because they have the '<u>wrong</u>' number of neutrons in them.

4) Each time a <u>uranium</u> atom <u>splits up</u>, it also spits out <u>two or three neutrons</u>, which can hit <u>other</u> uranium nuclei, causing them to <u>split</u> also, and so on and so on. This is a <u>chain reaction</u>.

Nuclear Power Stations are Really Glorified Steam Engines

Nuclear power stations are powered by <u>nuclear reactors</u>. In a nuclear reactor, a <u>controlled chain reaction</u> takes place in which uranium atoms <u>split up</u>. The <u>heat energy</u> released by nuclear fission is used to <u>boil water</u> to drive a <u>steam turbine</u>, which turns a <u>generator</u> to generate <u>electrical energy</u>.

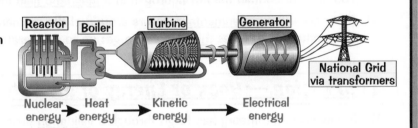

Nuclear energy → Heat energy → Kinetic energy → Electrical energy

Chain Reactions in Reactors Must be Carefully Controlled

1) The <u>neutrons</u> released by fission reactions in a nuclear reactor have <u>a lot</u> of energy. These neutrons will only cause <u>other</u> nuclear fissions (and cause a chain reaction) if they are <u>moving slow</u> enough to be <u>captured</u> by the uranium nuclei in the fuel rods.

2) To do this, the uranium <u>fuel rods</u> are placed in a <u>moderator</u> (for example, graphite) to <u>slow down</u> the fast moving neutrons.

3) This creates a <u>steady rate</u> of nuclear fission, where <u>one new neutron</u> produces another fission.

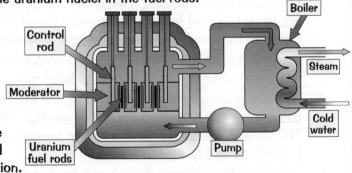

4) <u>Control rods</u>, often made of <u>boron</u>, limit the rate of fission by <u>absorbing</u> excess neutrons. They are placed <u>in between</u> the fuel rods and are <u>raised</u> and <u>lowered</u> into the reactor to <u>control</u> the chain reaction.

5) If the chain reaction in a nuclear reactor is <u>left to continue unchecked</u>, large amounts of <u>energy</u> are <u>released</u> in a very <u>short time</u>. <u>Many new fissions</u> will follow each fission, causing a <u>runaway reaction</u> which could lead to an <u>explosion</u>.

Revise nuclear power — full steam ahead...

When nuclear fission is used to produce energy in power stations, the chain reaction has to be <u>controlled</u> so that <u>safe</u> amounts of energy are released. More of a problem are the <u>radioactive products</u> (see page 101).

Nuclear Fusion

Loads of energy's released either when you break apart <u>really big nuclei</u> or join together <u>really small nuclei</u>. You can't do much with the ones in the middle, I'm afraid. (Don't ask, you don't want to know.)

Nuclear Fusion — _The Joining of Small Atomic Nuclei_

1) <u>Nuclear fusion</u> is the opposite of nuclear fission.

2) In nuclear fusion, two <u>light nuclei collide</u> at high speed and <u>join</u> (fuse) to create a <u>larger</u> nucleus. For example, <u>hydrogen</u> nuclei can fuse to produce <u>helium nuclei</u>. ➡

3) Fusion releases <u>a lot</u> of <u>energy</u> (<u>more</u> than fission for a given mass) — all the energy released in <u>stars</u> comes from fusion. So people are trying to develop <u>fusion reactors</u> to make <u>electricity</u>.

4) Fusion <u>doesn't</u> leave behind a lot of radioactive <u>waste</u> (see p.101) and there's <u>plenty</u> of hydrogen knocking about to use as <u>fuel</u>.

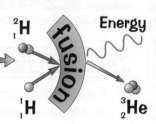

Fusion _Only Happens at_ High Temperatures _and_ Pressure

1) The <u>big problem</u> is that fusion only happens at <u>really high pressures and temperatures</u> (about <u>10 000 000 °C</u>). It doesn't happen at <u>low temperatures</u> and <u>pressures</u> due to the <u>electrostatic repulsion</u> of <u>protons</u> (like charges repel each other, see p.74).

2) It's <u>really hard</u> to create the <u>right conditions</u> for fusion. <u>No material</u> can withstand that kind of temperature — it would just be <u>vaporised</u>. So fusion reactors are <u>really hard</u> and <u>expensive</u> to try to build.

3) You have to contain the hot hydrogen in a <u>magnetic field</u> instead of a physical container.

4) There are a few <u>experimental</u> reactors around at the moment, but none of them are generating electricity yet. It takes <u>more</u> power to get up to temperature than the reactor can produce.

> BEWARE: the filling of this fruit pie is hotter than the conditions needed for fusion.

Cold Fusion — _Hoax_ or _Energy of the Future_?

1) A new scientific theory has to go through a <u>validation</u> process before it's accepted. This means making the <u>research results public</u> — usually in a <u>journal</u> such as <u>Nature</u>, so that other scientists can <u>repeat</u> the experiments. If lots of scientists get the <u>same results</u>, the theory is likely to be <u>accepted</u>.

2) An example of a theory which <u>hasn't</u> been accepted yet is '<u>cold fusion</u>'. Cold fusion is <u>nuclear fusion</u> which occurs at around <u>room temperature</u>, rather than at millions of degrees Celsius.

3) In 1989 two scientists, <u>Stanley Pons</u> and <u>Martin Fleischmann</u>, reported to a press conference that they had succeeded in releasing energy from cold fusion, using a simple experiment. This caused a lot of <u>excitement</u> — cold fusion would make it possible to generate lots of electricity, easily and cheaply. However, many scientists were <u>sceptical</u>, believing that fusion is only possible at very high temperatures.

4) Before the press conference, Pons and Fleischmann's work hadn't been <u>peer reviewed</u> — this meant other scientists hadn't <u>validated</u> their work before they went public.

5) After the press conference, other scientists tried to <u>repeat</u> Pons and Fleichmann's work. But <u>few</u> managed to reproduce the results <u>reliably</u>. When a group at <u>MIT</u> (Massachusetts Institute of Technology) <u>discredited</u> the theory, the feeling against cold fusion was so strong that some scientific journals <u>refused to publish</u> papers on it.

6) Despite all the setbacks, there is still <u>funding</u> available for cold fusion research, and Pons and Fleichmann's results have actually been <u>repeated</u> many times now — although <u>not reliably enough</u> for the theory to be accepted by the scientific community.

Pity they can't release energy by confusion...*

At about the same time as research started on fusion reactors, physicists were working on a <u>fusion bomb</u>. These "hydrogen bombs" are incredibly powerful — they can release a few thousand times more energy than the nuclear fission bombs that destroyed Hiroshima and Nagasaki at the end of World War II.

*There'd be plenty of physics books to use as fuel.

Background Radiation and Half-life

We're constantly exposed to <u>very low levels</u> of radiation — and all without us noticing. Sneaky.

Background Radiation *Comes from* Many Sources

Background radiation is the <u>low-level</u> radiation that's around us <u>all the time</u>. Background radiation comes from:

1) Radioactivity of naturally occurring <u>unstable isotopes</u> which are <u>all around us</u> — in the <u>air</u>, in <u>food</u>, in <u>building materials</u> and in the <u>rocks</u> under our feet.

2) Radiation from <u>space</u>, which is known as <u>cosmic rays</u>. These come mostly from the <u>Sun</u>. Luckily, the Earth's <u>atmosphere protects</u> us from much of this radiation, and its <u>magnetic field</u> deflects cosmic rays away from us.

3) Radiation due to <u>human activity</u>, e.g. <u>fallout</u> from <u>nuclear explosions</u> or <u>dumped nuclear waste</u> (see p.101). But this represents a <u>tiny</u> proportion of the total background radiation.

The RELATIVE PROPORTIONS of <u>background radiation</u>:

- 51% Radon gas
- 10% Cosmic rays
- 12% Food
- 12% Medical X-rays
- 14% Rocks and Building materials
- Just 1% from the Nuclear Industry

The Level of Background Radiation *Changes Depending on* Where You Are

1) Certain <u>underground rocks</u> (e.g. granite) can cause higher levels of background radiation at the <u>surface</u>, especially if they release <u>radioactive radon gas</u>, which tends to get <u>trapped inside people's houses</u>.

2) The <u>radon concentration</u> in people's houses <u>varies widely</u> across the UK, depending on the type of <u>rock</u> the house is built on.

3) So, the amount of <u>radon gas</u> that people are exposed to also depends on the <u>region</u> of the country they're living in.

Millom

Coloured bits indicate more radiation from rocks

The Radioactivity *of a Source Always* Decreases *Over Time*

The <u>activity</u> of a radioactive source <u>decreases</u> over time, <u>regardless</u> of what the source is.

1) Each time a radioactive nucleus <u>decays</u> (see page 93), and radiation is emitted, one more <u>radioactive nucleus disappears</u>.

2) As the <u>unstable nuclei</u> all steadily disappear, the <u>activity as a whole</u> will <u>decrease</u>. So the <u>older</u> a source becomes, the <u>less radiation</u> it will emit.

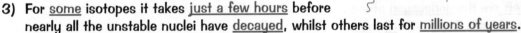

one half-life   one half-life

3) For <u>some</u> isotopes it takes <u>just a few hours</u> before nearly all the unstable nuclei have <u>decayed</u>, whilst others last for <u>millions of years</u>.

4) The problem with trying to <u>measure</u> this is that <u>the activity never reaches zero</u>, which is why we have to use the idea of <u>half-life</u> to measure how quickly the activity <u>drops off</u>.

5) A <u>short half-life</u> means the <u>activity falls quickly</u>, because <u>lots</u> of the nuclei decay <u>quickly</u>.

The <u>HALF-LIFE</u> of a radioactive isotope is the <u>TIME TAKEN</u> for <u>HALF</u> of the <u>undecayed nuclei</u> to <u>DECAY</u>.

6) A <u>long half-life</u> means the activity <u>falls more slowly</u> because <u>most</u> of the nuclei don't decay <u>for a long time</u> — they just sit there, <u>basically unstable</u>, but kind of <u>biding their time</u>.

7) The <u>activity</u> of a radioactive isotope is measured in <u>becquerels</u> (Bq). <u>1 Bq</u> is <u>1 decay per second</u>. This can be measured with a <u>Geiger-Muller</u> (G-M) tube.

Background radiation — the ugly wallpaper of the Universe...

Background radiation was discovered <u>accidentally</u>. Scientists were measuring radioactivity of materials, but they detected radioactivity when there was <u>no material</u> being tested. They realised it must be natural background radiation.

<u>Calculating Half-life</u>

<u>Half-life</u> is a tricky concept, but it can be calculated quite simply by looking at the activity of a sample over time.

<u>Calculating Half-Life</u> *is Best Done* Step by Step

Do half-life questions <u>STEP BY STEP</u>. Like this one:

> <u>A VERY SIMPLE EXAMPLE:</u> The activity of a radioisotope is 640 Bq.
> Two hours later it has fallen to 40 Bq. Find the half-life of the sample.
>
> <u>ANSWER:</u> You must go through it in <u>short simple steps</u> like this:
>
> | INITIAL count: | | after ONE half-life: | | after TWO half-lives: | | after THREE half-lives: | | after FOUR half-lives: |
> |---|---|---|---|---|---|---|---|---|
> | 640 | (÷2) → | 320 | (÷2) → | 160 | (÷2) → | 80 | (÷2) → | 40 |
>
> Notice the careful <u>step-by-step method</u>, which tells us it takes <u>four half-lives</u> for the activity to fall from 640 to 40. Hence <u>two hours</u> represents four half-lives, so the <u>half-life is 30 minutes</u>.

<u>Measuring</u> *the* <u>Half-Life</u> *of a Source Using a Graph*

1) This can <u>only be done</u> by taking <u>several readings</u> of the source's <u>activity</u>, usually using a <u>G-M tube and counter</u> (p.97).

2) The results can then be <u>plotted</u> as a <u>graph</u>, which will <u>always</u> be shaped like the one to the right. ⟹

3) The <u>half-life</u> is found from the graph, by finding the <u>time interval</u> on the <u>bottom axis</u> corresponding to a <u>halving</u> of the <u>activity</u> on the <u>vertical axis</u>. Easy peasy really.

4) <u>One trick</u> you need to know is about the <u>background radiation</u> (p.97), which also enters the G-M tube and gives <u>false readings</u>. Measure the background count <u>first</u> and then <u>subtract it</u> from <u>every reading</u> you get, before plotting the results on the <u>graph</u>.

<u>You Can Use</u> Models <u>to</u> *Simulate Radioactive Decay*

The <u>radioactive dice model</u> is one way of <u>simulating</u> the <u>radioactive decay</u> of a sample:

1) 24 dice represent 24 atoms of an <u>unstable isotope</u> that could decay at any moment.

2) Each <u>roll</u> of all 24 dice <u>represents one unit of time</u> (seconds, minutes, hours etc.). All the dice that come up with a <u>six</u> are said to have '<u>decayed</u>' and are removed.

3) <u>The dice that are left</u> are the <u>undecayed</u> atoms. The dice are rolled <u>multiple times</u> until <u>all</u> the radioactive isotope dice have decayed.

4) Plot your results in a <u>graph</u> like the one on the right with a <u>best fit curve</u>. ⟹

5) Use the graph to find the <u>time interval</u> on the bottom axis that you get by <u>halving the activity</u> and hey presto — you've got a <u>half life</u>.

6) This model <u>simulates radioactive decay</u> because it's <u>completely random</u> which dice will come up with a six on each roll, but each one will eventually — just like each unstable atom will <u>eventually decay</u>. The shape of the <u>decay curve</u> on the graph that you produce is the <u>same</u> as the one you would get from measuring the <u>activity of a radioactive source</u>.

<u>Half-life of a box of chocolates — about five minutes...</u>

When calculating the half-life of an isotope from a graph, find half the <u>initial activity</u> on the y-axis, draw a horizontal line across until you reach the activity curve, then draw a line vertically down to the x-axis. Sorted.

Uses of Radioactivity

With radioactive sources belting out all those emissions, some clever scientists thought up some uses for it all.

Household Fire Alarms — Use Alpha Radiation

1) A <u>weak</u> source of alpha radiation (p.94) is placed in a smoke detector, close to <u>two electrodes</u>.

2) The source causes <u>ionisation</u>, and a <u>current</u> flows.

3) If there is a fire then smoke will <u>absorb</u> the radiation
— the current stops and the <u>alarm sounds</u>.

Sterilisation of Food and Equipment Using Gamma Rays

1) <u>Food</u> can be <u>irradiated with</u> (exposed to) a <u>high dose</u> of <u>gamma rays</u> which will <u>kill</u> all <u>microbes</u>. This means that the food doesn't go bad as quickly as it would do otherwise.

2) Similarly, <u>medical equipment</u> can be <u>sterilised</u> using gamma rays instead of being <u>boiled</u>.

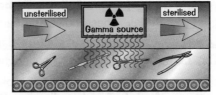

3) <u>Irradiation</u> is a particularly good method of sterilisation because, unlike boiling, it doesn't involve <u>high temperatures</u>, so <u>fresh fruit</u> or <u>plastic instruments</u> can be totally <u>sterilised</u> without being <u>damaged</u>.

4) The radioactive source used for this needs to be a <u>very strong</u> emitter of <u>gamma rays</u> with a <u>reasonably long half-life</u> (at least several months) so that it doesn't need <u>replacing</u> too often.

Radiation is Used in Tracers and Thickness Gauges

1) Certain radioactive isotopes can be used as <u>tracers</u>. A <u>medical</u> tracer is <u>injected</u> into a patient (or <u>swallowed</u>) and its progress around the body is followed using an <u>external detector</u>. A <u>computer</u> uses the reading from the detector to produce an <u>image</u> to follow the flow of the injected isotope. This method can be used to <u>detect</u> and <u>diagnose medical conditions</u> (e.g. cancer).

2) <u>All isotopes</u> which are taken <u>into the body</u> must be <u>BETA or GAMMA</u> emitters (never alpha), so that the radiation <u>passes out of the body</u> — and they should only last <u>a few hours</u>, so that the radioactivity inside the patient <u>quickly disappears</u> (i.e. they should have a <u>short half-life</u>).

3) <u>Gamma emitting tracers</u> are also used in <u>industry</u> to detect <u>leaks</u> in <u>underground pipes</u>.

4) <u>Beta radiation</u> is used in <u>thickness control</u>. You direct radiation through the stuff being made (e.g. paper), and put a detector on the other side, connected to a control unit. When the amount of <u>detected</u> radiation changes, it means the paper is coming out too thick or too thin, so the control unit adjusts the rollers to give the correct thickness.

5) The radioactive source used needs to have a fairly long half-life so it doesn't decay away <u>too quickly</u>.

6) It also needs to be a <u>beta</u> source, because then the paper will <u>partly block</u> the radiation (see p.94). If it <u>all</u> goes through (or <u>none</u> of it does), then the reading <u>won't change</u> at all as the thickness changes.

Gamma Rays Can Be Used to Treat Cancer

1) High doses of gamma rays will <u>kill all living cells</u>. For this reason, they can be used to <u>treat cancers</u>.

2) <u>Radiotherapists</u> have to be very careful when treating a patient to <u>direct</u> the gamma rays right at the <u>cancerous</u> cells, so they can <u>minimise</u> the damage done to <u>healthy</u> cells.

Ionising radiation — just what the doctor ordered...

Radiation has many important uses — especially in <u>medicine</u>. Make sure you know which type of radiation is used in each application and why. Examiners just love to ask you questions on this stuff.

Dangers of Radioactivity

Attitudes towards the dangers of radioactivity changed a lot over the last century.

1) When Marie Curie discovered the radioactive properties of radium in 1898, nobody knew anything about its dangers. People were fascinated by radium — it was used in medicines and to make luminous paint. You could buy everyday products made using this paint, e.g. glow-in-the-dark watches.

2) However, by the 1930s people were starting to link health problems to radiation — many watch dial painters developed cancer as a result of exposure to radium. More recently, we've learnt a lot about the dangers of radiation from the long-term effects of terrible events like the nuclear attacks on Japan in 1945 and the Chernobyl disaster in 1986.

Ionising Radiation *Can Cause* Tissue Damage *and* Cell Mutation

Alpha, beta and gamma radiation will cheerfully enter living cells and collide with molecules of genetic material. These collisions cause ionisation, which leads to tissue damage.

1) Lower doses tend to cause minor damage without killing the cell. This can give rise to mutant cells which divide uncontrollably. This is cancer.

2) Higher doses tend to kill cells completely, which causes radiation sickness if a lot of body cells all get battered at once.

3) The extent of the harmful effects depends on two things:

   a) How much exposure you have to the radiation.

   b) The energy and penetration of the radiation, since some types are more hazardous than others, of course.

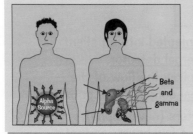

Outside the body, beta and gamma sources are the most dangerous. This is because beta and gamma can get inside to the delicate organs, whereas alpha is much less dangerous because it can't penetrate the skin. Inside the body, an alpha source is the most dangerous. Alpha sources do all their damage in a very localised area. Beta and gamma sources on the other hand are less dangerous inside the body because they mostly pass straight out without doing much damage.

You Should Protect Yourself *in the* Laboratory...

You should always act to minimise your exposure to radioactive sources.

1) Never allow skin contact with a source. Always handle sources with tongs.

2) Keep the source at arm's length to keep it as far from the body as possible.

3) Keep the source pointing away from the body and avoid looking directly at it.

4) Always put the source back in a labelled lead box, as soon as the experiment is over, to keep your exposure time short.

...and If You Work *with* Nuclear Radiation

1) Industrial nuclear workers wear full protective suits to prevent tiny radioactive particles being inhaled or lodging on the skin or under fingernails etc.

2) Lead-lined suits, lead/concrete barriers and thick lead screens are used to prevent exposure to gamma rays from highly contaminated areas (alpha and beta radiation are stopped much more easily — see p.94).

3) Workers use remote-controlled robot arms to carry out tasks in highly radioactive areas.

Revision sickness — never mind, it'll wear off...

It's quite difficult to do research on how radiation affects humans. This is partly because it would be very unethical to do controlled experiments, exposing people to huge doses of radiation just to see what happens. We rely mostly on studies of populations affected by nuclear accidents or nuclear bombs.

Nuclear Power

Nuclear power may be the best solution to future electricity supply problems, but it is a very <u>controversial</u> area for science. Intrigued? I bet you are. Get reading to find out more...

Nuclear Waste <u>is a</u> <u>Big Problem</u> <u>for the Nuclear Industry</u>

1) <u>Nuclear fission</u> releases a lot of energy that can be used to generate electricity (see page 95), but it also creates <u>radioactive waste products</u> that can't just be <u>thrown away</u>.

2) The waste products from nuclear fission <u>can't</u> usually be recycled to create more electricity. They also have <u>very long half-lives</u>, meaning they will be <u>radioactive</u> for <u>hundreds</u> or even <u>thousands</u> (or millions) of <u>years</u>.

3) This radioactive waste can be <u>really dangerous</u> (see previous page) so it needs to be put somewhere <u>far away</u> from <u>people</u> to stop it causing any <u>harm</u>.

4) At the moment, nuclear power stations usually deal with the most dangerous nuclear waste by <u>vitrification</u> — this means they melt the waste with other materials to form a type of <u>glass</u>. The liquid glass is sealed inside <u>steel canisters</u> and buried deep <u>underground</u>.

5) Another way to deal with nuclear waste is to pack it into <u>thick metal containers</u> and/or bury the waste in a deep hole and then fill the hole with <u>tons of concrete</u>.

6) Generally, the important thing when you're <u>storing</u> nuclear waste is to make sure there are plenty of materials to <u>absorb the</u> <u>radiation</u> long before it can reach the surface of the Earth.

Using Nuclear Power <u>Has Its</u> <u>Pros</u> <u>and</u> <u>Cons</u>

Nuclear power has a lot going for it, but some people are completely against it being used.

1) <u>Public perception</u> of nuclear power can be <u>very negative</u> — it's often seen by many to be <u>very dangerous</u>.

2) Some people worry that nuclear waste can <u>never be disposed of safely</u>. There is always a danger that the nuclear waste could <u>leak out</u> and <u>pollute</u> land, rivers and oceans. In the past there have been <u>serious accidents</u> that have <u>contaminated huge areas</u> with radioactivity. Some people say that the energy generated by nuclear power is <u>not worth the risk</u> of nuclear waste accidents.

3) <u>Nuclear power</u> also carries the risk of <u>leaks</u> from the power station or a <u>major catastrophe</u> like <u>Chernobyl</u>.

4) However, nuclear power is generally a <u>pretty safe</u> way of generating electricity — it's not as <u>risky</u> as <u>some people may think</u> it is.

5) And it's not all doom and gloom. Nuclear power is a <u>very reliable</u> energy resource and reduces the need for fossil fuels (which are already running out).

6) <u>Fossil fuels</u> (coal, oil and gas) all release carbon dioxide (CO_2) when they're burnt. This adds to the <u>greenhouse effect</u> and <u>global warming</u>. Burning coal and oil also releases <u>sulphur dioxide</u> that can cause <u>acid rain</u>. Nuclear power <u>doesn't</u> release these gases, so in this way it is a very <u>clean</u> source of energy.

7) <u>Huge</u> amounts of energy can be generated from a relatively <u>small</u> amount of <u>nuclear material</u>. Nuclear <u>fuel</u> (i.e. the uranium) is <u>cheap</u> and <u>readily available</u>.

8) However, the <u>overall cost</u> of nuclear power is <u>high</u> due to the initial cost of the <u>power plant</u> and final <u>decommissioning</u> — dismantling a nuclear plant safely takes <u>decades</u>.

Eating radioactive sheep? That's probably bad for ewe...

In 1986 the <u>Chernobyl</u> nuclear power plant in Ukraine overheated when too many of the <u>control rods</u> were removed in a system test. The resulting explosions released <u>100 times</u> the radiation of the bombs that were dropped on Japan, and nearby cities had to be totally evacuated. Today, the areas around Chernobyl <u>remain deserted</u>.

Revision Summary for P2b Topics 4, 5 & 6

Right, you've conquered three revision topics — time to see if any of it has stuck. Good luck chaps.

1) What are the two different parts of the overall stopping distance of a car?
2) List two factors which affect each of the two parts of the stopping distance.
3)* Write down the formula for momentum. Find the momentum of a 78 kg sheep falling at 15 m/s.
4)* A gymnast (mass 50 kg) jumps off a beam and hits the floor at a speed of 7 m/s.
   She bends her knees and stops moving in 0.5 s. What is the average force acting on her?
5) Explain how seat belts, crumple zones and airbags are useful in a crash.
6) What's the connection between 'work done' and 'energy transferred'?
7)* Write down the formula for work done. A crazy dog drags a big branch 12 m over the next-door
   neighbour's front lawn, pulling with a force of 535 N. How much energy is transferred?
8) What's the formula for power? What are the units of power?
9)* An electric motor transfers 540 kJ of electrical energy in 4½ minutes. What is its power output?
10)* What's the formula for kinetic energy? Find the kinetic energy of a 78 kg sheep moving at 23 m/s.
11)* Write down the formula for gravitational potential energy. Calculate the increase in gravitational potential
    energy when a box of mass 12 kg is raised through 4.5 m. (Assume g = 10 N/kg.)
12)* A roller coaster train of mass 15 000 kg starts from the top of a hill. As it travels down the hill it drops a
    vertical distance of 50 m. How much gravitational potential energy does it lose in this time?
13) Write down the principle of the conservation of energy.
14)* Assuming no air resistance, calculate the kinetic energy of a 78 kg sheep just as it hits the floor after
    falling from a height of 20 m. How fast is the sheep travelling as it hits the floor?
15) Explain what the mass number and atomic number of an atom represent.
16) Write down the number of protons and neutrons in an atom of $^{230}_{90}$Th.
17) Explain what isotopes are. Give an example. Do stable or unstable isotopes undergo nuclear decay?
18) Describe in detail the nature and properties of the three types of ionising radiation:
    a) alpha,   b) beta,   c) gamma.
19) Name a substance that will block each of the three types of nuclear radiation.
20) What type of particle is U-235 bombarded with to make it split?
21) Draw a diagram to illustrate the fission of uranium-235 and explain how the chain reaction works.
22) Explain in terms of energy transfers how electricity is produced in a nuclear power station.
23) What is nuclear fusion? Why is it difficult to construct a working fusion reactor?
24) What is 'cold fusion'? Why are many scientists still sceptical about cold fusion as a
    way of releasing energy?
25) Describe the process that new scientific theories have to go through before they are accepted.
26) Give three sources of background radiation.
27) Give a proper definition of half-life.
28) Sketch a typical graph of activity against time for a radioactive source.
    Show how you can find the half-life from your graph.
29)*The activity of a radioisotope sample is 840 Bq. Four hours later it has fallen to 105 Bq.
    Find the half-life of the sample.
30) Describe in detail how radioactive sources are used in each of the following:
    a) smoke detectors,   b) sterilisation of food,   c) tracers in medicine,   d) treating cancer.
31) Explain what kind of damage ionising radiation causes to body cells. What are the effects of high doses?
    What damage can lower doses do?
32) Which kinds of radioactive source are most dangerous: a) inside the body, b) outside the body?
33) List four safety precautions that should be taken when handling radioactive materials in the school lab.
34) Give one reason for using nuclear power rather than fossil fuels.
35) What is the main environmental problem associated with nuclear power?

*Answers on page 107.

The Perfect Cup of Tea

The making and drinking of tea are important life skills. It's not something that will crop up in the exam, but it is something that will make your revision much easier. So here's a guide to making the perfect cuppa...

1) Choose the Right Mug

A good mug is an essential part of the tea drinking experience, but choosing the right vessel for your tea can be tricky. Here's a guide to choosing your mug:

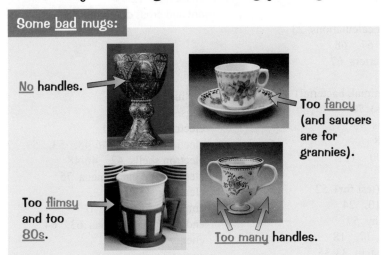

Some bad mugs:

No handles.

Too fancy (and saucers are for grannies).

Too flimsy and too 80s.

Too many handles.

The perfect mug:

Holds just the right amount of tea.

Wide enough to dunk a biscuit.

Has a design that complements your personality (yes, I'm a bit hippy).

Nice, easy to hold handle.

2) Get Some Water and Boil It

For a really great brew follow these easy step-by-step instructions:

1) First, pour some water into a kettle and switch it on. (Check it's switched on at the wall too.)

2) Let the kettle boil. While you're waiting, see what's on TV later and check your belly button for fluff. Oh, and put a tea bag in a mug.

3) Once the kettle has boiled, pour the water into the mug.

4) Mash the tea bag about a bit with a spoon. Remove the tea bag.

5) Add a splash of milk (and a lump of sugar or two if you're feeling naughty).

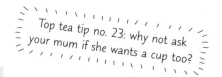

Top tea tip no. 23: why not ask your mum if she wants a cup too?

Note: some people may tell you to add the milk before the tea. Scientists have recently confirmed that this is nonsense.

3) Sit Back and Relax

Now this is important — once you've made your cuppa:

1) Have a quick rummage in the kitchen cupboards for a cheeky biscuit. (Custard creams are best — steer clear of any ginger biscuits — they're evil.)

2) Find your favourite armchair/beanbag. Move the cat.

3) Sit back and enjoy your mug of tea. You've earned it.

Phew — time for a brew I reckon...

It's best to ignore what other people say about making cups of tea and follow this method. Trust me, this is the most definitive and effective method. If you don't do it this way, you'll have a shoddy drinking experience. There, you've been warned. Now go and get the kettle on. Mine's milk and two sugars...

Index

Index

Index

Answers

Revision Summary for B2 Topic 1 (page 21)

3) $\times$ 25 magnification

15) a) pH 1.6

b) stomach

Revision Summary for B2 Topic 2 (page 30)

6) a) 60 beats per minute

b) 2 minutes

c) 70 beats per minute

Revision Summary for C2a Topics 1, 2 & 3 (page 58)

7) 20.18

15) a) KF

b) $AlCl_3$

c) NaOH

25) ionic lattice

29) 0.375

Bottom of page 69

NaOH: 40, Fe_2O_3: 160, C_6H_{14}: 86, $Mg(NO_3)_2$: 148

Bottom of page 70

1) a) 30.0%

b) 88.9%

2) CH_4

Bottom of page 71

1) 21.4 g

2) 38.0 g

Revision Summary for C2b Topics 4, 5 & 6 (page 73)

18)

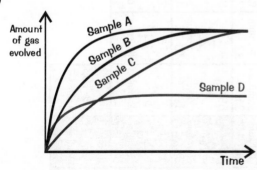

22) a) 44

b) 84

c) 78

d) 81

e) 106

23) 16.5%

24) CaF_2

25) a) 186.8 g

b) 80.3 g

Revision Summary for P2a Topics 1, 2 & 3 (page 87)

9) $I = Q \div t$, $t = 10 \times 60 = 600$ s

$I = 900 \div 600 = 1.5$ A

14) $R = V \div I$, $R = 12 \div 2.5 = 4.8 \ \Omega$

17) $I = P \div V$, $I = 1100 \div 230 = 4.8$ A

19) $s = d \div t$, $s = 3.2 \div 35 = 0.091$ m/s

$d = s \times t$, $d = 0.091 \times (25 \times 60) = 136.5$ m

20) No. speed = distance $\div$ time

speed = $6.3 \div 0.5 = 12.6$ m/s

22) $a = (v - u) \div t$, $a = (14 - 0) \div 0.4 = 35$ m/s^2

32) $F = m \times a$, $a = F \div m$

$a = 30 \div 4 = 7.5$ m/s^2

Revision Summary for P2b Topics 4, 5 & 6 (page 102)

3) momentum = mass $\times$ velocity

momentum = $78 \times 15 = 1170$ kg m/s

4) $F = (mv - mu) \div t$

$u = 7$ m/s, $v = 0$ m/s, $m = 50$ kg, $t = 0.5$ s

$F = (0 - (50 \times 7)) \div 0.5 = -700$ N

(i.e. 700 N upwards)

7) Work done = force $\times$ distance moved in the direction of the force

$E = F \times d = 535 \times 12 = 6420$ J

9) $P = E \div t = 540\ 000 \div (4.5 \times 60) = 2000$ W

10) K.E. = $\frac{1}{2} \times m \times v^2 = \frac{1}{2} \times 78 \times (23^2) = 20\ 631$ J

11) G.P.E. = $m \times g \times h = 12 \times 10 \times 4.5 = 540$ J

(g = 10 N/kg).

12) G.P.E. = $m \times g \times h$

$= 15\ 000 \times 10 \times 50 = 7\ 500\ 000$ J

(= 7500 kJ)

14) K.E. gained = G.P.E. lost (ignoring air resistance).

K.E. = $m \times g \times h = 78 \times 10 \times 20 = 15\ 600$ J

(= 15.6 kJ)

K.E. = $\frac{1}{2} \times m \times v^2$

$v^2 = 2 \times$ K.E. $\div m$

$v^2 = 2 \times 15\ 600 \div 78 = 400$ m/s

$v = 20$ m/s

29) $840 \div 2 = 420 \rightarrow$ 1 half life

$420 \div 2 = 210 \rightarrow$ 2 half lives

$210 \div 2 = 105 \rightarrow$ 3 half lives

3 half lives pass in 4 hours.

4 hours = $(4 \times 60) = 240$ mins.

1 half life = $240 \div 3 = 80$ mins.

The Periodic Table

Periods	Group 1	Group 2															Group 3	Group 4	Group 5	Group 6	Group 7	Group 0
1								1 H Hydrogen 1														4 He Helium 2
2	7 Li Lithium 3	9 Be Beryllium 4															11 B Boron 5	12 C Carbon 6	14 N Nitrogen 7	16 O Oxygen 8	19 F Fluorine 9	20 Ne Neon 10
3	23 Na Sodium 11	24 Mg Magnesium 12															27 Al Aluminium 13	28 Si Silicon 14	31 P Phosphorus 15	32 S Sulfur 16	35.5 Cl Chlorine 17	40 Ar Argon 18
4	39 K Potassium 19	40 Ca Calcium 20	45 Sc Scandium 21	48 Ti Titanium 22	51 V Vanadium 23	52 Cr Chromium 24	55 Mn Manganese 25	56 Fe Iron 26	59 Co Cobalt 27	59 Ni Nickel 28	63.5 Cu Copper 29	65 Zn Zinc 30	70 Ga Gallium 31	73 Ge Germanium 32	75 As Arsenic 33	79 Se Selenium 34	80 Br Bromine 35	84 Kr Krypton 36
5	85 Rb Rubidium 37	88 Sr Strontium 38	89 Y Yttrium 39	91 Zr Zirconium 40	93 Nb Niobium 41	96 Mo Molybdenum 42	99 Tc Technetium 43	101 Ru Ruthenium 44	103 Rh Rhodium 45	106 Pd Palladium 46	108 Ag Silver 47	112 Cd Cadmium 48	115 In Indium 49	119 Sn Tin 50	122 Sb Antimony 51	128 Te Tellurium 52	127 I Iodine 53	131 Xe Xenon 54
6	133 Cs Caesium 55	137 Ba Barium 56	57-71 Lanthanides	178 Hf Hafnium 72	181 Ta Tantalum 73	184 W Tungsten 74	186 Re Rhenium 75	190 Os Osmium 76	192 Ir Iridium 77	195 Pt Platinum 78	197 Au Gold 79	201 Hg Mercury 80	204 Tl Thallium 81	207 Pb Lead 82	209 Bi Bismuth 83	210 Po Polonium 84	210 At Astatine 85	222 Rn Radon 86
7	223 Fr Francium 87	226 Ra Radium 88	89-103 Actinides															

Atomic number

Key Stage 4 / GCSE

OnCourse

Maths
Foundation and Intermediate Tiers
Summary and Practice Book
WITH FULL ANSWERS

Stanley Thornes (Publishers) Ltd

Paul Metcalf, Liz Hamilton and Anne Haworth

Assessment

The GCSE Mathematics syllabus is assessed at three overlapping tiers:

- Foundation tier – covering grades D, E, F and G
- Intermediate tier – covering grades B, C, D and E
- Higher tier – covering grades A*, A, B and C

Within each tier, the syllabus content is divided into four attainment targets with the following weightings:

- Ma 1   Using and applying mathematics   20%
- Ma 2   Number and algebra   40%
- Ma 3   Shape, space and measure   20%
- Ma 4   Handling data   20%

Written papers

For your GCSE examination you will be required to take two written papers covering attainment targets Ma 2 to Ma 4 (worth 80% of the overall mark). You will not be allowed to use a calculator on the first written paper, although you will be expected to have a calculator for the second paper.

Both papers may assess any topic in the subject content for the tier.

Coursework

All candidates are required to carry out investigations and practical tasks during KS4. The GCSE examination will test your ability to use and apply mathematics (MA 1) through coursework set and marked by the centre (SEG Syllabus 2510T and NEAB Syllabus A), or coursework set and marked by the board (SEG Syllabus 2510X) or else by terminal examination (NEAB Syllabus B).

Preparing for the examination

Before the examination

- Get a copy of the syllabus document and identify the topics you need to work on.
- Read through the Summary pages of this book and make notes.
- Work through the Practice Exercises and Examination Questions and check your answers. Make a note of any mistakes you make and revisit these topics to make sure that you understand them.
- Put together a revision timetable and remember that quality is better than quantity!
- Make sure that you know how to use all the equipment you will need in your exam, e.g. calculator, protractor, compasses, etc.
- Don't rely on good luck – there is no substitute for revision and practice.

On the day of the examination

- Get to the examination in plenty of time and make sure you bring all the correct equipment you need with you.
- Make sure you read the instructions on the front of the examination paper and answer **all** the questions.
- Read each question carefully before answering.
- Write clearly and draw your diagrams accurately. Remember to show all of your working.
- Keep an eye on the time so you don't spend too long on early questions and then don't have time to finish the paper. If your are stuck on a question, leave it and come back to it later.
- Check your answers are reasonable and include units where appropriate.

Contents

Topic 1
The rules
of number

Note: The decimal point separates the units from the tenths.

Note: You should always cancel fractions down where possible.

Note: You can also use the fact that 9% = 0.09

Summary

Working with decimals

The place of a figure in a number tells you its value and decimals are all about place values. Dead easy!

Place value table

| ...... | thousands | hundreds | tens | units | . | tenths | hundredths | thousandths | ...... |

Like this

Write 4068.125 using the appropriate decimal place values.

4	0	6	8	.	1	2	5
4 thousands	0 hundreds	6 tens	8 units		1 tenth	2 hundredths	5 thousandths

Working with fractions

You do not change a fraction if you multiply or divide the numerator (top) and denominator (bottom) by the same number. The fractions you get are called equivalent fractions.

Like this

$\frac{6}{14} = \frac{3}{7}$ (divide by 2)   or $\frac{6}{14} = \frac{30}{70}$ (multiply by 5)

Finding a fraction of a quantity

To find a fraction of a quantity you multiply the quantity by the fraction.

Like this

Find $\frac{3}{5}$ of 450

$\frac{3}{5}$ of 450 is $\frac{3}{5} \times 450 = 270$

One quantity as a fraction of another

To find one quantity as a fraction of another you must remember to put each quantity in the same units.

Like this

I spend 35 minutes on my mathematics homework. My total homework time is 2 hours. What fraction of my homework time is spent on my mathematics?

Converting everything to the same units – in this case minutes

2 hours $= 2 \times 60$ minutes $= 120$ minutes

Fraction is $\frac{35}{120} = \frac{7}{24}$

Working with percentages

Percent means per 100 or out of 100 or just divide by 100.

27% means   27 per 100   or 27 out of 100   or $\frac{27}{100}$ or 0.27

Finding a percentage of a quantity

To find a percentage of a quantity you multiply the quantity by the percentage.

Like this

Find 9% of 300

9% is 9 divided by 100 or $\frac{9}{100}$

9% of 300 is $\frac{9}{100} \times 300 = 27$

Practice Exercise

1 (a) Put these into circles with others of the same value. 0.5, $\frac{1}{4}$, 5% and $\frac{1}{5}$ have already been done for you.

20% $\frac{5}{100}$ $\frac{2}{10}$ 50% $\frac{2}{40}$ 0.2 $\frac{50}{100}$

$\frac{25}{100}$ $\frac{1}{2}$ 25%   0.05 $\frac{1}{20}$

0.25 $\frac{5}{10}$ $\frac{5}{20}$ $\frac{20}{100}$

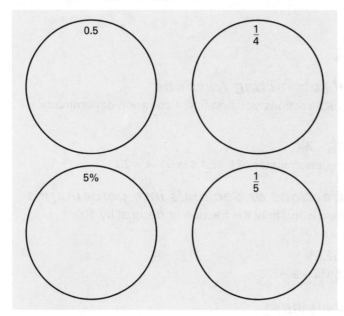

(b) What fraction of the whole set goes in each circle?

(c) What percentage of the whole set goes in each circle?

Which is the best mark, 80%, $\frac{15}{20}$ or $\frac{33}{40}$?

2

3 Say whether these statements are true or false.

Statement	True or false
12% of £15 $= \frac{12}{100} \times$ £15	
12% of £15 $= \frac{£15}{12}$	
12% of £15 $=$ £1.80	
12% of £15 $= \frac{£15}{100} \times 12$	
12% of £15 $= \frac{£15}{12} \times 100$	
12% of £15 $= \frac{£12}{15} \times 100$	

1 (b) Answer ....

1 (c) Answer ....

2 Answer ....

Topic 1
The rules
of number

Note: Remember to cancel your fractions down where possible.

Note: Remember to put each quantity in the same units.

Summary

Changing fractions to decimals

To change fractions to decimals you divide the numerator by the denominator. Easy!

Like this

$\frac{3}{8} = 3 \div 8 = 0.375$

Changing decimals to fractions

All you have to remember is your decimal place values!

Like this

$0.2 = \frac{2}{10} = \frac{1}{5}$ and

$0.002 = \frac{2}{1000} = \frac{1}{500}$

Adding and subtracting fractions

To add or subtract fractions you first find a common denominator.

Like this

$1\frac{2}{5} + 2\frac{1}{4} = 1\frac{8}{20} + 2\frac{5}{20} = 3\frac{13}{20}$

As the common denominator of 5 and 4 is $5 \times 4 = 20$

Changing fractions or decimals into percentages

All you have to do is multiply the fraction or decimal by 100.

Like this

$\frac{5}{8} = \frac{5}{8} \times 100\% = 62.5\%$

$0.39 = 0.39 \times 100\% = 39\%$

Percentage changes

To find a percentage change you first have to find the actual increase/decrease or profit/loss.

Like this

(a) A washing machine is advertised at £450 plus VAT at $17\frac{1}{2}\%$. What is the cost of the washing machine?

VAT is $17\frac{1}{2}\%$ of £450 $= \frac{17.5}{100} \times £450 = £78.75$

Cost of washing machine $= £450 + £78.75 = £528.75$

(b) After one year a car which cost £15 596.00 is sold at a loss of 7%. What is the selling price?

Loss is 7% of £15 596.00 $= \frac{7}{100} \times £15 596 = £1091.72$

Price of car after one year is £15 596.00 $- £1091.72 = £14 504.28$

Writing one quantity as a percentage of another

To find one quantity as a percentage of another you first have to find one quantity as a fraction of the other – then multiply the fraction by 100 to give a percentage.

Like this

I spend £104.50 on a new watch and then sell it for £90. What is my percentage loss?

Loss $= £104.50 - £90 = £14.50$

Fraction is $\frac{£14.50}{£104.50}$

Percentage is $\frac{£14.50}{£104.50} \times 100\% = 13.9\%$ (approximately)

Practice Exercise

1 Find numbers for the blanks so that the lists are in order of size.

    (a) 47, ..., ..., 48

    (b) 2.3, ..., ..., 2.4

    (c) 0.25, ..., ..., 0.267

    (d) 0.037, ..., ..., 0.043

2 Match the numbers in Column 1 with those in Column 2.

Column 1	Column 2
0.3	$\frac{57}{100}$
$\frac{1}{4}$	$\frac{4}{5}$
57%	0.22
0.15	30%
0.8	0.25
22%	$\frac{3}{20}$

3 Choose an instruction from the list to put into each of the boxes a–c.

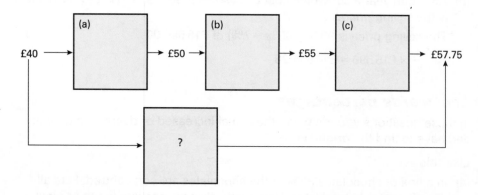

Instructions

increase by 20%

increase by 5%

increase by 10%

increase by 25%

Explain why the answer in the box marked '?' is not the same as the sum of boxes a, b and c.

....

....

Topic 1
The rules
of number

Note: Convert back to mixed numbers when you have finished.

Multiplying fractions

To multiply two fractions you must remember to make them into improper fractions and cancel where possible.

Like this

(a) $\dfrac{4}{3} \times \dfrac{1}{11} = \dfrac{4 \times 1}{3 \times 11} = \dfrac{4}{33}$

(b) $1\dfrac{3}{5} \times 2\dfrac{1}{4} = \dfrac{8}{5} \times \dfrac{\overset{2}{9}}{\underset{1}{4}} = \dfrac{18}{5} = 3\dfrac{3}{5}$

Dividing fractions

Remember to turn the 'divide' fraction upside down and then multiply.

Like this

$1\dfrac{3}{5} \div 1\dfrac{1}{3} = \dfrac{8}{5} \div \dfrac{4}{3} = \dfrac{\overset{2}{8}}{5} \times \dfrac{3}{\underset{1}{4}} = \dfrac{6}{5} = 1\dfrac{1}{5}$

Finding a percentage change

An alternative method to find a percentage change uses a single multiplier.

Like this

(a) A washing machine is advertised at £450 plus VAT at $17\frac{1}{2}\%$. What is the cost of the washing machine?

The new cost of the washing machine is

$117\frac{1}{2}\%$ $(100\% + 17\frac{1}{2}\%)$ of £450 $= \dfrac{117.5}{100} \times £450 = £528.75$

(b) After one year a car which cost £15 596.00 is sold at a loss of 7%. What is the selling price?

The selling price is 93% (100% − 7%) of £15 596.00

$= \dfrac{93}{100} \times £15\,596 = £14\,504.28$

Backwards percentages

In these questions you are given the actual increased or decreased quantity and have to find the **original** quantity.

Like this

Note: 100% is the original amount.

(a) In a box of chocolates 35% of the chocolates are soft centred. I ate all 21 soft centred-chocolates. How many chocolates were in the original selection?

35% of number of chocolates is 21

1% of number of chocolates is $\frac{21}{35}$ (dividing by 35 to find 1%)

100% of number of chocolates is $\frac{21}{35} \times 100$ (multiplying by 100 to find 100%)

Original number of chocolates is $\frac{21}{35} \times 100 = 60$

(b) In the sales all goods had a reduction of 25%. What was the original price of a mug whose sale price was 60p?

Reduction! Sale price is 75% (100% − 25%)

So 75% of the price of a mug is 60p

1% of the price of a mug is $\frac{60}{75}$p   (dividing by 75 to find 1%)

100% of the price of a mug is $\frac{60}{75} \times 100$ (multiplying by 100 to find 100%)

Original price is $\frac{60}{75} \times 100 = 80$p

Practice Exercise

1 Find a fraction whose value is between $\frac{2}{3}$ and $\frac{3}{4}$

1 Answer ....

2 Which of these are correct?
To increase an amount by 15% you multiply by:

(a) 0.15   (b) 1.15   (c) $\frac{100}{15}$ (d) $\frac{115}{100}$ (e) 1.5

2 Answer ....

....

3 The washing machine on the opposite page cost £528.75 including 17.5% VAT.

Show how to find the pre-VAT price of £450.

4 Which of these are correct?

450 g as a percentage of 2 kg is:

(a) $\frac{450}{200}\%$

(b) $\frac{450}{2000} \times 100\%$

(c) $\frac{450}{100} \times 2\%$

(d) $\frac{45\,000}{2000}\%$

(e) $22\frac{1}{2}\%$

(f) $\frac{450}{2} \times 100$

4 Answer ....

....

....

Topic 1
The rules of number

Examination Questions

1. The diagram shows a fence with fencing rails which are 3.9 metres long.

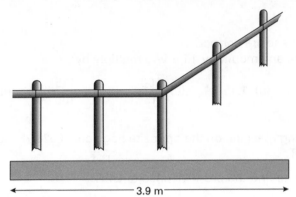

(a) How many rails are needed for a fence 200 metres long?

....

(b) A fencing post is shown.

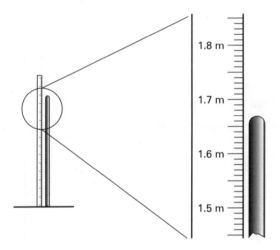

What is the height of the fencing post?

....

(SEG – specimen paper)

2. (a) Write the number 1750 in words.

....

(b) What is the value of the 5 in the number 1750?

....

(c) Write the number 1750 to the nearest thousand.

....

(SEG – specimen paper)

3. (a) Rachel has a bar of chocolate.
It has 20 pieces.

Rachel breaks off five pieces. What fraction of the bar is this?

....

(b) Sally also has a bar of chocolate with 20 pieces.
She has eaten $\frac{1}{5}$ of it.

How many pieces has she eaten?

....

(SEG – specimen paper)

4. (a) 6.08 m of carpet is cut from a 7.50 m length.
How much is left?
Give your answers in centimetres.

....

(b) A bookcase is 1.65 m long.
How many bookcases can be put along a wall which is 6.08 m long?

....

(SEG, Summer 1998 – Paper 12)

5. In class 9B there are 15 girls in the class of 30 pupils. In class 9C there are 17 girls out of 39 pupils.

Which class has the higher proportion of girls? Explain how you worked out your answer.

....

....

6. (a) What is the value of 6 in the number 5630?

....

(b) The number 5630 is multiplied by 10.
What is the value of 6 in the answer?

....

(c) The number 5630 is divided by 10.
What is the value of 6 in the answer?

....

(SEG – specimen paper)

Number

Topic 1
The rules of number

7. (a) Arrange the following numbers in order of size, smallest first.

0.085,   0.55,   0.56,   0.555,   0.058,   1,   0

....

(b) Express as decimals

(i) 54% ....

(ii) $\frac{4}{5}$ ....

8. Oranges are normally sold in packs of 15 oranges.
A special offer pack has 20% extra free.
How many oranges are in the special offer pack?

....

(SEG – specimen paper)

9. In 1990 Elm Tree House was bought for £88 000.

(a) In 1992 Elm Tree House was sold at a loss of 12.5%.
What was the sale price?

....

....

(b) In 1996 Elm Tree House was sold again. The sale price was 1.5% higher than its value in 1990. By how much had the value of the house increased between 1992 and 1996?

....

....

(SEG, Summer 1997 – Paper 3)

10. Bryan buys 21 litres of petrol at 65.9 pence per litre. How much will he be charged?

....

....

Examination Questions

11. Which of the following are integers?

$\frac{4}{8}$, $\frac{8}{4}$, 5, 0.5, 56, 5.6

....

12. Arrange the following in order of size, smallest first.

0.$\dot{6}$, 0.7, 0.67, 0.666, 0.6

....

13. A farm has an area of 324 hectares of land.
$\frac{1}{6}$ of the land is woodland and $\frac{5}{18}$ of the land is pasture.
The rest of the land is arable.

(a) What fraction of the land is arable?

....

(b) Calculate the area of the arable land.

....

(NEAB – specimen paper)

14. Skirts were priced at £13.80. In the sale, they cost £12.30.
What percentage discount is this?
Give your answer to an appropriate degree of accuracy.

....

(SEG – specimen paper)

15. In a sale a pair of trainers costs £25. This is a saving of 20%.
What was the original price of the shoes?

....

(NEAB – specimen paper)

16. In a sale a dress costs £32.40. The original price has been reduced by 10%.
What was the original price?

....

(NEAB, Summer 1998 – Intermediate Paper 2I)

Number

Topic 2
More
number

Note: *No sign in front of a number means that the number is positive.*

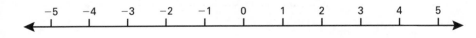
Summary

Working with negative numbers

A number line can be used to show negative numbers.

A horizontal number line

$$-5 \quad -4 \quad -3 \quad -2 \quad -1 \quad 0 \quad 1 \quad 2 \quad 3 \quad 4 \quad 5$$

Negative numbers (also called directed numbers) can be added or subtracted as follows:

You first remember:

add (+4)	or	+(+4)	means	+4
add (−4)	or	+(−4)	means	−4
subtract (+4)	or	−(+4)	means	−4
subtract (−4)	or	−(−4)	means	+4

Then you think in terms of temperature:
'+ is going up and − is going down'

Like this

$$-6 - (-4) = -6 + 4 = -2 \qquad \text{Start at } -6 \text{ then go up 4 to } -2$$

Take care here

$$-4 + (-9) = -4 - 9 = -13 \qquad \text{Start at } -4 \text{ then go down 9 to } -13$$

Rounding numbers

It is often helpful to round off a number.

When rounding numbers, the rule is to look at the next place:

if the figure is less than 5 then ignore it
if the figure is 5 or more then round up

To round to the nearest unit you look at the tenths,

to round to the nearest ten you look at the units,

to round to the nearest hundred you look at the tens, ... etc.

A vertical number line

(vertical number line: 10, 9, 8, 7, 6, 5, 4, 3, 2, 1, 0, −1, −2, −3, −4, −5, −6, −7, −8, −9, −10)

Note: *Remember that you may need to 'pad' your number with some 0s to make the number the right size. 4378 rounded to the nearest 100 is 4400.*

Like this

Round off 253.6

(a) to the nearest unit

To round to the nearest unit you look at the tenths.
The figure is 6 so round the units up

253.6 = 254 (to the nearest unit)

(b) to the nearest ten

To round to the nearest ten you look at the units.
The figure is 3 so ignore it

253.6 = 250 (to the nearest ten)

(c) to the nearest hundred

To round to the nearest hundred you look at the tens.
The figure is 5 so round the hundreds up

253.6 = 300 (to the nearest hundred)

Practice Exercise

1 Multiply each of the following quantities by 100. You should be able to do it without a calculator and without writing anything down!

(a) 5 metres

(b) £23

(c) 17p

(d) 2560

1 a Answer ....

1 b Answer ....

1 c Answer ....

1 d Answer ....

2 Tick one answer. 23 572 rounded to the nearest 100 is

236	23 600	2350
235	2360	23 500

3 Without using a calculator, find the cost of 25 computers at £752 each.

....

....

4 Estimate the answer to $5 \times \sqrt{7}$.

....

....

Now work it out with a calculator and find out how near you were!

5 Match up the quantities with the sensible rounding. The first one has been done for you.

ingredients in a recipe	nearest 10 miles
prices in a supermarket	nearest centimetre
your height	nearest penny
your weight	nearest half kilogramme
distance to London	nearest 5 grammes

Number

Topic 2
More
number

Note: Compare this

with $\frac{6}{14} = \frac{3}{7} = \frac{30}{70}$

Note: The rest is spent on boring necessities!

Working with ratios

If two brothers are 3 and 7 years old you can say the ratio of their ages is 3 compared to 7.

You can write 3 compared to 7 (you usually say 3 to 7) as $3:7$.

Writing ratios in different forms

You work with ratios in the same way as you work with fractions.
You do not change a ratio if you multiply or divide both sides of the ratio by the same number.

Like this

$6:14 = 3:7$ (divide by 2) $6:14 = 30:70$ (multiply by 5)

It is sometimes useful to write a ratio in the form $1:n$.
You can write the ratio $3:7$ in the form $1:n$ by dividing both sides by 3.

Like this

$3:7 = 1:\frac{7}{3} = 1:2\frac{1}{3}$

Dividing an amount in a given ratio

You earn £126 and divide it between partying, boring necessities and travel in the ratio $3:7:2$. How much do you spend on partying and how much do you spend on travel?

Rules for dividing an amount in a given ratio

1   Add the numbers in the ratio together. $3 + 7 + 2 = 12$

2   Divide the amount by 12 to get 1 part.

One part is £126 ÷ 12 = £10.50

3   Work out 3 parts and 2 parts.

Partying: Three parts is £10.5 × 3 = £31.50

Travel: Two parts is £10.5 × 2 = £21.00

I spend £31.50 on partying and £21 on travel

Rounding numbers to decimal places

You can round numbers to any number of decimal places.

When rounding numbers, the rule is to look at the next decimal place:

> **if the next decimal place is less than 5 then ignore it**
> **if the next decimal place is 5 or more then round up**

Like this

(a) Write 3.86 to one decimal place (1 dp).
To round to 1 decimal place you look at the next (second) decimal place which is 6 so round up.

3.86 = 3.9 (1 dp)

(b) Write 4.6745 to two decimal places.
To round to 2 decimal places you look at the next (third) decimal place which is 4 so ignore it.

4.6745 = 4.67 (2 dp)

Practice Exercise

1 Find a set of 6 different positive and negative numbers that add up to zero.

.... + ... + ... + ... + ... + ... = 0

2

Salad dressing

4 parts oil to
1 part vinegar

To make 100 ml of dressing,

you need .... ml oil

and .... ml vinegar.

3 30% of the students in a class are female.

The ratio of males to females is ....

4 Tick one answer.
2.478 rounded to 2 decimal places is

2.4	2.47	2.5	25	0.47
24	24.7	2.48	0.48	48

5 Use your common sense (not your calculator!) to decide which of these statements are reasonable:

✓ or ✗

(a) 53 meals at £4.95 each cost £262.35.   ....

(b) 152 units of electricity at 5.83p per unit cost £1342.16.   ....

(c) 12.3 square metres of carpet at £16.20 per square
    metre cost £1992.60.   ....

(d) The average of 16.2, 17.9, 27.8 and 15.2 is 77.1.   ....

(e) A salary of £22 531 a year is £1877.58 a week.   ....

Topic 2
More
number

Summary

Working with negative numbers

When you multiply or divide two numbers which are either both positive or both negative then the answer is positive.

When you multiply or divide two numbers one positive and the other negative then the answer is negative.

Like this

$$+5 \times +6 = 30 \qquad +10 \div +2 = 5 \qquad +10 \times -2 = -20 \qquad +14 \div -7 = -2$$
$$-3 \times -7 = 21 \qquad -12 \div -4 = 3 \qquad -3 \times +2 = -6 \qquad -12 \div +3 = -4$$

Direct proportion

If two quantities are directly proportional, then as one quantity increases so does the other quantity, keeping the ratio of the quantities the same.

Like this

Find the cost of a railway journey of 105 miles when a railway journey of 20 miles costs £3.20

20 miles costs £3.20

1 mile costs $\dfrac{£3.20}{20}$ = £0.16

105 miles costs $105 \times £0.16$ = £16.80

Inverse proportion

If two quantities are inversely proportional, then as one quantity increases the other quantity decreases so that the product remains the same.

Like this

You have provided enough food for 5 happy campers for one week (7 days). It rains and only two campers arrive at the camp.

How long will the food last the 2 campers?

5 campers have food for 7 days
1 camper has food for 7×5 = 35 days
2 campers have food for $35 \div 2$ = 17 days (and a half day!)

Rounding numbers to significant figures

You can also round numbers to any number of significant figures.

When rounding numbers, the rule is to look at the next significant figure:

if the next significant figure is less than 5 then ignore it
if the next significant figure is 5 or more then round up

Like this

(a) Write 4357 to 3 significant figures.
The next (fourth) significant figure is 7, so round up.

$4357 = 4360$ (3 sf)

(b) Write 0.002 718 to 2 significant figures.
The next (third) significant figure is 1, so ignore it.

$0.002 718 = 0.0027$ (2 sf)

Note: Remember that the first significant figure here is 2 as you do not count 0s in front of the number.

Rounding numbers to one significant figure is a useful way of approximating for mental calculations.

Like this

Find an approximate answer for 62.1×19.8
Rounding each number to 1 significant figure $60 \times 20 = 120$

Practice Exercise

1 When the number 3039.673 is rounded to:

3 significant figures	1 decimal place	nearest whole number	1 significant figure	
it becomes: 3000	3	3040	3039.7	3039

Match these up. Which numbers are left over?

....

....

2 Two quantities are inversely proportional.
If one quantity is doubled, what happens to the other?
Illustrate your answer with an example.

....

....

....

....

3 Arrange these in order of size. (Don't use a calculator!)

6.3×10^4 63×100 0.63×10^3 $6.3 \div 10^2$ 0.0063

................., ..., ..., ..., ...

4 Match the questions and the answers:

$0.9 \div -0.3 =$	-30
$-3 \times -9 =$	$+30$
$-9 \div 0.3 =$	-3
$-3 \div 9 =$	$-\frac{1}{3}$
$-9 \div -0.3 =$	$+27$

Topic 2
More number

Examination Questions

1. *'Our average daily sales are 758 885 copies.'*
   Daily Star

   Write this number of daily sales to the nearest thousand.

   ....

   (NEAB – specimen paper)

2. Mohini says:
   '21 × 29 is about 600'

   (a) Mohini did not work this out exactly. She estimated the answer to be about 600. Explain how she did it.

   ....

   ....

   (b) Show how you would find an estimate for 1980 ÷ 43.
   Write down your estimate for 1980 ÷ 43.

   ....

   (SEG – specimen paper)

3. Use your calculator to work out $\sqrt{(6 \times 9)}$, correct to the nearest whole number.

   ....

   (SEG – specimen paper)

4. This is a recipe for 24 scones.

600 g flour
250 g butter
100 g dried fruit
water to mix

   (a) How much dried fruit is needed for 6 scones?

   ....

   ....

   (b) How much flour is needed for 40 scones?

   ....

   ....

Examination Questions

5. (a) Arrange these numbers in order of size, smallest first.

$$0, \quad -5, \quad 2, \quad -8, \quad 4, \quad -2, \quad -1$$

....

(b) Find the sum of the numbers in part (a).

....

6. In a class there are 12 boys and 16 girls.

(a) Find the boy : girl ratio in its simplest form.

....

(b) What percentage of the class are boys?

....

7. A town has a population of 645 166 people.
The ratio of retired people to the rest of the population is 1 : 3.
How many people are retired?
Give your answer correct to three significant figures.

....

(SEG, Summer 1998 – Paper 13)

8. 80 million pounds of lottery funds was given to the sports of swimming and
athletics. This money was shared between these two sports in the ratio

swimming : athletics
3 : 1

Calculate the amount that was given to swimming.

....

....

(NEAB, 1998 – Intermediate Paper 1I)

9. Anne drives 559 miles using 53.7 litres of diesel. Calculate how far she drives on
one litre of diesel, giving your answer to an appropriate degree of accuracy.

....

Topic 2
More
number

Examination Questions

10. Evaluate $5 \times (-6) + (-10)$

....

11. A petrol pump takes 20 seconds to fill an 8 litre can. How long will it take to fill a 70 litre car fuel tank?

....

....

12. (a) Work out $\dfrac{4.7 \times 20.1}{5.6 - 1.8}$. Write down your full calculator display.

....

(b) Use estimation to check your answer.

....

(NEAB, Summer 1998 – Paper 2I)

13. In 1995 Mr Royles drove 7764 miles in his car. His car does 37 miles per gallon. Petrol costs 52 pence per litre.

(a) By taking one gallon to be 4.55 litres, calculate, in £, how much Mr Royles spent on petrol in 1995.

....

....

(b) Show how you can use approximation to check that your answer is of the right order of magnitude. You **must** show all your working.

....

....

(SEG – specimen paper)

14. (a) Mr Grey receives an electricity bill for £42.91. The bill includes a quarterly charge of £10.33 and the cost per unit is 7.49 pence. Mr Grey writes down the following calculation to work out the number of units of electricity he has used.

$$\text{Units used} = \frac{(42.91 - 10.33) \times 100}{7.49}$$

Calculate, to the nearest whole number, how many units he has used.

....

....

(b) In the next quarter he uses 578 units. The quarterly charge is the same and the cost per unit is the same. Calculate this quarterly bill.

....

....

(SEG – specimen paper)

15. Jean is told to estimate the value of $876 \div 32$. She says it is about 30. Explain how you could do this by estimation.

....

....

....

(NEAB – specimen paper)

16. Complete the following:

(a) $-4 - \ldots\ldots\ldots = -9$

(b) $6 - \ldots\ldots\ldots = 8$

(NEAB, Winter '98 – Intermediate Paper 11)

17. In 1954, Roger Bannister ran a mile in a time of 239.2 seconds, correct to the nearest tenth of a second. What is the shortest time that it could actually be?

....

(SEG – specimen paper)

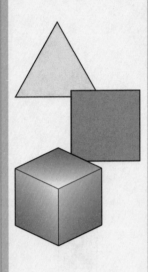

Topic 3
Describing number

Summary

Factors and multiples

Factors are numbers which divide into another number exactly.
So the factors of 12 are 1, 2, 3, 4, 6 and 12
and the factors of 30 are 1, 2, 3, 5, 6, 10, 15 and 30

Multiples are numbers which occur as the answers to multiplication tables.
So the multiples of 7 are 7, 14, 21, 28, 35, ...
and the multiples of 12 are 12, 24, 36, 48, 60, 72, ...

Triangles, squares and cubes

Triangular numbers are numbers that can be arranged as a triangle.

Like this

$3 + 2 + 1 = 6$

The triangular numbers are   1, 3, 6, 10, 15, 21, ...

1   3   6   10   ...

Square numbers are numbers that can be made into a square.

Like this

Three squared $= 3^2 = 3 \times 3 = 9$

The square numbers are: 1, 4, 9, 16, 25, 36, 49, ...

1   4   9   16   ...

Cube numbers are numbers (wait for it!) that can be arranged as a cube.

Like this

Two cubed $= 2^3 = 2 \times 2 \times 2 = 8$ arrange 8 as a cube.

The cube numbers are: 1, 8, 27, 64, 125, 216, 343, ...

Practice Exercise

1 Draw arrows to link the equal answers. Two arrows have been drawn for you.

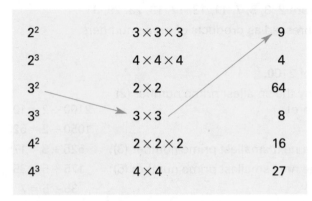

2^2	$3 \times 3 \times 3$	9
2^3	$4 \times 4 \times 4$	4
3^2	2×2	64
3^3	3×3	8
4^2	$2 \times 2 \times 2$	16
4^3	4×4	27

2

1	2	3	4	5	6	7	8	9	10
11	12	13	14	15	16	17	18	19	20
21	22	23	24	25	26	27	28	29	30
31	32	33	34	35	36	37	38	39	40
41	42	43	44	45	46	47	48	49	50
51	52	53	54	55	56	57	58	59	60
61	62	63	64	65	66	67	68	69	70
71	72	73	74	75	76	77	78	79	80
81	82	83	84	85	86	87	88	89	90
91	92	93	94	95	96	97	98	99	100

Use different colours to shade in:

(a) multiples of 3

(b) multiples of 5

(c) multiples of 9.

What do you notice about the multiples?

....

....

3 Complete this list of factors of 180 – each factor has a partner in the other half of the list.

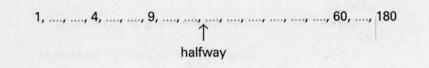

1, ..., ..., 4, ..., ..., 9, ..., ..., ..., ..., ..., ..., ..., ..., 60, ..., 180

↑
halfway

Which four factors are square numbers? ...., ..., ..., ...

Topic 3 Describing number

Summary

Prime numbers

A prime number is a number which has only 2 factors (1 and itself). So the prime numbers are 2, 3, 5, 7, 11, 13, 17, 19, 23, 29, 31, ...

All numbers can be expressed as products of prime numbers.

Like this

Find the prime factors of 2100.

You must divide 2100 by the smallest prime number (2) until it will divide no more!

$$2100 \div 2 = 1050$$
$$1050 \div 2 = 525$$

Now try to divide by the next smallest prime number (3): $\quad 525 \div 3 = 175$

Now try to divide by the next smallest prime number (5): $\quad 175 \div 5 = 35$

$$35 \div 5 = 7$$

Now try to divide by the next smallest prime number (7): $\quad 7 \div 7 = 1$

As you cannot divide any further then the prime factors of 2100 are 2, 2, 3, 5, 5 and 7, so $2100 = 2 \times 2 \times 3 \times 5 \times 5 \times 7$

Working with standard form

Standard form is a way to write very large numbers such as those used in space exploration, or very small numbers such as those used when dealing with molecules.

First be certain that you are happy multiplying and dividing by powers of 10 without using your calculator.

Like this

(a) To multiply by 10^2 move the decimal point two places to the right.
$4567.0 \times 10^2 = 456\,700$

(b) To divide by 10^4 move the decimal point four places to the left.
$4567.0 \div 10^4 = 0.4567$

Rules for writing a number in standard form

1 Write the number so that it is greater than 1 but less than 10.
2 Count the number of decimal places moved.
3 Multiply the new number by $10^{\pm \text{ the number of places moved}}$

Like this

(a) Write 135.0 in standard form.
  1 Write the number as 1.35
  2 So move decimal point 2 places to the left.
  3 Multiply 1.35 by 10^2.
  In standard form $135.0 = 1.35 \times 10^2$

(b) Write these numbers in standard form:
  (i) 24 609.3
      $= 2.460\,93 \times 10^4 \qquad$ move the decimal point 4 places left
  (ii) 0.07
      $= 7.0 \times 10^{-2} \qquad$ move the decimal point 2 places right
  (iii) 50 million
      $= 50\,000\,000$
      $= 5.0 \times 10^7 \qquad$ move the decimal point 7 places left

Practice Exercise

1 Which of these are correct?

45 million in standard form is

(a) 45×10^6

(b) 4.5×10^7

(c) 4.5^6

(d) 4.5^7

(e) $45\,000\,000$

Note: There is only one right answer!

1 Answer ....

2 Complete this process to express 240 as a product of prime factors.

$240 = 2 \times$ ....

$= 2 \times 2 \times$ ....

$= 2 \times 2 \times 2 \times$ ....

$= 2 \times 2 \times 2 \times 2 \times$ ....

$= 2 \times 2 \times 2 \times 2 \times$ .... $\times$ ....

$= 2^4 \times$ .... $\times$ ....

3 Draw lines to match up the pairs of equal numbers.

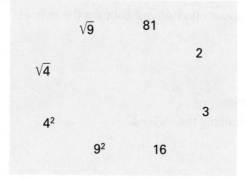

$\sqrt{9}$ 81

2

$\sqrt{4}$

3

4^2

9^2 16

4 Write these standard form numbers out in full.

(a) 4.32×10^5 (b) 2.06×10^2 (c) 8.15×10^{-3}

Number

Topic 3
Describing
number

*Note: You can work
out powers on your
calculator by using the
x^y or y^x button.*

Note:
$2^2 \times 2^3 = 4 \times 8 = 32$

Note:
$2^2 \div 2^3 = 4 \div 8 = \frac{1}{2}$

*Note: You cannot find
the reciprocal of 0.*

A little about square and cube roots

Square root $\sqrt{\ }$

$\sqrt{25} = 5$ You say the square root of 25 is 5 (since $25 = 5 \times 5$)

Cube root $\sqrt[3]{\ }$

$\sqrt[3]{8} = 2$ You say the cube root of 8 is 2 (since $8 = 2 \times 2 \times 2$)

Powers or indices

Positive indices

2^5 means $2 \times 2 \times 2 \times 2 \times 2 = 32$ You say two to the power of five.

Zero index

Any number to the power of 0 is 1.

Like this

$7^0 = 1$ $10\,000\,002^0 = 1$ and so on!!!

The rules of indices

Adding and subtracting

You have to slog it out: work out each term and then add or subtract.

Like this

$2^4 + 2^3 = 16 + 8 = 24$
$2^4 - 2^3 = 16 - 8 = 8$

Multiplying indices

To multiply different powers of the *same* number you add the indices.

Like this

$2^2 \times 2^3 = 2^{2+3} = 2^5$

Dividing indices

To divide different powers of the *same* number you subtract the indices.

Like this

$2^2 \div 2^3 = 2^{2-3} = 2^{-1}$

Raising powers to a power

To raise powers to a power you multiply the indices.

Like this

$(5^3)^2 = 5^{3 \times 2} = 5^6 = 15\,625$

Reciprocal

To find the reciprocal of a number you turn it upside down (simple!).

Like this

The reciprocal of $\frac{3}{5}$ is $\frac{5}{3}$

The reciprocal of 3 is $\frac{1}{3}$ you need to write 3 as $\frac{3}{1}$

Practice Exercise

1 Put these terms into circles with others which are equivalent

$$ab \times ab \qquad\qquad bab \qquad\qquad ba^2$$

$$\sqrt{a^2b^2} \qquad\qquad \sqrt{a^4b^4} \qquad\qquad b^2a \qquad\qquad (ab)^2$$

$$\frac{a^2}{a} \times \frac{b^2}{b} \qquad \frac{a^3b^3}{ab} \qquad a \times a \times b \qquad \frac{(ab)^2}{ab}$$

ab^2	a^2b^2	a^2b	ab

2 Arrange these in order of size, starting with the smallest.

$$4.8 \times 10^{-3} \qquad 2.4 \qquad 2.4 \times 10^{-3} \qquad 0.48$$

$$0.00048 \qquad 240 \qquad 2.4 \times 10^3 \qquad 4.8 \times 10^2$$

....

....

3 Link the reciprocal pairs.

2	$\frac{2}{9}$
4	0.5
$3\frac{1}{3}$	$\frac{1}{4}$
100	0.01
$4\frac{1}{2}$	$\frac{3}{10}$

4 Complete the following:

(a) The highest common factor (HCF) of two numbers is

....

(b) The lowest common multiple (LCM) of two numbers is

....

Topic 3
Describing number

Examination Questions

1. Five numbers are shown below.

$$23 \quad 26 \quad 56 \quad 73 \quad 74$$

(a) Which two of these numbers have a total of 100?

....

(b) Which two of these five numbers have a difference of 50?

....

(c) What is the highest number you can make by multiplying two of these five numbers?

....

(d) From these five numbers write down one which is a multiple of 7.

....

(NEAB, Summer 1998 – Paper 1F, part question)

2. Paul has five numbered discs.

④ ⑧ ② ⑥ ⑦

(a) (i) Which of Paul's numbers is a square number?

....

(ii) Which of Paul's numbers is a multiple of 4, other than 4 itself?

....

(SEG, Summer 1998 – Paper 11, part question)

3. (a) What is the value of 3^2?

....

(b) What is the value of 2^3?

....

(SEG, Summer 1998 – Paper 11, part question)

4. Belinda is thinking of a number.

My number is less than 10.
It is a multiple of 2.
It can be divided exactly by 3.

What is Belinda's number?

....

(SEG – specimen paper)

Examination Questions

5. Tony used his calculator and from the display he thought that the answer was 4.5^{10}.
   William said that this was the number 45.
   Susan said it was 4.500 000 000 0.
   Joseph said that it was 45 000 000 000.
   Who was correct?

   ....

   (NEAB – specimen paper)

6. Which of these numbers have exact square roots?

   4,   8,   12,   16,   20,   24

   ....

7. (a) Work out the value of 2^5.

   ....

   ....

   (b) A pupil worked out 5^2 instead of 2^5. Calculate the difference between the two
   answers.

   ....

   ....

   (NEAB – specimen paper)

8. A light year is the distance travelled by light in 365 days. The speed of light is
   3.0×10^5 kilometres per second. The distance to the nearest star is 4.0×10^{13} km.
   How many light years is it to the nearest star? Give your answer to an appropriate
   degree of accuracy.

   ....

   ....

   ....

   ....

   ....

   (SEG – specimen paper)

Topic 3
Describing
number

Examination Questions

9. Calculate the difference between $\sqrt{5}$ and $\sqrt[3]{10}$. Give your answer correct to two decimal places.

....

....

(NEAB – specimen paper)

10. 500 sheets of paper make a pile 5 cm high. Express the thickness of one sheet of paper in cm in standard form.

....

....

11. Express these in the form 3^n

   (a) $3^2 \times 3^5$ ....

   (b) $\dfrac{3^6}{3^2}$ ....

12. (a) Find, as a single integer, the highest common factor of 216 and 168.

....

....

   (b) A rectangular field measures 21.6 m by 16.8 m. Fencing posts are placed along its sides at equal distances apart so that fence panels of equal size can be fastened between them. The posts are as far apart as possible. What is the distance between them?

....

....

(SEG – specimen paper)

13. Which is bigger, the square root of 200 or the cube root of 2000? Show how you obtained your answer.

....

....

Examination Questions

Number

**Topic 3
Describing
number**

Intermediate Tier Only

14. (a) In Britain there are 5.80×10^7 people.
The number of retired people is 1.04×10^7.
What percentage of people in Britain are retired?
Give your answer to an appropriate degree of accuracy.

....

....

....

(b) 13.8% of the world's population live in Europe.
The population of the world is 5.72×10^9.
Calculate the population of Europe.

....

....

....

(SEG, Summer 1998 – Higher Paper 15)

15. The distance from Earth to the planet Kronos is 35 000 000 000 000 000 miles.

(a) Write this distance in standard form.

....

(b) Light travels at a speed of 5.9×10^{12} miles per year. How many years will it
take to travel from Kronos to Earth? Give your answer to a reasonable degree
of accuracy.

....

....

....

(NEAB – specimen paper)

Topic 4
Application of number

Summary

Hire purchase

Hire purchase is a way of paying for goods or services over a period of time. Hire purchase usually involves the payment of a deposit plus regular (weekly or monthly) payments of a fixed amount.

Like this

A television is priced £1800 but can be bought with a 15% deposit and 30 monthly payments of £59.50.

Find: (a) the amount of the deposit
     (b) the total credit price
     (c) the amount saved by paying cash.

(a) the amount of the deposit is 15% of £1800 $= \dfrac{15}{100} \times £1800 = £270$

(b) the total credit price is deposit + 30 monthly payments of £59.50
$$= £270 + £1785 = £2055$$

(c) the amount saved by paying cash is credit price − cash price
$$= £2055 − £1800 = £255$$

Money, money, money

Questions on wages and salaries are very popular in the examination.

Like this

An employee is paid £280 for a basic 40 hour week and overtime is paid at double time (i.e. twice the basic rate).

Calculate: (a) the basic hourly rate
     (b) the overtime rate
     (c) the amount of pay for 5 hours overtime

(a) the basic hourly rate is $\dfrac{£280}{40} = £7$ per hour

(b) the overtime rate is 2 times the basic hourly rate $= 2 \times £7 = £14$ per hour

(c) the amount of pay for 5 hours overtime is $5 \times$ overtime rate
$$= 5 \times £14 = £70$$

Time

Time can be described in many different ways – five fifteen pm, seventeen fifteen hours, fifteen minutes past five, quarter past five, etc. The most common way of describing time is to use the twelve or twenty four hour clock.

Like this

A traveller leaves home at 0825 and arrives at her destination at 1218. How long did the journey take?

To work out the time taken it is useful to divide the time up as follows:

	hours	minutes
0825 to 0900		35
0900 to 1200	3	
1200 to 1218		18
	3	53

The journey takes 3 hours and 53 minutes.

Note: *Do remember that there are 60 minutes in an hour (and 60 seconds in a minute) **not** 100. If your answer in the minutes column is greater than 60 you need to split it into hours and minutes*

Practice Exercise

1 A train leaves Preston at 0620 and arrives in London at 0925. The distance is 220 miles.

The time taken by the train is ....

The average speed is approximately (estimate – no calculator!)

....

2 Arrange these in order of size, smallest first:

120 mm	1 foot	10 cm	1 metre
4 feet	10.01 cm	120 cm	2 inches

....

....

3 Jane earns £15.95 an hour. Here is the record of her working hours in one week:

Mon	Tue	Wed	Thur	Fri
0900–1230	0830–1230	1200–1600	0900–1230	0900–1200
1330–1700	1830–2130	1800–2030	1330–1800	

Find how much Jane earns this week.

....

....

....

....

....

....

3 Answer £............................

Topic 4
Application of number

Note: The amount of taxable income is found by subtracting the personal allowance from the annual income.

Note: The exchange rates fluctuate on a day-to-day basis so examination questions will provide you with the information needed.

Summary

Taxation at basic rate

Income tax is a tax on income earned which is paid to the government and is usually deducted automatically from a person's pay packet. The amount of income tax paid depends upon a number of factors such as the amount of money earned, the rate of tax and an individual's personal allowance.

Like this

A shopworker earns £545.60 per month. He has a personal allowance of £3765 and pays 20% on the first £3900 of his taxable income. How much income tax does he pay?

Annual income is £545.60 × 12 = £6547.20
Taxable income is annual income − personal allowance
= £6547.20 − £3765.00 = £2782.20

The shopworker pays 20% tax on the first £3900 of his taxable income.

$$\text{Tax} = 20\% \text{ of } £2782.20 = \frac{20}{100} \times £2782.20 = £556.44$$

The shopworker pays £556.44 income tax.

Foreign currency and exchange rates

The table gives the exchange rate for the British pound at the time of going to press.

You will be expected to answer questions on foreign currency and exchange rates.

Country	Exchange rate
Australia	£1 = 2.62 dollars
Austria	£1 = 18.94 schillings
Belgium	£1 = 55.73 francs
Denmark	£1 = 10.33 kroner
France	£1 = 9.03 francs
Germany	£1 = 2.70 marks
Greece	£1 = 453.55 dracma
Holland	£1 = 3.03 guilders
Ireland	£1 = 1.08 punts
Italy	£1 = 2688.00 lira
Japan	£1 = 193.88 yen
New Zealand	£1 = 3.10 dollars
Spain	£1 = 228.60 pesetas
Sweden	£1 = 13.17 kroner
United States	£1 = 1.61 dollars

Like this

(a) How many Swedish kroner would you get for £120?

The exchange rate is £1 = 13.17 kroner.
So £120 = 120 × 13.17 kroner
= 1580 kroner (to the nearest kroner)

(b) How much is 150 French francs worth?

The exchange rate is 9.03 francs = £1

$$1 \text{ franc} = \frac{£1}{9.03} \quad (\div 9.03 \text{ to find the value of 1 franc})$$

$$150 \text{ francs} = 150 \times \frac{£1}{9.03} \quad (\times 150 \text{ to find the value of 150 francs})$$

$$= £16.61 \quad (\text{to the nearest penny})$$

Working with simple interest

With simple interest you only get interest paid on the amount you originally invested (not very interesting at all).

Like this

A bank account gives 9.325% simple interest per annum (each year). Find out how much interest you earn on £3000 invested for 4 years.

$$\text{1st year's interest is } 9.325\% \text{ of } £3000 = \frac{9.325}{100} \times £3000 = £279.75$$

4 years' interest is £279.75 × 4 = £1119.00

Practice Exercise

1 Compare the prices of different sizes of shampoo:

Small size: 100 ml for £1.29 so 1 ml costs ....

Large size: 250 ml for £3.10 so 1 ml costs ....

Best buy is ....

Check your answer:

Small size: 100 ml for £1.29 so 1 penny buys ....

Large size: 250 ml for £3.10 so 1 penny buys ....

Best buy is ....

2 Mike chooses clothes costing £57.45 but he gets a 5% student discount. How much will he pay?

Discount = $\dfrac{............}{100}$ × £57.45 = ...

Price paid = £57.45 − £..................... = £.....................

3 Which of these calculations will give the correct answer for $\dfrac{3.2 + 21.9}{5.6}$?

(a) $3.2 + 21.9 \div 5.6$

(b) $(3.2 + 21.9) \div 5.6$

(c) $3.2 + (21.9 \div 5.6)$

(d) $5.6 \div (3.2 + 21.9)$

3 Answer ....

39

Number

Topic 4
Application of number

Note: Remember that per tells you to divide.

Note: For problems involving compound measure (that is per!) keep your wits about you and make sure you know when to divide and when to multiply.

Summary

Working with compound interest

With compound interest you get interest paid on your interest. To calculate compound interest you find the interest for the first year. You then add this interest to the original amount and find the interest on this new amount for the second year. And so on!

Like this

Find the compound interest on £200 invested for 3 years at 10% per annum.

10% as a decimal is 0.1	1st year interest is $0.1 \times £200$ = £20
New amount is £200 + £20 = £220	2nd year interest is $0.1 \times £220$ = £22
New amount is £220 + £22 = £242	3rd year interest is $0.1 \times £242$ = £24.20

For 3 years the total interest is £20 + £22 + £24.20 = £66.20

Working with compound measure

Examples of compound measure are:

> speed measured in miles per hour
> density measured in grams per cubic centimetre
> population density measured in people per square mile.

For a problem involving speed you may find it helps to use a **D**istance, **S**peed, **T**ime triangle.

$$\text{Distance} = \text{Speed} \times \text{Time}$$

$$\text{Speed} = \frac{\text{Distance}}{\text{Time}} \qquad \text{Time} = \frac{\text{Distance}}{\text{Speed}}$$

Like this

A car travels at 35 mph for 2 hours. It stops for 30 minutes, and then continues at a steady speed of 70 mph along the motorway for 3 hours 45 minutes. Find the car's average speed over the whole journey.

$$\text{Average speed} = \frac{\text{Total distance}}{\text{Total time}}$$

Total time is 2 h + 0.5 h + 3.75 h	= 6.25 h
Distance for first part of journey is 35 mph $\times$ 2 h	= 70 miles
Distance for second part of journey is 70 mph $\times$ 3.75 h	= 262.5 miles
Total distance is 70 miles + 262.5 miles	= 332.5 miles

$$\text{Average speed} = \frac{332.5}{6.25} \text{ mph} = 53.2 \text{ mph}$$

Similarly, for a problem involving density you may find it helps to use a **M**ass, **D**ensity, **V**olume triangle.

$$\text{Mass} = \text{Density} \times \text{Volume}$$

$$\text{Density} = \frac{\text{Mass}}{\text{Volume}} \qquad \text{Volume} = \frac{\text{Mass}}{\text{Density}}$$

Practice Exercise

1 Tax is paid at 20% per annum on the first £3900 of taxable income and at 23% on the remaining taxable income up to £27 000.

Find the tax paid by a person with £16 500 taxable income.

....

....

....

1 Answer £...........................

2 Explain how to find the mass of a cuboid whose measurements are given (in cm) and which is made of material with a density of 3 grams per cubic centimetre.

....

....

....

3 Complete these calculations to give the total amount after 2 years if £100 is invested at 3% per annum interest.

Interest for 1st year $= \dfrac{3}{100} \times £100 =$ ....

Amount at beginning of 2nd year $= £100 +$ .... $=$ ....

Interest for 2nd year $= \dfrac{\text{....................}}{\text{....................}} \times £$ .... $=$ ....

∴ Amount at end of 2nd year $=$ ....

4 (a) Calculate $£100 \times (1.03)^2$.

....

....

(b) Compare your answer with that for question 3 and comment.

....

....

....

Topic 4
Application
of number

Examination Questions

1. Chocolate bars cost 35p each.

   (a) Jason buys 5 bars.
   How much change does Jason get from £5?

   ....

   ....

   (b) How many bars of chocolate can Jason buy with £5?

   ....

   (c) A bag contains 1.1 kg of chocolate bars.
   Each bar weighs 55 g.

   How many chocolate bars are in the bag?

   ....

   ....

   (SEG, Summer 1998 – Paper 11)

2. (a) A coach will seat 46 pupils.

   (i) How many coaches are needed to take 197 pupils on a trip?

   ....

   (ii) The 197 pupils pay £2.60 each to cover the cost of the coaches.
   How much does it cost to hire each coach?

   ....

   ....

   (b) A coach took 3 hours to complete the journey of 132 miles.
   Calculate the average speed of the coach.

   ....

   ....

   (SEG, Summer 1998 – Paper 11)

Topic 4
Application
of number

3. A railway timetable is shown.

Bournemouth	0558	0616	0642	0654	0715	0754	0839	0900
Brockenhurst	0619	0639	0646	0722	0738	0823	0841	0921
Southampton	0634	0655	0714	0738	0754	0838	0908	0938
So'ton Parkway	0642	0703	0722	0746	0802	0848	0916	0947
Eastleigh	0646	0707	–	0750	–	0852	–	0951
Winchester	0656	0716	0733	0759	0812	0901	–	1001
Basingstoke	0716	0733	0753	0816	–	0918	–	1020
Woking	0738	–	0815	0845	0851	0938	–	1044
Waterloo	0804	0819	0844	0901	0917	1005	1018	1112

(a) David intends to catch a train from Eastleigh to Waterloo. He has to be in Waterloo by 9.30 am. What is the time of the latest train he can catch?

....

(b) Elisa misses the 0839 train from Bournemouth to Waterloo and catches the 0900 instead.
How much longer, in hours and minutes, does the journey take?

....

....

Answer .... hours .... minutes

(SEG – specimen paper)

4. The cost of hiring a concrete mixer is £15.40 per day plus a delivery charge of £12.

(a) How much would it cost to hire the mixer for three days including delivery?

....

....

Answer £ ....

(b) A builder hired the mixer and was charged a total of £135.20 including delivery. For how many days was the mixer hired?

....

....

Answer .... days

(SEG – specimen paper)

Topic 4
Application
of number

5. (a) Write the time 1410 in 12 hour clock time.

....

A bus timetable for journeys between Doncaster and York is shown.

Doncaster – York								
Doncaster			0910	1210	1410	1610	1810	1910
Bentley			0916	1216	1416	1616	1816	1916
Askern			0933	1233	1433	1633	1833	1933
Selby	0820	0920	1020	1320	1520	1720	1920	2020
York	0905	1005	1105	1405	1605	1805	2005	2105

(b) Usuf travels from Doncaster to York on the 1410 bus.

How long does his journey take?

....

Answer .... hours .... minutes

In York, Usuf visits the Jorvik Centre.
The admission prices are shown.

JORVIK CENTRE

Prices

ADULTS £8.00

UNDER 16 years ..... $\frac{3}{4}$ of the Adult Price

Usuf is 15 years old.

(c) Work out how much Usuf paid to get in.

....

....

Answer £ ....

(SEG, Summer 1998 – Paper 12)

6. A car park has the following charges.

Time	Cost
Up to 1 hour	60p
Up to 2 hours	£1
Up to 4 hours	£1.50
Up to 6 hours	£3
Over 6 hours	£5

Mrs Smith wants to pay for 1 hour.

(a) The machine takes 10p, 20p, 50p and £1 coins.

One way of paying for 1 hour would be using:

a **10p** and a **50p** coin.

Write down **three** other ways of paying 60p.

....

....

....

(b) Mrs Smith buys her 60p ticket at 09.35.

She later looks at her watch and sees that it is ten past ten.
How much longer has she got before her ticket runs out?

....

(NEAB – specimen paper)

Examination Questions

7. A man wants to exchange £450 for Singapore Dollars. The exchange rate is 3.4 Singapore Dollars for £1.

   (a) How many Singapore Dollars are equivalent to £450?

   ....

   (b) The man buys a watch which costs 27 Singapore Dollars. What is this worth in £? Give your answer to the nearest £.

   ....

   ....

   (NEAB – specimen paper)

8. The size and selling price of small and medium toothpaste are shown.

Small size 72 ml **50p**	Medium size 135 ml **90p**

   Which size of toothpaste gives better value for money? You **must** show all your working.

   ....

   ....

   ....

   (SEG – specimen paper)

9. Given that y is proportional to x^2, complete the table.

x	5		20
y	45	180	

   (SEG, Summer '98 – Higher Paper 15)

10. A car travels at 28 metres per second.
    What is its speed in kilometres per hour? Give your answer to an appropriate degree of accuracy.

    ....

    ....

    ....

Examination Questions

11. Kathy earned £27 000 in 1995. She did not pay tax on the first £3525 of her income. She paid tax on the rest of her income at the following tax rates. She paid tax at 20% on the first £3200 of her taxable income and at 25% on the rest of her taxable income. Calculate the total amount of tax that she paid in 1995.

....

....

....

....

(SEG – specimen paper)

12. (a) A train from London to Manchester takes 2 hours 30 minutes. It travels at an average speed of 80 miles an hour.
What is the distance from London to Manchester?

....

....

(b) The railway company is going to buy some faster trains. These new trains will have an average speed of 100 miles per hour.
How much time will be saved on the journey from London to Manchester?

....

....

....

(NEAB, Summer 1998 – Intermediate Paper 1I)

13. The formula for the population, P, of a country with a growth rate of $r\%$ per year in time t years, is given by $P = P_0\left(1 + \dfrac{r}{100}\right)^t$ where P_0 is the population this year. The population of Nigeria this year is 66.2 million. The growth rate is 3% per year. Calculate the population of Nigeria in five years time giving your answer to an appropriate degree of accuracy.

....

....

....

....

(SEG – specimen paper)

14. A cuboid measures 5 cm by 5 cm by 10 cm. Its mass is 0.354 kg. Calculate the density of the cuboid in grams per cubic centimetre.

....

....

....

Algebra

Topic 5
The language of algebra

Note: The letters x *and* y *are very common letters to use but you can use any letters.*

Note: The terms go with the + or − sign in front of them, i.e. the three terms in the expression 5a − 3b + 17 are +5a, −3b and +17.

*Note: You would be asked to **simplify** an expression and to **solve** an equation.*

Summary

Letters for numbers

In algebra, letters are used to represent numbers. Any letters can be used to represent the numbers.

Like this

Let x and y represent two numbers. Then:

the sum of the two numbers is $x + y$

the difference of the two numbers is $x - y$
(or $y - x$, especially if y is bigger than x)

the product of the two numbers is $x \times y$
(this is usually written more simply as xy)

the first number divided by the second number is $x \div y$ (or $\frac{x}{y}$)

Making expressions

In algebra you can use letters and symbols (as well as numbers) to make expressions.

Like this

(a) A girl is x years old. How old will she be in 10 years time?
In ten years time the girl will be $x + 10$ years old.

(b) A boy is y years old. How old was he last year?
Last year the boy was $y - 1$ years old.

(c) A pencil costs a pence. How much will 5 pencils cost?
5 pencils will cost $5 \times a$ pence or $5a$ pence.

(d) A pen costs b pence. How much will 3 pens cost?
3 pens will cost $3 \times b$ or $3b$ pence.

(e) A pencil cost a pence and a pen costs b pence. How much will 5 pencils and 3 pens cost?
5 pencils will cost $5a$ pence and 3 pens will cost $3b$ pence.
So 5 pencils and 3 pens will cost $5a + 3b$ pence.

(f) A rectangle measures x cm by y cm.
What is the perimeter of the rectangle?
Perimeter $= x + y + x + y = 2x + 2y$
(collecting like terms)

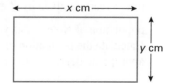

Some vocabulary for you to learn

You may find the following vocabulary helpful in your algebra.

Expression An expression is a series of terms linked by + and − signs.

$5a - 3b + 17$ is an expression which has three terms:
$5a$, $3b$ and 17.

Equation An equation is like an expression, but it has two sides with an equals sign between.

So $4x - 12$ is an expression, but $4x - 12 = 0$ is an equation.

Formula A formula is a statement expressed in words or symbols.

Examples of formulae (plural for formula) are:
Area of rectangle $=$ length $\times$ breadth
$V = \frac{1}{3}\pi r^2 h$ (formula to find the volume of a cone)

Practice Exercise

1 Write down a definition for each of the following:

An **expression** ....
....

An **equation** ....
....

A **formula** ....
....

2 What is the difference between an expression and an equation?

....
....

3 Let a and b represent two numbers.
Write the following more simply.

(a) The product of the two numbers.

(b) The difference of the two numbers.

(c) The first number multiplied by 4.

(d) The second number divided by 3.

(e) The first number multiplied by itself.

3 (a) Answer ....

3 (b) Answer ....

3 (c) Answer ....

3 (d) Answer ....

3 (e) Answer ....

4 Make expressions for each of the following:

(a) My brother is y years old. How old will he be next year?

(b) A book costs £x. How much will 3 books cost?

(c) A coat normally costs £c and is reduced by £15 in a sale. What is the sale price of the coat?

(d) A rectangle measures x cm by y cm. What is the area of the rectangle?

4 (a) Answer

.... years old

4 (b) Answer £ ....

4 (c) Answer £...................

4 (d) Answer ....cm²

Algebra

Topic 5
The language of algebra

Note: ab *and* 4ba *are like terms as* ab *is the same as* ba.

Note: The number in front of a term is sometimes called the coefficient. For 6xy the coefficient of xy is 6.

Note: $-(2x+4) = -2x-4$ *as you multiply each term inside the bracket by -1 (-1 times 2x plus -1 times 4).*

Note: Always check you have the correct answer by multiplying out.

Summary

Simplifying expressions

Addition and subtraction

You can only add and subtract like terms.

Like this

(a) $y + 2y = 3y$ (add like y terms)

(b) $y^2 - 3y^2 = -2y^2$ (subtract like y^2 terms)

(c) $ab + 4ba = 5ab$ or $5ba$ (as $ab = ba$)

(d) $3y^2 + 2y^3$ (you cannot add these because y^3 and y^2 are unlike terms)

Multiplication

To multiply two terms you multiply the numbers then the letters.

Like this

(a) $5y \times 7y = 5 \times 7 \times y \times y = 35y^2$

(b) $2ab \times 6bc = 2 \times 6 \times a \times b \times b \times c = 12ab^2c$

Division

To divide two terms you should cancel down where possible.

Like this

(a) $6xy \div 6y = \dfrac{{}^3\cancel{6}x\cancel{y}}{{}_1\cancel{2}\cancel{y}} = 3x$

(b) $4p^2qr^3 \div 3pq^2r^2 = \dfrac{4p^2\cancel{q}r^3}{3\cancel{p}q^2\cancel{r^2}} = \dfrac{4pr}{3q}$

Working with brackets

Expanding brackets

If there is a term outside the bracket then it must multiply every term inside the bracket. This process is called expanding the brackets.

Like this

(a) Expand $3(y + 4)$.

     $3(y + 4) = 3y + 12$ (you multiply each term inside the bracket by 3, i.e. 3 times y plus 3 times 4)

(b) Expand $-4y(y + 5)$.

     $-4y(y + 5) = -4y^2 - 20y$ (you multiply each term inside the bracket by $-4y$, i.e. $-4y$ times y plus $-4y$ times 5)

Factorising brackets

The opposite of expanding brackets is factorising brackets. Factorising means putting the brackets back by looking for common factors.

Like this

(a) Factorise $3x + 6$

     $3x + 6 = 3 \times x + 3 \times 2$

            $= 3(x + 2)$ (3 is the common factor)

(b) Factorise $y^2 + 4y$

     $y^2 + 4y = y \times y + 4 \times y$

            $= y(y + 4)$ (y is the common factor)

Practice Exercise

1 Use different colours to shade the boxes containing like terms.

Note: You should only need 4 different colours.

x	$2y$	z	xy
$7y$	$4z$	$3x$	xyx
$2xyz$	$5x$	$\frac{1}{2}zyx$	$-\frac{1}{2}y$
$3xy$	$\frac{1}{3}y$	$-yx$	$-2x$

2 Circle the correct answer(s).

(a) $y + 5y =$ $y + 5y$ $y + 6$ $6y$

(b) $ab + ba =$ $ba + ab$ $2ab$ $abba$

(c) $ab \times ab =$ $abab$ $2ab$ a^2b^2

(d) $6xy \div 2y =$ $12xy^2$ $6x$ $3x$

(e) $4(x + 2) =$ $4x + 2$ $4x + 8$ $4x + 42$

(f) $y(y - 3) =$ $yy - 3$ $y - 3y$ $y^2 - 3y$

3 Find the trios of equivalent expressions. One set has been done for you.

$3(x - 6)$ $18 - 3x$ $-3(-6 + x)$

$3(6 - x)$ $3x + 18$ $-3(x + 6)$

$3(x + 6)$ $-3x - 18$ $-3(-x - 6)$

$3(-x - 6)$ $3x - 18$ $-3(-x + 6)$

4 Think of a number.
Double it. Add 6.
Divide the answer by 2.
Take away the number you first thought of.
What number do you have now?

Show why the result will **always** be 3 no matter what number you start with.

....

....

5 Which of these expressions is the odd one out?

$abab$ b^2a^2 $(ab)^2$ $aabb$ ab^2 $baba$ a^2b^2 $(ba)^2$

5 Answer ....

Topic 5
The language of algebra

Summary

More working with brackets

Expanding two pairs of brackets

If there are two pairs of brackets then you must multiply each term in the first bracket by each term in the second bracket.

The word **FOIL** (standing for **First, Outside, Inside, Last**) will help you to remember how to do this.

Like this

Expand and simplify $(2x + 3)(x - 4)$

First	$2x \times x = 2x^2$	$(2x + 3)(x - 4)$
Outside	$2x \times -4 = -8x$	$(2x + 3)(x - 4)$
Inside	$3 \times x = 3x$	$(2x + 3)(x - 4)$
Last	$3 \times -4 = -12$	$(2x + 3)(x - 4)$

$$= 2x^2 - 5x - 12 \quad \text{(collecting together like terms)}$$

Factorising quadratics

To factorise quadratics of the form $x^2 + bx + c$ you must look for factors of the number term whose sum is the coefficient of the x term.

Like this

(a) Factorise $x^2 + 7x + 10$
Ask yourself which two numbers multiple to give $+10$ and add to make $+7$.
The numbers are **+2** and **+5**.
So $x^2 + 7x + 10 = (x + \mathbf{2})(x + \mathbf{5})$

(b) Factorise $x^2 + 1x - 6$
Ask yourself which two numbers multiply to give -6 and add to make $+1$.
The numbers are **−2** and **+3**.
So $x^2 + 1x - 6 = (x - \mathbf{2})(x + \mathbf{3})$

The rules of indices

These are the same as for numbers (see Topic 3).

Note: You cannot simplify $a^4 + a^5$ or $a^4 - a^5$ because you have unlike terms.

Multiplying indices

To multiply powers of the *same* letter you add the indices.

Like this
$a^4 \times a^5 = a^{4+5} = a^9$

Dividing indices

To divide powers of the *same* letter you subtract the indices.

Like this
$a^4 \div a^5 = a^{4-5} = a^{-1}$

Raising indices to a power

To raise indices to a power you multiply the indices.

Note: As with numbers, any letter to the power of 0 is 1 so that $a^0 = 1$, $x^0 = 1$, and so on.

Like this
$(a^4)^3 = a^{4 \times 3} = a^{12}$

Practice Exercise

1 The area of the whole rectangle is
$(x + 8)(x + 5)$.

Find the areas of the smaller
rectangles that make up the
whole rectangle and show that
$(x + 8)(x + 5) = x^2 + 13x + 40$

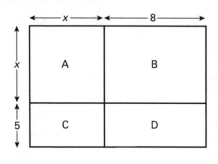

....

....

2 Why isn't $(x + 12)^2$ equal to $x^2 + 144$?

....

....

3 Expand and simplify the following expressions.

(a) $(x + 7)(x + 2)$

First .... × .... = ...

Outside .... × .... = ...

Inside .... × .... = ...

Last .... × .... = ...

Adding these and collecting like terms ....

(b) $(x - 3)(x + 8)$

....

....

(c) $(x - 5)(x - 11)$

....

....

4 Complete the following:

(a) $x^2 + 5x + 4$ $= (x + ...)(x + ...)$

(b) $x^2 + 6x - 7$ $= (x + ...)(x - ...)$

(c) $x^2 - x - 6$ $= (x ......)(x ......)$

(d) $x^2 - 11x + 24$ $= (.........)(.........)$

Algebra

Topic 5
The language of algebra

1. An examination booklet is made by stapling together four double sheets of paper, as shown.

(a) The middle pages are numbered 8 and 9. These are printed on the front of the top sheet. What page numbers are printed on the back of the top sheet?

....

(b) Another booklet is made in the same way, using **six** double sheets of paper.

(i) What are the numbers of the middle pages?

....

(ii) What is the number of the last page?

....

(SEG, Summer 1998 – specimen paper)

2. A quick way to convert °Fahrenheit into °Celsius is:

Subtract 30 from the °Fahrenheit and halve the answer

Use this quick way to change the following temperatures into °Celsius.

(a) 60°F

....

(b) 30°F

....

(c) 0°F

....

(NEAB – specimen paper)

3. (a) Simplify the expressions $2x + 5y - 3x + 8y$

....

....

(b) Multiply out the expression $2(x + 5)$

....

....

(NEAB – specimen paper)

4. (a) Write down an expression for the perimeter of this rectangle

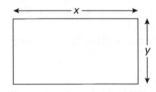

....

(b) Write down an expression for the area of this shape.

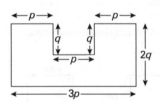

....

....

....

(NEAB – specimen paper)

Topic 5
The language of algebra

5.

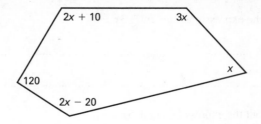

Write down and simplify an expression for the sum of the angles of this pentagon.

....

(NEAB, Summer 1998 – Paper 2H)

6. A square has sides of length $2y$ metres. A rectangle has sides of length $3y$ metres and breadth 3 metres.

(a) (i) The perimeter of the square is $2y + 2y + 2y + 2y$. Simplify this expression.

....

(ii) The perimeter of the rectangle is $3y + 3 + 3y + 3$. Simplify this expression.

....

(iii) The perimeter of the square is equal to the perimeter of the rectangle. Work out the value of y.

....

(b) The areas of these two rectangles are the same.

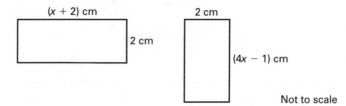

Not to scale

By solving the equation $2(x + 2) = 2(4x - 1)$ find the area of one of these rectangles.

....

....

(SEG – specimen paper)

Examination Questions

7. (a) Expand and simplify $(2x - 4)(x + 6)$

....

(b) Factorise

(i) $2x^2 - 4xy$

....

(ii) $x^2 + 10x - 24$

....

(NEAB, Summer 1998 – Paper 2H)

8. (a) Expand $x(3x^2 - 5)$

....

....

(b) Expand and simplify $(2x + 1)(3x - 2)$

....

(NEAB, Summer 1998 – Paper 2H)

9. Simplify

(a) $t^3 \times t^5$

....

(b) $p^6 \div p^2$

....

(c) $\dfrac{a^3 \times a^2}{a}$

....

(NEAB, Summer 1998 – Paper 1I)

Algebra

Topic 6
Making graphs

Note: The word axes is simply plural for the word axis. Remember: one axis, two axes!

Note: On most examination questions the scale is already given, but you may be asked to choose your own (sensible) scale.

Note: The first number of the co-ordinate gives the distance along the x axis and the second number gives the distance along the y axis.

Summary

Plotting graphs

Before you plot a graph you need to consider the frame of reference and choose a suitable scale.

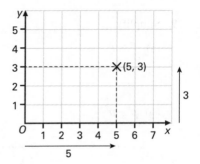

Vertical axis (y axis)

Origin

Horizontal axis (x axis)

Frame of reference

All graphs are drawn with reference to a set of axes which are drawn at right angles to each other, as shown.

The horizontal axis is usually called the x axis and the vertical axis is usually called the y axis.

The point of intersection of the two axes is called the origin.

Choosing a scale

The scale is determined from the smallest and largest values to be plotted on each of the axes. The scale on each axis should be as large as possible. You should choose the scale carefully so that the points are easy to plot.

Cartesian co-ordinates in one quadrant

Co-ordinates are used to mark the position of a point on a graph. Each co-ordinate must consist of two numbers separated by a comma in a pair of brackets.

Like this

The co-ordinate (5, 3) is drawn so that its position is 5 units along the x axis and 3 units up the y axis.

Practice Exercise

1 Write down the co-ordinates of the points in each diagram.

(a)

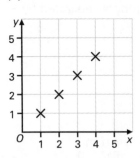

(b)

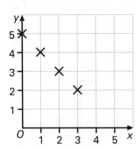

(c)

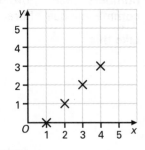

(d) Find another point on each of the lines.

2 Plot the following points and join them in order:
(2, 10), (7, 10), (7, 8), (4, 8), (4, 6), (6, 6), (6, 4), (4, 4), (4, 0), (2, 0), (2, 10).

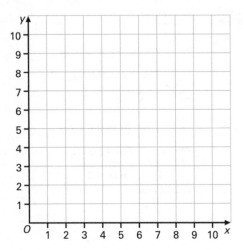

3 Draw your own shape and write down the co-ordinates. Ask a friend to plot your points and join them up.

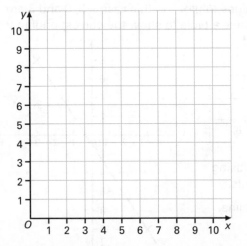

1 (a) Answer

(......, ...) (......, ...)

(......, ...) (......, ...)

1 (b) Answer

(......, ...) (......, ...)

(......, ...) (......, ...)

1 (c) Answer

(......, ...) (......, ...)

(......, ...) (......, ...)

1 (d) Answer

(......, ...) (......, ...)

(......, ...)

Topic 6
Making graphs

Summary

Cartesian co-ordinates in four quadrants

You can extend the axes of a graph to include both positive and negative numbers. Each co-ordinate must consist of two numbers separated by a comma in a pair of brackets.

Like this

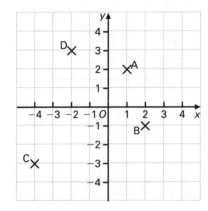

A (1, 2)
B (2, −1)
C (−4, −3)
D (−2, 3)

Note: Remember that the first number of the co-ordinate gives the distance along the x axis from the origin and the second number gives the distance along the y axis from the origin.

Plotting straight-line graphs

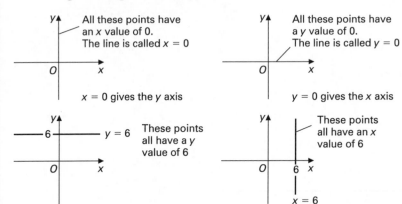

To plot more difficult lines you need to make a **table of values**.

You must choose your x values and work out the corresponding y values.

Like this

Draw the line $y = 3x - 1$

You start by choosing some x values to plot – in this case −3, 0 and 3 are suitable x values – and then produce a table to show the corresponding y values. The table of values would look like this:

x	−3	0	3
y	−10	−1	8
(x, y)	(−3, −10)	(0, −1)	(3, 8)

You can now draw a set of axes (using a suitable scale) and plot the points.

Join the points up with a straight line.

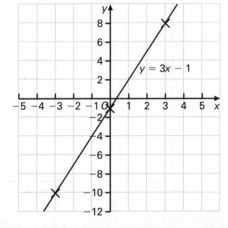

Note: Although you need only two points to define a straight line, it is always best to plot three points in case you've made a mistake.

Practice Exercise

1 (a) Write down the co-ordinates of the points in each diagram.

(i)

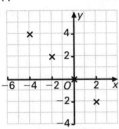

(ii)

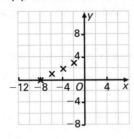

(iii)

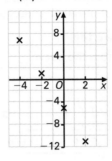

(b) Find another point on each of the lines.

2 Plot the following points and join them in order: (1, 4), (2, 4), (2, −3), (1, −3), (−2, 2), (−2, −3), (−3, −3), (−3, 4), (−2, 4), (1, −1), (1, 4).

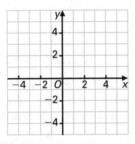

3 On the same axes draw

(a) $y = 2x$
$y = 3x$
$y = 5x$

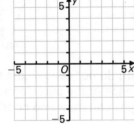

(b) $y = -2x$
$y = -3x$
$y = -5x$

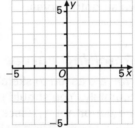

(c) $y = x + 1$
$y = x + 3$
$y = x - 2$

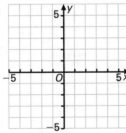

(d) $y = 2x + 3$
$y = 2x + 4$
$y = 2x - 1$

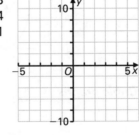

(e) What do you notice in each case?

....

....

....

....

Foundation and Intermediate Tiers

Summary

Topic 6
Making graphs

Note: In this case the x values of the points to be plotted are given. If they are not given you need to make a sensible choice of x values to use.

Plotting curves

To draw curves you need to make a **table of values**.
You must choose your x values and work out the corresponding y values.

Like this

Draw the curve $y = \dfrac{8}{x}$ between -8 and $+8$ on the x axis.

x	-8	-6	-4	-2	0	2	4	6	8
$y = \dfrac{8}{x}$	-1	-1.3	-2	-4	error	4	2	1.3	1
(x, y)	$(-8, -1)$	$(-6, -1.3)$	$(-4, -2)$	$(-2, -4)$		$(2, 4)$	$(4, 2)$	$(6, 1.3)$	$(8, 1)$

Since it is not easy to see what is going on around $x = 0$, it may be helpful to choose some extra x values.

x	-1	$-\frac{1}{2}$	$\frac{1}{2}$	1
$y = \dfrac{8}{x}$	-8	-16	16	8
(x, y)	$(-1, -8)$	$(-\frac{1}{2}, -16)$	$(\frac{1}{2}, 16)$	$(1, 8)$

Note: Check that your points do form a smooth line. If a point seems misplaced then check again.

You can now draw a set of axes (using a suitable scale) and plot the points. Join the points up with a smooth curve.

The graph $y = \dfrac{8}{x}$ has two separate parts, so in this case you need to join your points with two smooth curves.

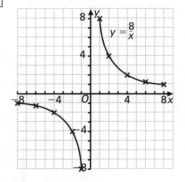

Sketching curves

If you are asked to sketch a graph then you do not need to draw the graph accurately. You should just 'sketch' the shape of the curve and show whether or not it passes through the origin. You may also need to show values where your graph crosses the axes.

Quadratic graphs

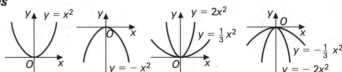

Cubic graphs

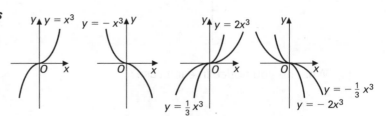

Reciprocal graphs
(where k is a constant)

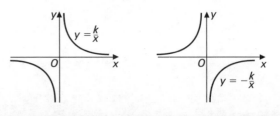

Note: Remember that reciprocal graphs come in two parts.

Practice Exercise

1 On the same axes draw:

(a) $y = x^2$
$y = x^2 + 3$
$y = x^2 - 1$

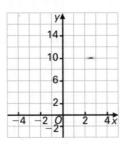

(b) $y = x^3$
$y = x^3 + 4$
$y = x^3 - 2$

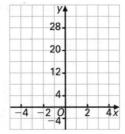

(c) $y = \dfrac{1}{x}$

$y = \dfrac{3}{x}$

$y = \dfrac{4}{x}$

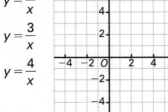

(d) $y = -\dfrac{1}{x}$

$y = -\dfrac{3}{x}$

$y = -\dfrac{4}{x}$

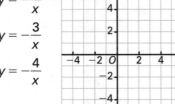

(e) What do you notice?

....

....

....

....

2 Match each description with the correct function.

(a)
> The graph of this function does not cut either of the axes and its gradient is always negative.

A $y = (x - 2)(x - 3)$

2 (a) Answer ....

(b)
> The graph of this function has a gradient which is never negative. The graph goes through the origin.

B $y = \dfrac{2}{x}$

2 (b) Answer ....

(c)
> The graph of this function cuts the x-axis in two places and cuts the y-axis at (0, 6).
> The gradient is first negative, then zero, then positive.

C $y = x^3$

2 (c) Answer ....

Examination Questions

Topic 6
Making graphs

1. (a) Plot the points (1, 3) and (4, 6).
Join the points with a straight line.

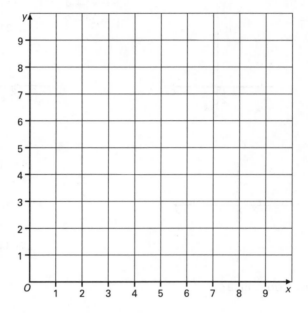

(b) The point P $(a, 5)$ lies on the line.
What is the value of a?

....

(SEG – specimen paper)

2. (a) Draw the graph of $y = 2x^2$ for values of x from 0 to 3.

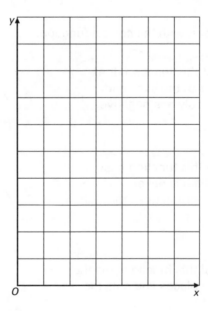

(b) Use your graph to find a value of x when $y = 12$.

....

(SEG, Summer 1997 – Intermediate Paper 3)

Examination Questions

Algebra

Topic 6
Making graphs

Foundation and Intermediate Tiers

Intermediate Tier Only

3. The following graph shows the line $y = 2x + 8$

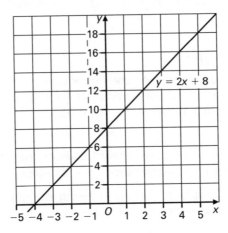

On the same graph draw the curve $y = x^2$

Write down the points of intersection of the straight line $y = 2x + 8$ and the curve $y = x^2$

Co-ordinates are (........., ...) and (........., ...)

4. The cross-section of a swimming pool is shown. It is filled, from empty, at a uniform rate. Sketch a graph of the water height against time, t, as the pool fills.

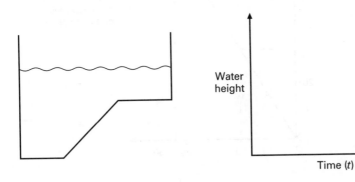

(SEG, Summer 1997 – Higher Paper 6)

Algebra

Topic 7
Using graphs

Note: *Although most conversion graphs will pass through the origin, remember that this is not always the case. For example, the conversion graph for temperatures in Fahrenheit and Celsius does not pass through the origin*

Summary

Real-life graphs

You need to be able to plot and draw graphs for everyday situations, such as conversion graphs.

Conversion graphs

Conversion graphs can be used to convert between distances in kilometres and miles, between temperatures in degrees Fahrenheit and degrees Celsius, between money in different currencies, etc.

Like this

Use the fact that 1 mile is approximately 1.6 kilometres to draw a graph to convert distances in miles into distances in kilometres.

Drawing conversion graphs is a bit like drawing straight line graphs. You need to make a table of values for at least three points.

Miles	0	10	50
Kilometres	0	16	80
(x, y)	(0, 0)	(10, 16)	(50, 80)

You can now draw a set of axes (using a suitable scale) and plot the points. Join your points up with a straight line.

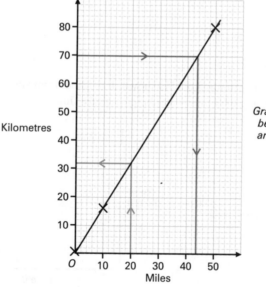

Graph to convert between miles and kilometres

The conversion graph can now be used to convert distances.

Like this

(a) How many kilometres are there in 20 miles?
(b) How many miles are there in 70 kilometres?

To carry out the conversions you need to draw a line from the given value on the correct axis to the conversion line and then read off the value on the other axis.

From the graph

(a) There are 32 kilometres in 20 miles.
(b) There are 44 miles in 70 kilometres.

Practice Exercise

1 The following conversion graph is used to convert between pounds sterling (£) and euros (€).

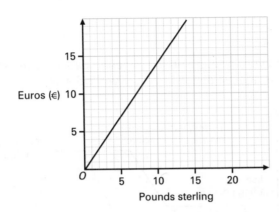

Use the graph to convert the following. (Remember to show the working on the graph)

(a) £2.50

(b) £8.00

(c) £10.50

(d) €3.00

(e) €7.00

(f) €12.00

2 Given that 1 kilogram (kg) = 2.2 pounds (lb) complete the following graph and use it to convert the weights in (a)–(d).

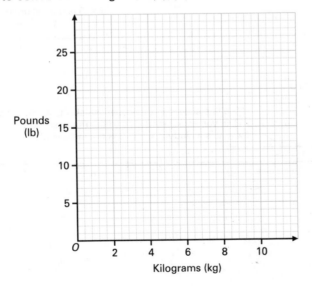

(a) 5 kg

(b) 7.5 kg

(c) 10 lb

(d) 16.2 lb

Topic 7
Using graphs

Note: The gradient, i.e. 'steepness', of the travel graph shows the speed. The steeper the line, the greater the speed.

Note: A closed circle means the number at the end of the range is included. An open circle means the number is not included.

Summary

Real-life graphs

You need to be able to plot and draw graphs of everyday situations such as travel graphs.

Travel graphs

Travel graphs are very popular on examination papers. They show time on the horizontal axis against distance on the vertical axis.

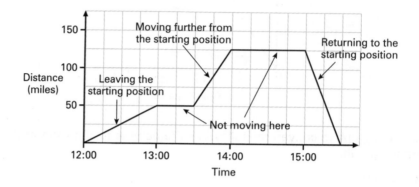

Inequalities and number lines

You must be able to use a number line to show an inequality.

Like this

Show the following inequalities on a number line:

(a) $x > 5$

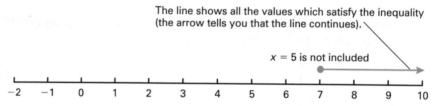

(b) $-3 < x \leq 0$

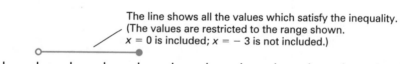

Practice Exercise

1 Here is a distance–time graph. Which description fits the graph?

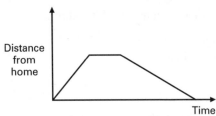

A Sally sets off from home walks up a hill across the top and down the other side.

B Sally sets off from home, increases her speed, goes at a steady speed for a while then slows down and stops.

C Sally travels at a steady speed, stops for a rest then returns home at a slower speed than before.

D Sally sets off from home, goes at a steady speed for a while, stops for a rest and then sets off in the same direction.

1 Answer ....

2 Complete the graph to show the following information:
A cyclist leaves Croyston at 12.00 noon and cycles to Darley 40 km away. The cyclist arrived at Darley at 2.00 pm. A motorist leaves Croyston at 12.30 pm and travels to Darley at a steady speed of 60 km/h.

From your graph:

(a) When does the motorist pass the cyclist?

(b) What time does the motorist arrive in Darley?

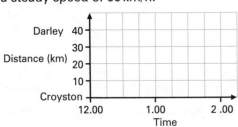

2 (a) Answer ....

2 (b) Answer ....

3 Show the following inequalities on this number line.

(a) $a \geq 5$ (b) $b \leq -3$ (c) $c > -2$ (d) $-3 \leq d < 8$

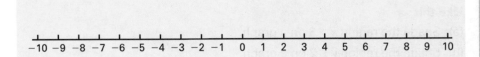

4 Write down the inequalities shown on the number lines.

(a)
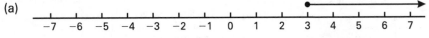

4 (a) Answer ....

(b)
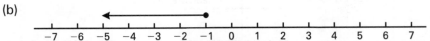

4 (b) Answer ....

(c)
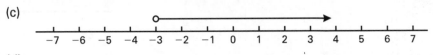

4 (c) Answer ....

(d)
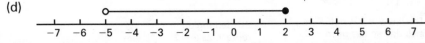

4 (d) Answer ....

Algebra

Topic 7
Using graphs

Gradient of a line

The gradient of a line is a measure of its 'steepness.'

$$\text{Gradient} = \frac{\text{vertical distance}}{\text{horizontal distance}}$$

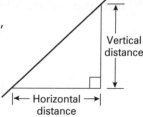

Gradients are positive if the slope is 'uphill' or negative if the slope is 'downhill.'

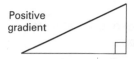

Positive gradient

Negative gradient

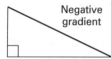

Note: *To find the gradient of a straight line you should choose two points on your line and create a right-angled triangle with sides parallel to the axes. It is best if you can choose your two points as far apart as possible so that the triangle you draw is quite large.*

The general equation of a straight line ($y = mx + c$)

The equation of any straight line can be written in the form $\mathbf{y = mx + c}$ where m is the gradient of the line and c is where the line cuts the y axis (i.e. c is the intercept on the y axis).

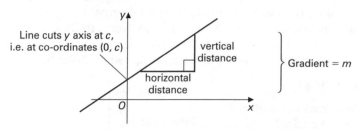

Line cuts y axis at c, i.e. at co-ordinates $(0, c)$

vertical distance

horizontal distance

Gradient $= m$

To find the equation of a given straight line you have to work out the gradient and find the value of y where the line cuts the y axis. Simple!

You then have $y = $ gradient $\times x + $ value where line cuts the y axis.

Note: *Always check whether the gradient is positive or negative.*

Note: *If the line goes through the origin then $c = 0$ and $y = $ gradient $\times x$.*

Inequalities and graphs

To show inequalities on a graph you must first plot the boundary line. You usually shade the region you don't want, but remember to **read the question carefully** to make sure. Just to keep you on your toes, some exam boards do it the other way round!

Like this

(a) Shade the region $x > 3$ on a graph.

(b) Shade the region $y \leq 2$ on a graph.

(c) Shade the region satisfied by $x < 2$ and $y \geq -1$ on a graph.

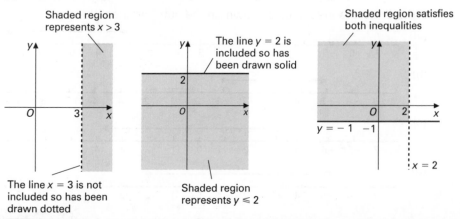

Shaded region represents $x > 3$

The line $x = 3$ is not included so has been drawn dotted

The line $y = 2$ is included so has been drawn solid

Shaded region represents $y \leq 2$

Shaded region satisfies both inequalities

$y = -1$

$x = 2$

Note: *Read the question carefully. Does the question ask you to shade the region required or the region not required?*

Practice Exercise

1 Arrange these lines in order of their gradients, smallest gradient first.

$y = 2x + 3$ .... Smallest gradient

$y = \dfrac{x}{2} + 10$ ....

$3y = x - 1$ ....

$5y = 8x$ .... Largest gradient

2 Which graph corresponds to each of these equations.

(a) $y = 2.5$

(b) $x + y = 3$

(c) $y = 2x$

(d) $y = \frac{1}{2}x + 1$

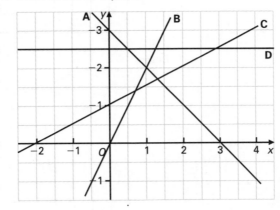

2 (a) Answer ....

2 (b) Answer ....

2 (c) Answer ....

2 (d) Answer ....

3 Show clearly on the diagram the region where all these inequalities are satisfied:

$y \geqslant 0 \qquad y \leqslant 2x \qquad x + y \leqslant 4$

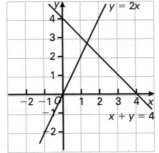

4 For each of the following equations identify the gradient (m) and the intercept on the y axis (c).

(a) $y = 3x + 2$ $\quad m = \ldots\ldots\ldots \quad c = \ldots\ldots\ldots$

(b) $y = -2x + 7$ $\quad m = \ldots\ldots\ldots \quad c = \ldots\ldots\ldots$

(c) $y = 2x - \frac{1}{2}$ $\quad m = \ldots\ldots\ldots \quad c = \ldots\ldots\ldots$

(d) $2y = x + 2$ $\quad m = \ldots\ldots\ldots \quad c = \ldots\ldots\ldots$

(e) $2x + y = 3$ $\quad m = \ldots\ldots\ldots \quad c = \ldots\ldots\ldots$

Topic 7
Using graphs

Examination Questions

1. The table below shows conversions for pounds to dollars

Pounds (£)	1	2	3	5	10
Dollars ($)	1.60	3.20	4.80	8.00	16.00

(a) Show this information on the graph below

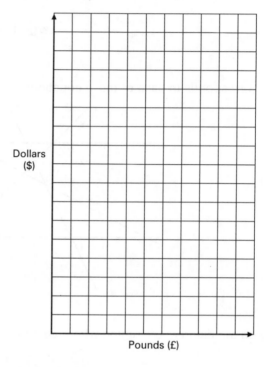

Dollars
($)

Pounds (£)

(b) Use your graph to find

(i)   the number of dollars equivalent to £8

....

(ii) the number of pounds equivalent to $6.00

....

Examination Questions

Algebra

Topic 7
Using graphs

Foundation and Intermediate Tiers

Intermediate Tier Only

2. Jane takes 15 minutes to walk half a mile from home to the bus stop. She waits at the bus stop for 5 minutes then catches the bus. The bus takes 15 minutes to travel the two miles to school.

Draw a distance–time graph to show Jane's journey to school.

3. (a) On the diagram draw and label the following lines.

$y = 2x$ and $x + y = 5$

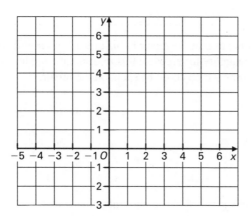

(b) Explain how to use your graph to solve the equation $2x = 5 - x$

....

....

(c) Show clearly the single region that is satisfied by **all** of these inequalities

$$x + y \leq 5 \qquad y \geq 2x \qquad x \geq 0$$

Label the region R.

(SEG, Summer 1998 – Intermediate Paper 14)

Topic 7
Using graphs

Examination Questions

4. Television repair charges depend on the length of time taken for the repair, as shown on the graph.

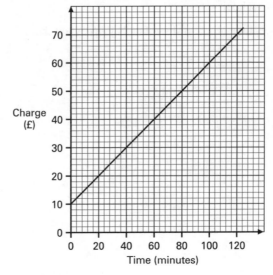

The charge is made up of a fixed amount plus an extra amount which depends on the time.

(a) Write down the equation of the line.

....

(b) Mr Swann hopes that the repair to his television set will cost £84 or less. Write down an inequality to represent this information and use it to calculate the maximum time which could be spent on the repair.

....

....

(SEG – specimen paper)

5. The distance–time graph shows the journeys made by a van and a car starting from Oxford, travelling to Luton, and returning to Oxford.

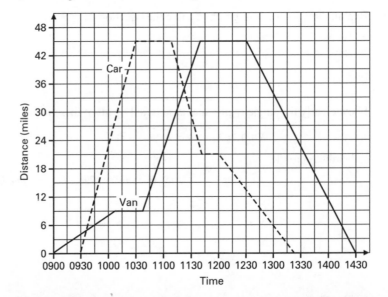

(a) How far had the car travelled when it met the van for the second time?

....

(b) Calculate, in miles per hour, the average speed of the car between 0950 and 1000.

....

(c) During which period of time was the van travelling at its greatest average speed?

....

(SEG – specimen paper)

6. The distance from Upton to Dorchester is 20 miles.

   The diagram shows the distance–time graph of a cyclist travelling from Upton to Dorchester.

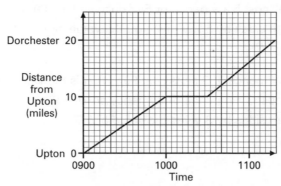

   At 0940 a motorist leaves Dorchester to travel to Upton along the same road as the cyclist. The motorist travels at an average speed of 40 mph.

   (a) On the same diagram draw the distance–time graph of the motorist.

   (b) At what time did the motorist pass the cyclist?

   ....

(SEG, Summer 1997 – Intermediate Paper 3)

7. The diagram shows the graph of $y = x^3$. By drawing the graph $y = x^2 + 1$ for $0 \leqslant x \leqslant 2$, estimate the solution of the equation $x^3 = x^2 + 1$.

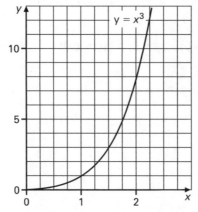

(SEG, Summer 1997 – Higher Paper 6)

Algebra

Topic 8
Using algebra

Making equations

Sometimes you can solve a problem by writing an equation.

Like this

(a) A girl is *x* years old. In 10 years time she will be 21 years old.

In ten years the girl will be $x + 10$ years old so $x + 10 = 21$ and $x = 11$
So the girl is 11 years old.

(b) A boy is *y* years old. Last year he was 15 years old.

Last year the boy was $y - 1$ years old so $y - 1 = 15$ and $y = 16$
So the boy is 16 years old.

The problems seem quite easy to solve without algebra, but is helpful to see how you are solving them.

Like this

(a) A pencil costs *a* pence. If 5 pencils cost 80p what is the value of *a*?

5 pencils will cost $5 \times a$ pence or $5a$ pence so $5a = 80$

Dividing both sides by 5 will give you the value of *a*.

$$a = \frac{80}{5} = 16$$

(b) A pen costs *b* pence. If 3 pens cost 90p what is the value of *b*?

3 pens will cost $3 \times b$ pence or $3b$ pence so $3b = 90$

Dividing both sides by 3 gives the value of *b*.

$$b = \frac{90}{3} = 30$$

Substitution

Substitution is where you replace a letter by a given number.

Like this

(a) Substitute $a = 2$ to find the values of $7a$ and $4a - 7$

$7a = 7 \times a = 7 \times 2 = 14$

$4a - 7 = 4 \times a - 7 = 4 \times 2 - 7 = 8 - 7 = 1$

(b) If $x = 5$ and $y = 0.2$, find the values of $10x$, $3y$, $10x + 3y$, xy and $\frac{3x}{10y}$.

$10x = 10 \times x = 10 \times 5 = 50$

$3y$ means $3 \times y = 3 \times 0.2 = 0.6$

$10x + 3y$ means $10 \times x + 3 \times y = 50 + 0.6 = 50.6$

$xy = x \times y = 5 \times 0.2 = 1$

$$\frac{3x}{10y} = (3 \times x) \div (10 \times y) = (3 \times 5) \div (10 \times 0.2) = 15 \div 2 = 7\tfrac{1}{2} \text{ (or 7.5)}$$

Practice Exercise

1 Write down equations to go with each of the following

(a) Three times a number, a, is equal to thirty.

....

(b) Five times a number b plus twelve equals twenty.

....

(c) Four times a number, c, minus six equals two.

....

(d) Half of a number, d, plus three equals four and a half.

....

2 If $a = 3$, $b = 2$, $c = 0$ and $d = -4$ then connect each expression to its answer. The first one has been done for you.

$a + b$	3
ab	-12
$a - c$	-2
abc	5
$\frac{1}{2}b$	1
ad	6
$\dfrac{d}{b}$	9
abd	0
a^b	-24

3 Work out the value of each expression when $x = 5$ and arrange the answers in order of size.

$3x + 2$ $\qquad$ $3(x - 2)$ $\qquad$ $3x - 2$ $\qquad$ $3(x + 2)$

biggest $\qquad\qquad\qquad\qquad\qquad\qquad\qquad\qquad$ smallest

.... 9
....

4 The area of this trapezium is $\dfrac{h}{2}(a + b)$.
Find the area when $a = 4\,\text{m}$, $b = 6\,\text{m}$ and $h = 2\,\text{m}$.

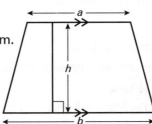

....

....

....

Algebra

Topic 8
Using algebra

Note: Once you have made your equation you should be able to solve it! This means finding the value of x (the number of tickets sold) which works in the equation.

Summary

Making equations

Sometimes you can solve a problem by writing an equation.

Like this

(a) It costs £50 to hire a hall for a disco (you provide the music!). If you sell x tickets at £1.50 each, write an expression for your profit, P, in £s.

You make £1.50 $\times x$ from selling the tickets, but you have to subtract the cost of hiring the hall from your profit. So
$P = 1.5x - 50$

(b) If your profit is £250, write an equation for x.
Your equation is $1.5x - 50 = 250$

Rules for solving linear equations

1 What you do to one side of an equation you must do to the other side. Think of your equation as a balance.

Like this

Solve $1.5x - 50 = 250$
To get the x term by itself add 50 to each side $1.5x = 300$
Now to get x divide each side by 1.5 $x = 200$

2 You must collect all the x terms on one side of the equation and the number terms on the other side.

Like this

Solve $9x + 8 = 7x - 3$
Subtract $7x$ from both sides $9x - 7x + 8 = 7x - 7x - 3$
                                $2x + 8 = -3$

Subtract 8 from both sides $2x + 8 - 8 = -3 - 8$
                                $2x = -11$

Divide both sides by 2 $x = -\dfrac{11}{2} = -5.5$

3 If you have any brackets you must get rid of them!

Like this

Solve $3(x + 2) = 4(x - 1)$
Work out the brackets $3x + 6 = 4x - 4$
Subtract $3x$ from both sides $3x - 3x + 6 = 4x - 3x - 4$
                             $6 = x - 4$

Add 4 to both sides $6 + 4 = x - 4 + 4$
                          $10 = x$ or $x = 10$

Note: It is easier to work on the side which keeps the x term positive.

Substitution

Remember that substitution is where you replace a letter by a given number.

Like this

If $a = 2$, $b = -3$ and $c = \frac{1}{2}$ find the values of $3a + 4c$, $3a - 5b$, abc, $\dfrac{b}{c}$, and b^a.

$3a + 4c = 3 \times 2 + 4 \times \frac{1}{2} = 6 + 2 = 8$

$3a - 5b = 3 \times 2 - 5 \times -3 = 6 + 15 = 21$ remember that $- \times - = +$

$abc = 2 \times -3 \times \frac{1}{2} = -3$

$\dfrac{b}{c} = \dfrac{-3}{\frac{1}{2}} = -6$

$ba = (-3)^2 = -3 \times -3 = 9$

Practice Exercise

1 Find the weight of one of the unknown containers in each of parts a–f. Where there is more than one unknown container, you may assume they are of equal weight.

(a)

(b)

(c)
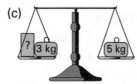

(d)

(e)
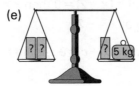

(f)

1 (a) Answer ....kg

1 (b) Answer ....kg

1 (c) Answer ....kg

1 (d) Answer ....kg

1 (e) Answer ....kg

1 (f) Answer ....kg

2 Which two of these equations have got the same solution?

A $3x - 6 = 9$

B $2x = 2.5$

C $\dfrac{x}{2} = 2.5$

D $3(x - 6) = 9$

2 Answer .... and ....

3 A quadrilateral has three angles of $x°$ and one angle of 75°. Make an equation to show this information and solve it to find the value of x.

....

....

4 If $a = 3$, $b = 2$, $c = \frac{1}{2}$, $d = -\frac{1}{3}$ then connect the expression to its answer. The first one has been done for you.

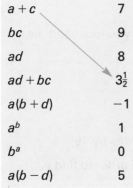

$a + c$	7
bc	9
ad	8
$ad + bc$	$3\frac{1}{2}$
$a(b + d)$	-1
a^b	1
b^a	0
$a(b - d)$	5

Topic 8
Using
algebra

Summary

Solving quadratic equations

Quadratic equations can be solved using the fact that if $A \times B = 0$, then either $A = 0$ or $B = 0$ (or both $A = 0$ and $B = 0$).

Like this

Solve $(x - 5)(x + 2) = 0$

Since $(x - 5)(x + 2)$ is the same as $(x - 5) \times (x + 2)$ then either $(x - 5) = 0$ or $(x + 2) = 0$

If $(x - 5) = 0$ then $x = 5$ and if $(x + 2) = 0$ then $x = -2$

So the solutions are $x = 5$ or $x = -2$

Quadratics of the form $ax^2 + bx + c = 0$ should be factorised and then solved in a similar manner.

Like this

Solve $x^2 - 3x - 10 = 0$

Factorising the left-hand side you get $(x - 5)(x + 2)$

So $(x - 5)(x + 2) = 0$ and you proceed as above.

Simultaneous linear equations

Simultaneous equations are two equations which have two unknown terms. You need to find the two answers which 'work' for both equations.

Like this

Solve the simultaneous equations $4x + y = 7$ and $2x - 2y = 11$.

Step 1 Label the equations.
$4x + y = 7$ [1]
$2x - 2y = 11$ [2]   No sweat yet!

Note: You could choose to make the x terms the same by multiplying equation [2] by 2.

Step 2 Choose to make the number in front of either the x or y term the same in both equations. In this case make the y terms the same by multiplying both sides of equation [1] by 2.

This gives $8x + 2y = 14$ [1] $\times$ 2
and you still have $2x - 2y = 11$ [2]

Note: If the chosen terms have the same signs, subtract the two equations. If the chosen terms have different signs, add the two equations.

Step 3 You must now get rid of your chosen term.

The chosen y terms have different signs so you must add the equations to get rid of these terms.

$$8x + 2y = 14$$
add $$\underline{2x - 2y = 11}$$
$$10x \quad\quad = 25$$

Step 4 Now find x. $10x = 25$
$x = 2.5$ (dividing both sides by 10)

Note: It is sensible to check your answers by substituting the values of x and y into equation [2];
$2x - 2y = 2 \times 2.5 - 2$
$\times -3 = 5 + 6 = 11$

Step 5 Substitute the value of x into equation [1] in order to find y.
$4x + y = 7$ [1]
$4 \times 2.5 + y = 7$
$y = -3$

You can also solve simultaneous equations using graphs. Plot graphs for the two equations you need to solve. The point of intersection of the two graphs (x, y) gives the solutions of the two simultaneous equations. If the graphs do not intersect, then the simultaneous equations have no solution.

Practice Exercise

1 Solve the following equations

(a) $(x - 3)(x + 7) = 0$

Either (....................) = 0   or   (....................) = 0

So $x =$ ....   or $x =$ ....

(b) $(x + 7)(2x - 5) = 0$

Either (....................) = 0   or   (....................) = 0

So $x =$ ....   or $x =$ ....

(c) $x^2 + 2x - 15 = 0$

$(x +$ ....$)$ $(x -$ ....$) = 0$

Either $(x +$ ....$) = 0$ or $(x -$ ....$) = 0$

So $x =$ ....   or $x =$ ....

(d) $x^2 - 3x - 28 = 0$

(....................) (....................) = 0

Either (....................) = 0   or   (....................) = 0

So $x =$ ....   or $x =$ ....

2 Match the equations and the solutions, then solve the equation left over.

$x^2 + 7x + 12 = 0$

$x = 4, x = 3$

$x^2 + x - 12 = 0$

$x = -4, x = 3$

$x^2 - x - 12 = 0$

$x = 4, x = -3$

$x^2 - 7x - 12 = 0$

2 Answer x = ...

x = ...

3 Solve the simultaneous equations:

(a) $2x + y = 11$
    $5x - 2y = 5$

(b) $2x + y = 1$
    $x - 2y = 8$

3 (a) Answer x = ..., y = ...

3 (b) Answer x = ..., y = ...

Algebra

Topic 8
Using algebra

1. Use the formula $s = 2t + 32$ to work out the following.

   (a) Find s when $t = -7$.

   ....

   (b) Find t when $s = 40$.

   ....

   ....

   (c) Show how to use the method of approximations to estimate the value of s when $t = 18.9$.

   ....

   ....

   (SEG, Summer 1998 – Specimen Paper 12)

2. Solve the equation $2(3x + 5) = 4x + 7$

   ....

   ....

   (SEG, Summer 1997 – Intermediate Paper 4)

3. P and Q are rectangles.
   The dimensions are given in centimetres.

   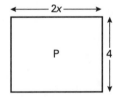
   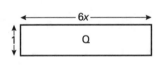

   (a) (i) Write down a simplified expression for the area of P.

   ....

   (ii) What is the perimeter of P in centimetres?

   ....

   The two rectangles have the same perimeter.
   The perimeter of P is $4x + 8$.
   The perimeter of Q is $12x + 2$

   (b) Solve the equation $4x + 8 = 12x + 2$

   ....

   ....

   (SEG, Summer 1997 – Intermediate Paper 3)

4. The height, h metres, of a stone t seconds after being thrown in the air is given by the formula

$$h = ut + \tfrac{1}{2}at^2$$

Find the height of the stone after 5 seconds when $u = 12.9$ and $a = -9.8$

....

....

5. Solve the simultaneous equations $3x - 2y = 8$ and
$$x + 4y = 5$$

....

....

(SEG, Summer 1997 – Intermediate Paper 3)

6. Solve these simultaneous equations $4x + 5y = 5$
$$2x - y = 6$$

....

....

....

....

Do not use a trial and improvement method.

(NEAB, Summer 1998 – Higher Paper 2H)

7. Jane buys 3 litres of oil and 40 litres of petrol for £30. Richard buys 2 litres of oil and 10 litres of petrol for £10. The cost of 1 litre of oil is £x. The cost of 1 litre of petrol is £y.

Therefore $3x + 40y = 30$
and $2x + 10y = 10$

(a) Draw the graph of these equations.

(b) What is the cost of 1 litre of petrol?

....

(SEG – Specimen Intermediate Paper 13)

Topic 9
More using algebra

Note: *The sequence 1, 1, 2, 3, 5, 8, ... is usually referred to as **the** Fibonacci sequence!*

Summary

All about sequences

A sequence is an ordered set of numbers that obeys a certain rule which you have to work out! Usually you have to find two more terms and then the nth term. It is easy(ish!) to work out the rule and use words to describe what is happening. The problem comes when you have to find the general – or nth – term.

Some sequences which you should recognise:

1   The sequence of squares.

   1, 4, 9, ... $1^2, 2^2, 3^2, ...$

   The next terms are 16 (4^2) then 25 (5^2) and the nth is n^2.

2   The sequence of cubes.

   1, 8, 27, ... $1^3, 2^3, 3^3, ...$

   The next terms are 64 (4^3) then 125 (5^3) and the nth term is n^3.

3   Fibonacci sequences

   In Fibonacci sequences the next terms are found by adding the two previous terms.

   e.g.   1, 1, 2, 3, 5, ...   the next term is $3 + 5 = 8$

   or   3, 4, 7, 11, 18, ...   the next term is $11 + 18 = 29$

Working with sequences

Most number sequences involve adding/subtracting or multiplying/dividing as the rule for finding the next term. You should continue the sequence to find subsequent terms.

Like this

Find the next three terms for each of the following sequences

(a)   2, 7, 12, 17, ...

   Each term is obtained from the previous term by adding 5. So the rule is 'add 5.'

   The next three terms are 22, 27 and 32.

(b)   2, 6, 18, 54, ...

   Each term is obtained from the previous term by multiplying by 3. So the rule is 'multiply by 3.'

   The next three terms are 162, 486 and 1458.

(c)   15, 11, 7, 3, ...

   Each term is obtained from the previous term by subtracting 4. So the rule is 'subtract 4.'

   The next three terms are -1, -5 and -9.

Practice Exercise

1 Match the sequences and the descriptions.

    (a) Each term in the sequence is double the one before.

                                    1, 1, 2, 3, 5, ...

    (b) The square numbers.

                                    2, 4, 6, 8, ...

    (c) The next number is found by adding together the two previous ones.

                                    2, 4, 8, 16, ...

    (d) The even numbers.

Find the sequence for the description left over.

2 Write down the next 4 terms in each of these sequences.

    (a) 3, 7, 11, 15, ..., ..., ..., ...,

    (b) 5, 3, 1, −1, ..., ..., ..., ...,

    (c) 3, 6, 12, 24, ..., ..., ..., ...,

    (d) 18, 9, $4\frac{1}{2}$, $2\frac{1}{4}$, ..., ..., ..., ...,

3 Write down the rule for each of the sequences in question 2.

    (a) ....

    (b) ....

    (c) ....

    (d) ....

4 Write down your own sequence and then ask a friend to write down the rule and the next 4 terms.

Sequence ....

Rule ....

Next 4 terms ....

Algebra

Topic 9
More using algebra

Sequences using the method of 'add one'

In the sequence 7, 10, 13, ... to find the next term you 'add on 3' each time.

The next two terms are 16 and 19.

The nth term is $7 + 3(n - 1) = 7 + 3n - 3 = 4 + 3n$

In general if there is an 'add on' or difference of d between each term, then

nth term = first term + $d \times (n - 1)$

Like this

Find the next two terms and the nth term in the sequence: $-2, 2, 6, ...$

To find the next term you 'add on 4' each time.

The next two terms are 10 $(6 + 4)$ and 14 $(10 + 4)$.

nth term $=$ first term $+ d \times (n - 1)$

nth term $= -2 + (n - 1) \times$ difference

$\qquad = -2 + (n - 1) \times 4$

$\qquad = -2 + 4n - 4$

$\qquad = -6 + 4n \quad$ or $\quad 4n - 6$

Solving linear inequalities

To solve linear inequalities you use the same procedure as solving linear equations except when you multiply or divide by a negative number.

When you multiply or divide by a negative number you must change the direction of the inequality.

You have $\qquad 3 > 1$

Multiply by $-1 \quad -3 < -1$

You must change the direction of the inequality to make the statement correct.

Transforming or changing the subject of formulae

This is a fancy way of saying find one letter in terms of another letter (or other letters).

You must isolate the letter term you want on one side of the formula. The rules of linear equations apply!

Like this

(a) Find t given that $v = u + at$

Subtract u from both sides to isolate the t term $\qquad v - u = at$

Divide both sides by a to get t by itself $\qquad \dfrac{v - u}{a} = t$

Turn the equation around to make t the subject $\qquad t = \dfrac{v - u}{a}$

(b) Find r, the radius of a circle, given that $A = \pi r^2$

Divide both sides by π to isolate the square term $\qquad \dfrac{A}{\pi} = r^2$

Take the square root each side $\qquad \sqrt{\dfrac{A}{\pi}} = r$

Turn the equation around to make r the subject $\qquad r = \sqrt{\dfrac{A}{\pi}}$

Practice Exercise

1 Match the sequences and the *n*th terms.
Find the *n*th term for the sequence left over.

5, 6, 7, 8, ...	$4n$
5, 8, 11, 14, ...	$n+3$
4, 8, 12, 16, ...	$n+4$
4, 5, 6, 7, ...	$3n+2$
6, 12, 18, 24, ...	....

2 Find the *n*th term of the sequence

18, 15, 12, 9, ...

....

....

....

3 Use the signs $>$ or $<$ to complete the following:

(a) 5 3

(b) −2 4

(c) 3^2 6

(d) 0.25 .... 0.2

4 Complete the following to make x the subject of the formula.

$y = mx + c$

.... Subtract c from both sides of the formula

.... Divide both sides of the formula by m

$x = $ .... Turn the formula around to make x the subject

Algebra

Topic 9
More using algebra

Summary

Sequences using the method of differences

If the rule to obtain a sequence is not obvious to you, try the method of differences. The method of differences involves finding the difference between successive terms of the sequence.

Like this

To find the next two terms of the sequence 3, 8, 15, 24, 36, ..., draw a diagram to find the differences.

$$3, \quad 8, \quad 15, \quad 24, \quad 36, ...$$

(+5) +7 +9 +11 First differences

(+2) +2 +2 Second differences

The number +5 is called the first difference (of the set of first differences)

The number +2 is called the second difference (of the set of second differences)

As the second differences are all the same then

nth term = first term + 1st difference $\times (n-1)$ + 2nd difference $\times \frac{1}{2}(n-1)(n-2)$

Like this

Find the nth term of the sequence above.

$$\begin{aligned} n\text{th term} &= \text{first term} + \text{1st difference} \times (n-1) + \text{2nd difference} \times \tfrac{1}{2}(n-1)(n-2) \\ &= 3 + (n-1) \times 5 + \tfrac{1}{2}(n-1)(n-2) \times 2 \\ &= 3 + 5n - 5 + 1(n^2 - 3n + 2) \\ &= n^2 + 2n \end{aligned}$$

Inequalities

To solve inequalities you proceed in exactly the same way as you do with equalities (equations) except when you multiply or divide by a negative number. When you multiply or divide by a negative number you must change the direction of the inequality.

Note: *To solve inequalities of the form $6 > x+3 > -1$ you must write these as two separate inequalities (i.e. $6 > x+3$ and $x+3 > -1$) and then solve each part separately.*

Like this

Solve $19 - 2x > 9$

Add $2x$ to each side $\qquad 19 > 2x + 9$

Subtract 9 from each side $\qquad 19 - 9 > 2x$

$\qquad\qquad\qquad\qquad\qquad 10 > 2x$

Divide each side by 2 $\qquad 5 > x \quad$ or $\quad x < 5$

Solving cubic equations

Cubic equations can be solved using a trial and improvement method.

Like this

Use trial and improvement to solve $x^3 - x^2 = 10$. Give your answer to 1 dp.

First find the two integer values between which the solution lies.

Try $x = 2 \qquad 2^3 - 2^2 = 8 - 4 = 4 \qquad$ too small

Try $x = 3 \qquad 3^3 - 3^2 = 27 - 9 = 18 \qquad$ too big $\qquad$ so $2 < x < 3$

Note: *It is often useful to draw a sketch of the cubic graph to give you an idea of appropriate starting points for your first approximations.*

Then find the two values of 1 dp between which the solution lies.

Try $x = 2.6 \quad 2.6^3 - 2.6^2 = 17.576 - 6.76 = 10.816 \quad$ too big

Try $x = 2.5 \quad 2.5^3 - 2.5^2 = 15.625 - 6.25 = 9.375 \quad$ too small $\quad$ so $2.5 < x < 2.6$

To decide if the answer to 1 dp is 2.5 or 2.6 you must try 2.55.

Try $x = 2.55 \qquad 2.55^3 - 2.55^2 = 16.581... - 6.5025 = 10.078... \qquad$ too big

So $2.5 < x < 2.55$ and $x = 2.5$ (correct to 1 dp)

Practice Exercise

1 What is a correct algebraic description of the nth term of the sequence 2, 6, 12, 20, ...?

A $n^2 + n$ C $2n^2$

B $n^2 + 2$ D $n^2 + 1$

1 Answer ....

2 Use a table of differences to find the nth term of the sequence 3, 6, 11, 18, ...

....

....

....

3 Find a formula for the total number of rods in the nth pattern in this sequence:

....

4 Solve the following inequalities.

(a) $3x + 5 > 17$

....

(b) $4x + 3 \leqslant 3x + 9$

....

(c) $4(x + 4) > 2x + 21$

....

5 Which number line shows the solution to the inequality $-5 < 3x - 2 < 4$?

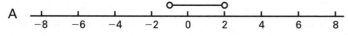
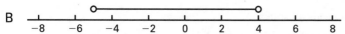
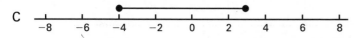
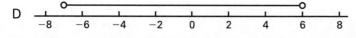

Algebra

Topic 9
More using algebra

Examination Questions

1. A sequence begins 1, 3, 7, 15, ...
   The rule for continuing the sequence is shown.

   MULTIPLY THE LAST NUMBER BY 2 AND ADD 1

   (a) What is the next number in the sequence?

   ....

   (b) This sequence uses the same rule.   −2, −3, −5, −9, ...
       What is the next number in the sequence?

   ....

   (SEG, Summer 1998 – Paper 11)

2. Black tiles and white tiles are used to make tiling patterns.

   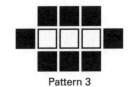

   Pattern 1   Pattern 2   Pattern 3

   (a) How many black tiles will Pattern 4 have?

   ....

   (b) (i) Explain the rule for finding the number of black tiles in a pattern when
           you know the pattern number.

       ....

       (ii) How many black tiles will Pattern 50 have?

       ....

   (SEG, Summer 1998 – Paper 12)

3. Patterns of triangles are made using sticks.
   The first three patterns are drawn below.

   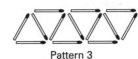

   Pattern 1   Pattern 2   Pattern 3

   (a) How many sticks are needed to make Pattern 4?

   ....

   (b) A pattern needs 45 sticks.
       What is the number of this pattern?

   ....

   ....

   (SEG, Summer 1998 – specimen paper)

Examination Questions

4. (a) A sequence begins 2, 9, 16, 23, ...

(i) What must be added to 23 to give the next number in the sequence?

....

(ii) Explain how you could use the first term in the sequence to find the 10th term without writing down all the terms.

....

....

(b) A new sequence begins 4, 10, 16, 22, ...

(i) What is the 20th term in the sequence?

....

(ii) Write an expression for the nth term in this sequence.

....

....

(SEG, Summer 1998 – specimen paper)

5. Emma made these shapes with matchsticks.

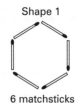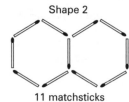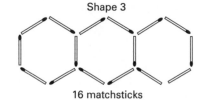

Shape 1   Shape 2   Shape 3

6 matchsticks   11 matchsticks   16 matchsticks

(a) Draw shape 4 for Emma.

(b) (i) Complete this table

Shape number	1	2	3	4	5
Number of matchsticks	6	11	16		

(ii) What pattern do you notice in the 'number of matchsticks' row?

....

(iii) How many matchsticks are needed to make shape 9?
Explain how you can work it out **without** doing any drawings.

....

....

(NEAB, Summer 1998 – Paper 2F)

Topic 9
More using algebra

6. The first four terms in a sequence are 2, 8, 18, 32.

   What is the next term in the sequence?

   ....

   (SEG, Summer 1997 – Intermediate Paper 4)

7. Hexagons are used to make a sequence of patterns as shown.

   | **Pattern 1** | **Pattern 2** | **Pattern 3** |
   | 10 outside edges | 14 outside edges | 18 outside edges |

   (a) How many outside edges has Pattern 8?

   ....

   (b) Write down a rule to find the number of outside edges for Pattern *n*.

   ....

   ....

   (SEG, Summer 1997 – Intermediate Paper 3)

8. (a) What is the next number in this sequence?

1, 3, 7, 15, ...

(b) Find a formula, in terms of n, for the number of sticks in the nth shape in this sequence.

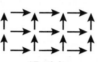

      7 sticks   12 sticks   17 sticks

....

....

(c) Find a formula, in terms of n, for the nth term in this sequence.

2, 6, 12, 20, 30, ...

(SEG – specimen paper)

9. (a) Write down the nth term for each of the following sequences.

(i) 1, 4, 9, 16,

....

(ii) 4, 16, 36, 64,

....

(b) The nth term of another sequence is $(n + 1)(n + 2)$.
Explain why every term of the sequence is an even number.

....

....

(NEAB, Summer 1998 – Higher Paper 2H)

Algebra

Topic 9
More using algebra

Examination Questions

10. (a) The volume of a cone is given by the formula $V = \frac{1}{3}\pi r^2 h$. Rearrange the formula to give r in terms of V and h.

....

....

(SEG – specimen Higher Paper 15 part question)

11. Solve the equation $x^3 = 22$ by trial and improvement.

Start with $x = 2$.

Give your final answer correct to **one** decimal place.

You **must** show all your working.

....

....

....

....

....

....

(SEG, Summer 1997 – Intermediate Paper 4)

12. Katy is using trial and improvement to find an answer to the question $x^3 - x = 35$.

This table shows her first two tries.

x	$x^3 - x$	Comment
3	24	too small
4	60	too big

Continue the table to find a solution to the equation.

x	$x^3 - x$	Comment
3	24	too small
4	60	too big

Give your answer to **1 decimal place**

....

(NEAB, Summer 1998 – Higher Paper)

13. (a) (i) Factorise fully the expression $2r^2 + 2rh$.

....

....

(ii) Multiply out $(2x + 3)(x - 4)$. Simplify your answer.

....

....

(b) A possible points system for the high jump event in athletics is given by

$P = a(M - b)^2$.

M is the height jumped in cm, P is the number of points awarded and a and b are non-zero positive constants.

(i) Zero points are scored for a height jumped of 75 cm. What is the value of the constant b?

....

....

(ii) Express M in terms of P, a, b.

....

....

(SEG – specimen paper)

Shape, Space and Measures

Topic 10
Angle properties

Summary

Clockwise and anticlockwise

You need to be able to distinguish between clockwise and anticlockwise (sometimes called counterclockwise).

Clockwise

Anticlockwise

Of course it is much easier if you haven't got a digital watch!

Angles

Angles can be measured in terms of turning.

Like this

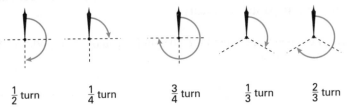

$\frac{1}{2}$ turn $\frac{1}{4}$ turn $\frac{3}{4}$ turn $\frac{1}{3}$ turn $\frac{2}{3}$ turn

Unfortunately, such measurements can be difficult so a full turn is divided into 360 equal parts. Each part is called a **degree** and the symbol ° is used to represent a degree.

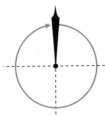

1 full turn = 360°

Similarly, a half turn is 180° and a quarter turn is 90°. A quarter turn is sometimes called a right angle as follows:

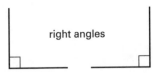

right angles

Note: Two lines which meet at right angles are called perpendicular lines.

You can use the properties of turning to work out missing angles.

Like this

Find the missing angles

Right angle = 90°
So $x° = 90 - 55$
$= 35°$

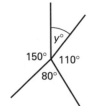

Angles in a full turn = 360°
So $y° = 360 - (150 + 110 + 80)$
$= 360 - 340 = 20°$

Angles in a half turn = 180°
So $z° = 180 - (30 + 15)$
$= 180 - 45 = 135°$

Practice Exercise

1 Label each of these diagrams as clockwise or anticlockwise.

(a)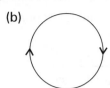

(b)

1 (a) Answer

....

1 (b) Answer

....

2 Identify each of these turns and match them to their description.
The first one is done for you.

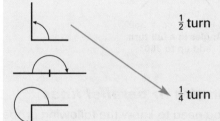

(a) $\frac{1}{2}$ turn

(b)

(c) $\frac{1}{4}$ turn

(d) $\frac{3}{4}$ turn

(e)

(f) $\frac{1}{3}$ turn

(g) $\frac{2}{3}$ turn

3 Write down the size of angles a–d in degrees.

(a)

(b)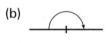

(c)

(d)

3 (a) Answer ....°

3 (b) Answer ....°

3 (c) Answer ....°

3 (d) Answer ....°

4 What can you say about the angles a, b, c, d?

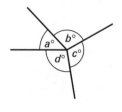

....

....

....

....

....

Topic 10
Angle properties

Angle properties

You need to know the following angle properties

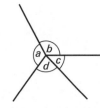

$a + b + c + d = 360°$
Angles in a full turn add up to 360°

$e + f = 180°$
Angles on a straight line add up to 180°

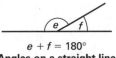

$g = i$ ⎱ two pairs of **vertically**
$i = k$ ⎰ **opposite** angles

Vertically opposite angles are equal

Angles in parallel lines

You need to know the following properties of angles in parallel lines

Note:

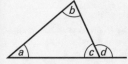

Angles *r* and *s* are also **alternate angles** or **Z angles**.

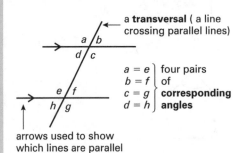

a **transversal** (a line crossing parallel lines)

$a = e$ ⎫ four pairs
$b = f$ ⎬ of
$c = g$ ⎬ **corresponding**
$d = h$ ⎭ **angles**

arrows used to show which lines are parallel

Corresponding angles are equal

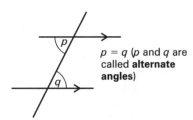

$p = q$ (*p* and *q* are called **alternate angles**)

Alternate angles between parallel lines are equal

Angles in triangles and quadrilaterals

The angle sum (or sum of the angles) of a triangle is 180°

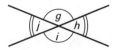

$a + b + c = 180°$

Note:

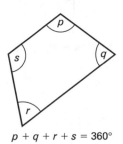

$d = a + b$ (exterior angle = sum of interior opposite angles)

The angle sum of a quadrilateral is 360°

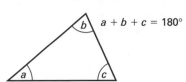

$p + q + r + s = 360°$

Practice Exercise

1 Find the missing angles.

(a)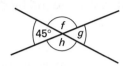

(b)

(c)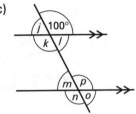

(d)

(e)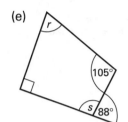

1 (a) Answer f = ...°

g = ...°

h = ...°

1 (b) Answer i = ...°

1 (c) Answer j = ...°

k = ...°

l = ...°

m = ...°

n = ...°

o = ...°

p = ...°

1 (d) Answer q = ...°

1 (e) Answer r = ...°

s = ...°

2 Match the statements with the reasons.

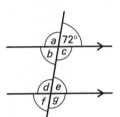

$a = 108°$	vertically opposite angles
$c = d$	corresponding angles
$b = 72°$	alternate angles
$e = 72°$	angles on a straight line

3 Say whether each of these statements (a)–(f) is true or false.

(a) The angles of a triangle add up to 90°

(b) The angles of a quadrilateral add up to 180°

(c) Opposite angles are equal

(d) Angles on a straight line are equal

(e) Alternate angles are equal

(f) Interior angles add up to 360°

3 (a) Answer ....

3 (b) Answer ....

3 (c) Answer ....

3 (d) Answer ....

3 (e) Answer ....

3 (f) Answer ....

4

(a) Explain why DA is not parallel to CB.

....

....

(b) Find the sizes of the other two angles of the quadrilateral ABCD, stating any angle properties you use.

Topic 10
Angle properties

Note: *You should notice that for an n-sided polygon the angle sum is* $(n - 2) \times 180°$

Summary

Angle sums

The angle sum (or the sum of the angles) of shapes can be found by dividing them into triangles

Like this

$a + b + c = 180°$
Angle sum = 180°

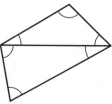

A quadrilateral can be split into two triangles

Angle sum = 2 × 180°
= 360°

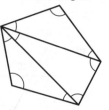

A pentagon can be split into three triangles

Angle sum = 3 × 180°
= 540°

Angle properties of circles

Angle in a semicircle is 90°.

Note: *Work on angles in a semicircle will only be tested on the higher tier by NEAB.*

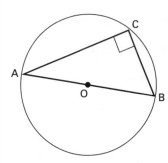

If AB is a diameter of the circle (i.e. passes through the centre) then angle ACB (written ∠ACB or AĈB) is 90°

Chords and radii

A radius which goes through the centre of a chord is perpendicular to the chord.

Note: *The property works 'the other way round' so that if XC bisects chord AXB at right angles then XC goes through O, and so is a radius.*

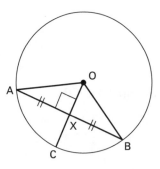

OC is a radius and cuts the chord AB at X such that AX = XB.
So radius OC is perpendicular to chord AXB.

Practice Exercise

1 Split these shapes into triangles and find their angle sum.

(a)

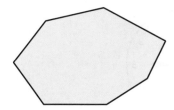

(b)

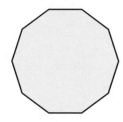

Angle sum = ...°   Angle sum = ...°

2 (a) Use the formula for the sum of angles of an *n*-sided polygon to show that the sum of the angles of a hexagon (a six-sided shape) is 720°.

....

....

(b) Show how you can get the same result by dividing a hexagon into triangles.

(c) What is the size of each angle of a **regular** hexagon?

....

....

3 Look at the diagram and then say whether each of the statements (a)–(e) is true or false.

(a) AE = EC

(b) *a* and *d* are 60°

(c) $p = a + d$

(d) $d = b$

(e) *c* is a right angle

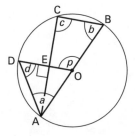

3 (a) Answer ....

3 (b) Answer ....

3 (c) Answer ....

3 (d) Answer ....

3 (e) Answer ....

(f) Write down another true statement about this diagram

....

Topic 10
Angle
properties

1. The diagram shows a clock.

The clock shows the time in the afternoon.

(a) Write down the time using the 24 hour clock.

....

(b) What is the angle between the hands of the clock?

....

2. Find the sizes of the angles marked by the letters in these diagrams

(a)

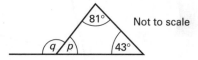

Not to scale

....

(b)

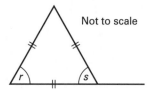

Not to scale

....

(c)

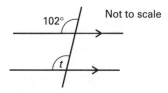

Not to scale

....

(NEAB – specimen paper)

3. AB is parallel to CD. CP = DP. Angle CPD = 110°.

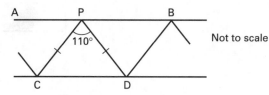

Not to scale

(a) (i) Which of the following correctly describes the angle CPD?

right angle   acute angle   obtuse angle   reflex angle

....

(ii) Which of the following correctly describes the triangle CPD?

right angled   isosceles   equilateral   scalene

....

(b) Work out the size of angle CDP.

....

(c) Write down the size of the angle BPD. Give a reason for your answer.

....

....

(SEG, Summer 1998 – Paper 11)

**Shape, Space
and Measures**

Topic 10

Angle
properties

4. The diagram shows two straight lines
AB and PQ which cross at O.

The line OT is perpendicular to AB.

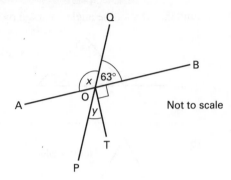

Not to scale

Angle BOT = 90°

Angle QOB = 63°

Work out the sizes of angle x and angle y.

....

....

$x =$ .... degrees

$y =$ .... degrees

(SEG, Winter 1998 – Paper 13)

5. The diagram shows a regular 12 sided polygon
(called a dodecagon).
Each interior angle is 150°.

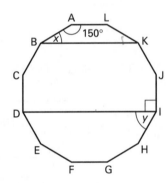

The lines BK and DI have been drawn.

(a) (i) What is the special name for the polygon ALKB?

....

(ii) Calculate the size of the angle marked x.

....

(b) Calculate the size of the angle marked y.

....

(c) Calculate the sum of the angles in the polygon DEFGHI.

....

....

(NEAB – specimen paper)

Examination Questions

Shape, Space and Measures

Topic 10
Angle properties

Foundation and Intermediate Tiers

Intermediate Tier Only

6. (a) The regular octagon shown below has eight sides. One side of the octagon has been extended to form angle x.

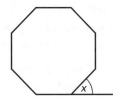

Calculate the size of angle x.
You must show all of your working

....

....

.... degrees

(b) The regular pentagon shown below has five sides.

Calculate the size of angle y?
You must show all of your working

....

....

.... degrees

7. The diagram shows a regular octagon with centre O.

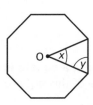

(a) Work out the size of angle x.

....

....

.... degrees

(b) Work out the size of angle y.

....

....

.... degrees

(SEG, Summer 1998 – Paper 13)

Summary

About length

The **perimeter** of a shape is measured by working out the distance round the outside edge of the shape.

Perimeter of a square is 4 × length of side
Perimeter of this square is $4 \times a = 4a$

Perimeter of a rectangle is 2 × (length + breadth)
Perimeter of this rectangle is $a + b + a + b$.
$= 2a + 2b = 2(a + b)$

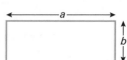

About area

The area of a shape is measured by working out how many square units the shape covers.

Area of an irregular figure
To find the area of an irregular shape, you draw a grid and count the approximate number of squares which the shape covers.

Like this
The area of the leaf is approximately 9 squares
1 square represents $1\,cm^2$ so area $= 9\,cm^2$

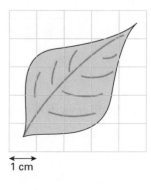

1 cm

Area of a square is (length)²
Area of this square is $a \times a = a^2$.

Area of a rectangle is length × breadth
Area of this rectangle is $a \times b = ab$

About volume

The volume of a solid is measured by working out how many cubic units the solid contains.

A **cube** has all sides equal. You can think of a cube as a 3D square, or an ice cube.

Volume of cube is length × length × length
Volume of this cube is $a \times a \times a = a^3$

A **cuboid** does not have all sides equal. You can think of a cuboid as a 3D rectangle, or a packet of cornflakes!

Volume of a cuboid is length × breadth × height
Volume of this cuboid is $a \times b \times c = abc$

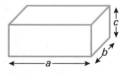

Practice Exercise

1 These rectangles each have area 24 cm². Work out the perimeter of each rectangle.

(a)

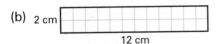

24 cm — 1 cm

(b) 2 cm

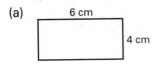

12 cm

(c) 3 cm

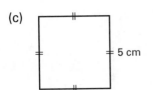

8 cm

(d)

4 cm

6 cm

1 (a) Answer .... cm

1 (b) Answer .... cm

1 (c) Answer .... cm

1 (d) Answer .... cm

2 Find the area of rectangles (a)–(d).

(a) 6 cm

4 cm

(b)

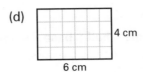

12 cm

1 cm

(c)

5 cm

(d)

10 cm

$\frac{1}{2}$ cm

2 (a) Answer .... cm²

2 (b) Answer .... cm²

2 (c) Answer .... cm²

2 (d) Answer .... cm²

3 (a) How many centimetre cubes are used to make this cuboid?

(b) Write down the dimensions of another cuboid with the same number of centimetre cubes.

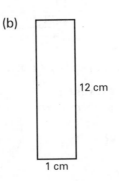

2 cm

4 cm   3 cm

3 (a) Answer ....

3 (b) Answer ....

4 Find the volume of cuboids (a) and (b).

(a)

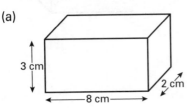

3 cm

2 cm

8 cm

(b)

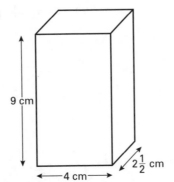

9 cm

4 cm $2\frac{1}{2}$ cm

4 (a) Answer .... cm³

4 (b) Answer .... cm³

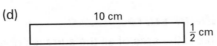
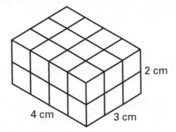

Topic 11
Length, area
and volume

Note: Where you are allowed to use your calculator, it is best to use the $\boxed{\pi}$ key for your calculations.

Note: You must be able to use the circumference formula 'the other way round' so that if $C = \pi \times d$ then $d = \dfrac{C}{\pi}$

Note: You must be able to use the formula for the area of a circle 'the other way round' so that if $A = \pi r^2$ then $r = \sqrt{\dfrac{A}{\pi}}$

Summary

About length

Circumference is the special name for the perimeter of a circle.

Circumference of a circle $= \pi \times$ diameter

The circumference of this circle is $\pi \times d = \pi d$

π is a number which is approximately 3.142

About area

Area of a triangle $=$ half $\times$ base $\times$ height

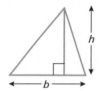

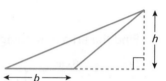

Area of all these triangles is $\frac{1}{2} \times b \times h = \frac{1}{2}bh$

Area of circle $= \pi \times$ (radius)^2

Area of this circle is $\pi \times r^2 = \pi r^2$

About surface area

This is the area of all the surfaces of a 3D shape. You could think of it as the 'skin area'.

Surface area of a cube $= 6 \times$ area of a face

This cube has 6 faces each of area $a \times a = a^2$

Surface area is $6a^2$

Surface area of a cuboid $= 2 \times$ area of top face $+ 2 \times$ area of front face
$+ 2 \times$ area of side face

For this cuboid: area of top face is $a \times b = ab$
area of front face is $a \times c = ac$
area of side face is $b \times c = bc$

Surface area is $2ab + 2ac + 2bc$
$= 2(ab + ac + ab)$

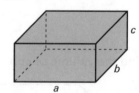

Practice Exercise

1 Which of these triangles have area 15 cm²?

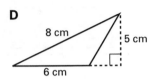

A

5 cm   4 cm

6 cm

B

3 cm

5 cm

C

6 cm   7.8 cm

5 cm

D

8 cm   5 cm

6 cm

E

5 cm

3 cm

4 cm

F

6 cm

5 cm

1 Answer ....

2 Complete the following information to find the area of this shape.

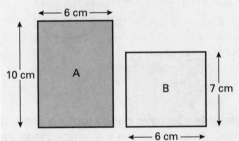

← 6 cm →

10 cm

A

B

7 cm

← 12 cm →

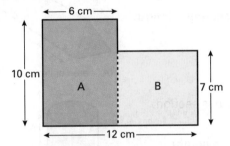

← 6 cm →

10 cm

A

B

7 cm

← 6 cm →

Area of A = ... = ...

Area of B = ... = ...

Total area = ... + ...

= .... cm²

3 Find the area of these shapes.

(a)

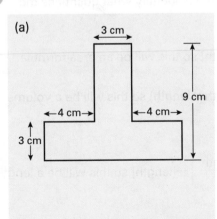

3 cm

9 cm

←4 cm→   ←4 cm→

3 cm

(b)

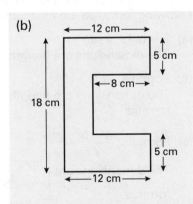

← 12 cm →

5 cm

←8 cm→

18 cm

5 cm

← 12 cm →

3 (a) Answer ....

3 (b) Answer ....

Shape, Space and Measures

Topic 11

Length, area and volume

Note: Because area involves 2 dimensions make sure that you use the same units of length for each.
Do not, *for example, mix metres and centimetres.*

Note: You may find it useful to think of a cylinder as a 'prism' with a circular cross section

Note: The dimension of a [length + length] is a [length] dimension.

Note: 4 and π are numbers which don't have units so don't affect the dimensions.

More about area

Area of parallelogram = base × height
Area of this parallelogram is $b \times h = bh$

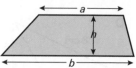

Area of a trapezium = half height × sum of parallel sides
Area of this trapezium is $\frac{1}{2} \times h \times (a + b) = \frac{1}{2}h(a + b)$

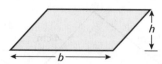

About volume

A **prism** is a shape with a constant polygonal cross section. You can think of a Toblerone or 'T' bar.

Volume of a prism = area of cross section × length
Volume of this prism is $A \times l = Al$

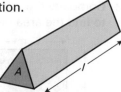

(A = area of cross section)

A **cylinder** is a shape with circular cross section. You can think of a can of cola!

Volume of a cylinder = area of base × height
Volume of this cylinder is $\pi \times r^2 \times h = \pi r^2 h$

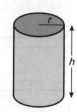

About dimensions

You can recognise what type of quantity you have got by looking at the units in which it is measured. For example, if you are given a quantity measured in m² you would know you are dealing with area.

Like this

If a, b, c and d are numbers for length units, identify what quantities the following formulae are measuring:

(a) Formula: $4\pi ab$
The dimensions are [length × length] so this will be an area formula.

(b) Formula: $ab(c + d)$
The dimensions are [length × length × length] so this will be a volume formula.

(c) Formula: $\dfrac{4\pi ab}{c}$
The dimensions are $\left[\dfrac{\text{length} \times \text{length}}{\text{length}} \right]$ = [length] so this will be a length formula.

Practice Exercise

1 Complete the following:

Area of parallelogram = ...

Area of trapezium = ...

Volume of a cylinder = ...

2 Arrange these triangles, rectangles, parallelograms and trapeziums in ascending order of their areas.

A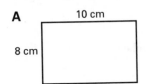
10 cm
8 cm

B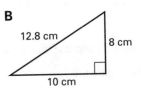
12.8 cm
8 cm
10 cm

C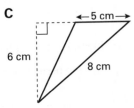
←5 cm→
6 cm
8 cm

D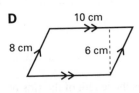
10 cm
8 cm 6 cm

E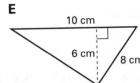
10 cm
6 cm 8 cm

F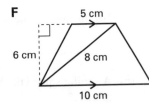
5 cm
6 cm 8 cm
10 cm

Smallest area ...., ..., ..., ..., ..., ... largest area

3 Work out the volume of the prisms in (a)–(d).

(a)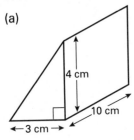
4 cm
10 cm
←3 cm→

(b)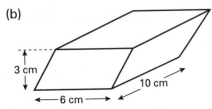
3 cm
10 cm
←6 cm→

(c)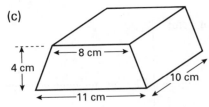
8 cm
4 cm
10 cm
11 cm

(d)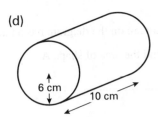
6 cm
10 cm

3 (a) Answer .... cm³

3 (b) Answer .... cm³

3 (c) Answer .... cm³

3 (d) Answer .... cm³

4 If a, b, and c are lengths, put these formulae into the correct sets

$$\pi a^2 \quad a+b+c \quad ab+ac \quad abc \quad a^2b$$
$$a^2+b^2 \quad 2a+2b \quad 4(a+b+c)$$

Lengths .... Areas .... Volumes ....

....

111

Topic 11

Length, area
and volume

1. The following picture shows a square tile which is drawn to the correct size.

(a) Measure the length of the side and use this to calculate:

(i) the perimeter of the square tile

.... cm

(ii) the area of the square tile.

.... cm^2

(b) A similar square tile has an area of 64 cm^2. What is the length of the side of this tile?

....

.... cm

2. The diagram shows two shapes

Each square on the diagram has an area of 1 cm^2

(a) Find the area of shape A

....

.... cm^2

(b) Find the perimeter of shape B

....

.... cm

(SEG, Summer 1998 – Paper 11)

Examination Questions

3. The dimensions of a metal waste bin are 30 cm by 10 cm by 40 cm.

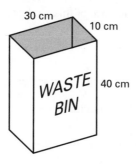

Calculate the volume of the bin, stating your units

....

....

(SEG – specimen paper)

4. Calculate the area of a circle with a diameter of 15 cm.
Give your answer to an appropriate degree of accuracy.

....

....

(NEAB, Winter 1998 – Paper 1)

5. A spinning top which consists
of a cone of base radius 5 cm,
height 9 cm and a hemisphere
of radius 5 cm is illustrated.

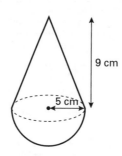

(a) Calculate the volume of the spinning top.

....

....

(b) Calculate the total surface area of the spinning top.

....

....

....

(SEG – specimen paper)

Examination Questions

6. (a) A circle has a diameter of 7 cm.

(i) Calculate the circumference of this circle.

....

....

(ii) Calculate the area of this circle.

....

....

(b) A plastic beaker has a height of 10 cm and a circular base of diameter 7 cm.

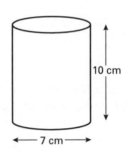

Calculate the volume of the beaker.

....

....

....

(NEAB, Summer 1997 – Paper 2)

7.

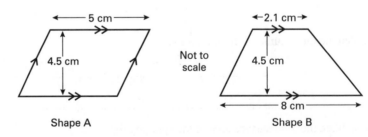

Shape A   Shape B

Which of these shapes has the larger area?
You must show all your working clearly.

....

....

....

(NEAB – specimen paper)

8. The cylinder is 20 cm high and holds 1000 cm³ of water.

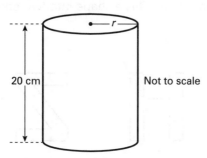

20 cm   Not to scale

    Find the radius of the cylinder.

    ....

    ....

    ....

    ....

    (SEG, Summer 1998 – Paper 14)

9. Ice cream is sold in a box that is the shape of a prism.
    The ends are parallelograms.
    The size of the prism is shown in the diagram.
    The length of the prism is 12 cm.

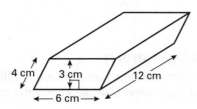

4 cm   3 cm   12 cm
        6 cm

    Calculate the volume of the ice cream in the box.

    ....

    ....

    ....

    ....

    ....

    (NEAB, Summer 1998 – Paper 2)

Topic 12
Symmetry and transformations

Note: You can check whether a shape has line symmetry by folding it in half, using tracing paper or using a mirror.

Summary

Line symmetry

A line (or axis) of symmetry divides a shape into two equal halves.

Like this

Line of symmetry

An isoceles triangle has one line of symmetry

The letter H has two lines of symmetry

The letter Z has no lines of symmetry

An equilateral triangle has three lines of symmetry

Rotational symmetry

Rotational symmetry (or point symmetry) is where a shape can be rotated and look exactly the same as when it started.

Like this

Starting point

Rotate 120°

Rotate another 120° (total 240°)

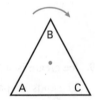
Rotate another 120° and it is back to the starting position (total 360°)

Order of rotational symmetry

The order of rotational symmetry tells you how many different positions look exactly the same. For the equilateral triangle above the order of rotational symmetry is 3.

The letter Z has rotational symmetry of order 2

This shape has rotational symmetry of order 4

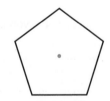
A regular pentagon has rotational symmetry of order 5

Note: All shapes have rotational symmetry of order 1

This irregular shape has rotational symmetry of order 1

Practice Exercise

1 Draw all the lines of symmetry on these shapes.

   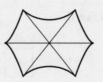

2 Which of the letters have rotational symmetry? For those letters with rotational symmetry, write down the order.

(a)   (b)   (c)   (d)

....

3 Reflect the lines in the mirror to make a word.

 mirror

4 Here is a tiling pattern.

Shade one shape which has rotational symmetry of order 2 and 0 lines of symmetry.

Note: You should check your reflection is correct by folding along the given line using tracing paper or using a mirror.

Note: You should check your rotation is correct by using tracing paper.

Summary

Plane symmetry

A plane of symmetry divides a solid into two equal halves.

Like this

Reflection

You must be able to reflect a figure in a given line.

Like this

Object   Image after reflection

Object

Image after reflection

Rotation

You must be able to rotate a figure through $\frac{1}{4}$, $\frac{1}{2}$, or $\frac{3}{4}$ turns about a given point (called the centre of rotation).

Like this

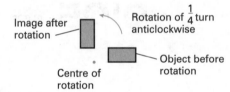

Image after rotation

Rotation of $\frac{1}{4}$ turn anticlockwise

Object before rotation

Centre of rotation

Enlargement

Enlargement with positive scale factor.

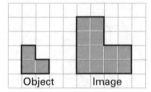

Here the enlargement has scale factor 2 (or all of the lengths are multiplied by 2)

Translation

A translation can be defined as a movement to the right (or the left) followed by a movement upwards (or downwards)

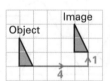

Here the shape has moved 4 units to the right followed by 1 unit up

Tessellations

If shapes fit together without any gaps then they are said to tessellate.

Shapes which tessellate   Shapes which do not tessellate

 *LOOK NO GAPS!*   *GAPS!*

Practice Exercise

1 How many planes of symmetry do the following solids have?

(a)
(b)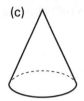
(c)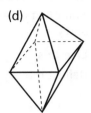
(d)

2 The diagram shows an L-shaped solid standing on a mirror.
Draw the reflection of the solid in the mirror.

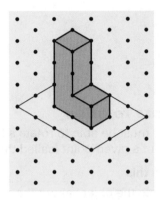

3

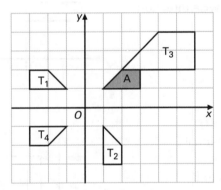

(a) Which shape is a rotation of A of $\frac{1}{4}$ turn clockwise about (0, 0)?

(b) Which shape is an enlargement of A with scale factor 2, centre (0, 0)?

(c) Which shape is a reflection of A in the *y* axis?

(d) Which shape is a rotation of A of $\frac{1}{2}$ turn about (0, 0)?

(e) On the same axes draw and label T_5, the reflection of A in the *x* axis.

4 Here is a trapezium with the mid-point of each side marked. Rotate the trapezium 180° about each mid-point and draw its new positions. Rotate the new trapeziums again and hence make a tessellation covering the dotted paper.

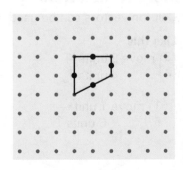

Summary

More reflection

You must be able to reflect a figure in a given line including the lines $y = x$ and $y = -x$.

Like this

Reflect the object in the line $y = x$

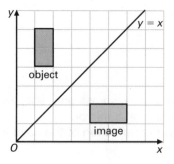

Note: Once again, you could check your reflection by folding along the given line, using tracing paper or using a mirror.

More rotation

You must be able to rotate a figure through any angle in a given direction about a given point (called the centre of rotation).

Like this

Rotate the object about the origin through 90° in a clockwise direction.

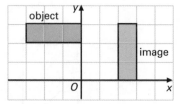

Note: Once again, you could check your rotation is correct by using tracing paper.

More enlargement

Enlargement with fractional scale factor (SF).

The enlargement of A to B is SF 3

The enlargement of B to A is SF $\frac{1}{3}$

(i.e. lengths in A are one-third those in B)

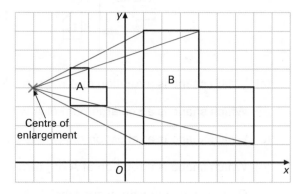

Note: A fractional scale factor (less than 1) makes the shape smaller.

More translation

Column vectors can be used to specify translations.

Like this

$\begin{pmatrix} 3 \\ 4 \end{pmatrix}$ move 3 units → 4 units ↑

$\begin{pmatrix} 2 \\ -5 \end{pmatrix}$ move 2 units → 5 units ↓

$\begin{pmatrix} -1 \\ 6 \end{pmatrix}$ move 1 unit ← 6 units ↑

$\begin{pmatrix} -5 \\ -8 \end{pmatrix}$ move 5 units ← 8 units ↓

Note: Work on column vectors will only be tested on the higher tier by NEAB.

Practice Exercise

1

```
        y
         │         ╱ y = x
         │      ╱
         │   ╱
         │╱    ┌─────┐ A
         │    ╱────┘
─────────┼──╱T₃──────── x
        O│╲
         │  ╲
         │    ╲
         │      ╲ y = −x
```

(a) Draw T_1, the reflection of A in the line $y = x$.

(b) Draw T_2, the rotation of T_1 90° anticlockwise about (0, 0).

(c) What **single** transformation would transform A onto T_2?

....

(d)

T_3 is an enlargement of A with scale factor ....

centre (..........., ...).

(e)

The co-ordinates of A after a translation with vector $\begin{pmatrix} 3 \\ 2 \end{pmatrix}$ are

(..........., ...), (..........., ...) and (..........., ...).

2 This is part of a tessellation of octagons and squares.

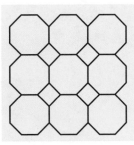

(a) On the diagram, mark:

    (i) a line of symmetry

    (ii) a point, A, about which there is rotational symmetry of order 4

    (iii) a point, D, about which there is rotational symmetry of order 2.

(b) Use the diagram to explain why each angle of a regular octagon is 135°.

....

....

Examination Questions

Topic 12

Symmetry and transformations

1. (a) The position of a point P is shown.

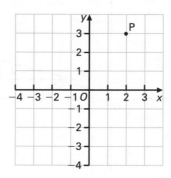

(i) What are the co-ordinates of point P?

....

(ii) P is reflected in the *x* axis.
On the diagram above, mark the new position of P with a cross.

(b) The triangle below is rotated half a turn about the point X.
Draw the new position on the diagram.

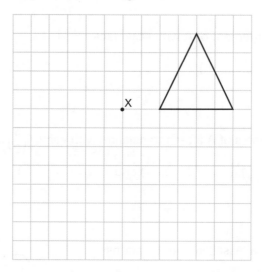

(SEG, Summer 1998 – Paper 11)

2.

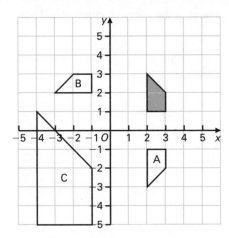

Describe fully a single transformation that would map the shaded shape on to

(a) shape A,

....

....

(b) shape B,

....

....

(c) shape C.

....

....

(NEAB, Summer 1997 – Paper 1)

3. (a) The diagram shows part of a wallpaper pattern.

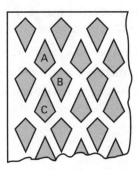

Using only one of the words, 'rotation, reflection or translation', describe the **single** transformation which maps:

(i) the shape A onto the shape B; ....

(ii) the shape A onto the shape C. ....

Examination Questions

(b) Draw an enlargement of the kite with centre P and scale factor 3.

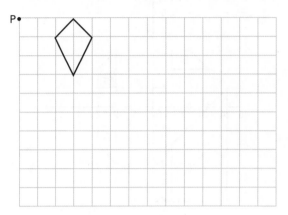

(SEG – specimen paper)

4. The diagram shows a triangle T.

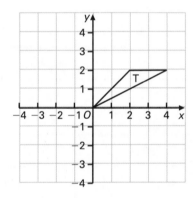

(a) Triangle A is obtained by rotating triangle T through 90° clockwise about O.
Draw and label triangle A on the diagram.

(b) Triangle B is obtained by reflecting triangle T in the *y* axis.
Draw and label triangle B on the diagram.

(c) Triangles T, A and B form part of a pattern which has line symmetry.

(i) Draw and label the triangle C which will complete the pattern.

(ii) How many lines of symmetry has the complete pattern?

(SEG – specimen paper)

Examination Questions

Shape, Space
and Measures

Topic 12

Symmetry and
transformations

Intermediate Tier Only

5. Patchwork cushion cover designs are made using the following shapes

Complete this design so that it has rotational symmetry.

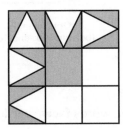

(SEG – specimen paper)

6. The diagram shows two transformations of the shaded rectangle PQRS.

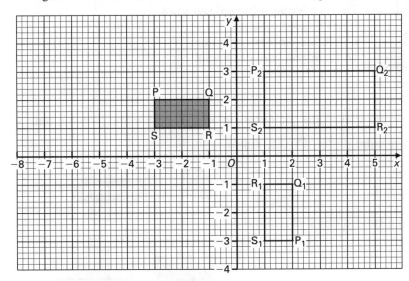

Describe fully the **single** transformation which maps:

(a) PQRS onto $P_1Q_1R_1S_1$

....

....

(b) PQRS onto $P_2Q_2R_2S_2$

....

....

(SEG – specimen paper)

Topic 13
Shapes and solids

Types of angles

Angles are classified according to their size

 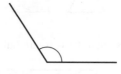

| Acute angle (less than 90°) | Right angle (= 90°) | Obtuse angle (between 90° and 180°) | Reflex angle (between 180° and 360°) |

The language of shape

You need to be familiar with the words **faces**, **vertices** and **edges**

This is a **cube**.
It has 6 square **faces** (flat surfaces),
8 **vertices** (corners or points),
and 12 **edges** (straight lines).

This is a (**square-based**) **pyramid**.
It has 5 **faces** (one square and four triangular),
5 **vertices** (corners or points),
and 8 **edges** (straight lines).

Nets

A net is the shape you get if you cut up a 3D shape and flatten it out.

Net of a cube (think of an ice cube)

Net of a cuboid (think of a cornflake packet)

Net of a pyramid (you know what a pyramid looks like!)

 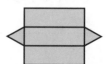

Net of a prism (think of your Toblerone box)

Net of a cylinder (think of a can)

 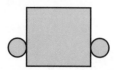

Practice Exercise

1 Here are some angles. Say which are acute, which obtuse and which reflex.

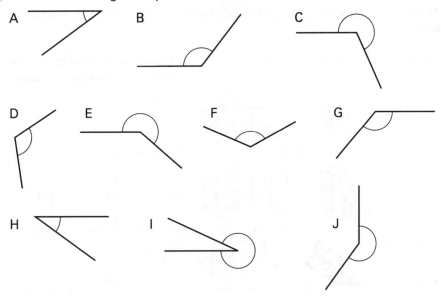

Acute ....

Obtuse...

Reflex...

2 Indicate by drawing arrows on this diagram where the items may be found:

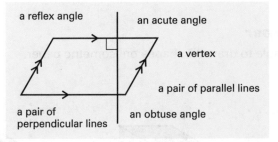

a reflex angle   an acute angle

a vertex

a pair of parallel lines

a pair of perpendicular lines   an obtuse angle

3 Draw the net of a triangular pyramid.

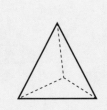

Shape, Space and Measures

Topic 13
Shapes and solids

Summary

Nets

Remember that a net is the shape you get if you cut open a 3D shape and flatten it out.

Name	Shape	Net	Number of faces	Number of vertices	Number of edges
Cube			6	8	12
Cuboid			6	8	12
Triangular-based prism			5	6	9
Triangular-based pyramid			4	4	6
Square-based pyramid			5	5	8
Cylinder			3	0	2

Isometric paper

You need to be able to draw 3D shapes on isometric paper.

Like this

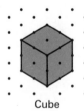

Cube

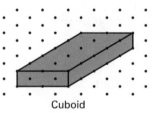

Cuboid

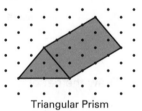

Triangular Prism

Practice Exercise

1 Match the nets with the shapes. Give the name of each of the shapes.

(a)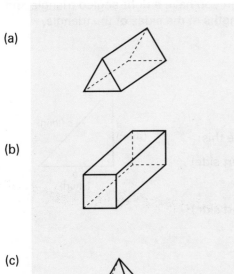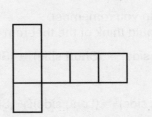

1 (a) Answer
....

(b)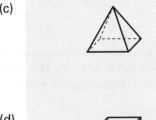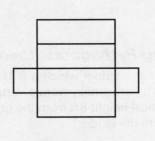

1 (b) Answer
....

(c)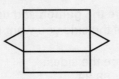

1 (c) Answer
....

(d)

1 (d) Answer
....

2 (a) Complete the following table.

Name of shape	No. of faces	No. of vertices	No. of edges
Cube	6	8	12
Cuboid			
Triangular prism			
Triangular pyramid			
Square pyramid			

(b) (i) What relationship do you notice between the number of faces, the number of vertices and the number of edges?

....
....

(ii) Does this always work?

....
....

Shape, Space and Measures

Topic 13
Shapes and solids

Working with right-angled triangles

Pythagoras' Theorem is used when you have a right-angled triangle and problems involving finding the lengths of the sides of the triangle.

Pythagoras' theorem

This states:
$$c^2 = a^2 + b^2$$

To help you remember you could think of the theorem like this:

(Long side)^2 = (Short side)^2 + (Short side)^2

and

(Short side)^2 = (Long side)^2 − (Short side)^2

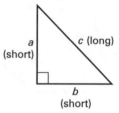

Using Pythagoras' theorem

You have a ladder which is 8.3 ft long. The ladder cannot be placed nearer than 3 ft horizontally from a vertical wall. Juliet is stuck upstairs at a window of vertical height 8 ft from the ground. If you were Romeo could you rescue her with the ladder?

1   Ignore the gumph and draw the correct right-angled triangle.
Label the side you want (height you can reach with your ladder) 'x ft'

2   Square the sides:
$8.3^2 = 68.89$
$3^2 = 9$

Note: *To show that a triangle is right-angled show that Pythagoras' theorem works!*

3   You want a short side so subtract.
$x^2 = 8.3^2 - 3^2$
$= 68.89 - 9$
$= 59.89$

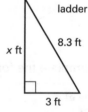

4   Find the square root to get x.
$x = \sqrt{59.89} = 7.738\,863$
As the window is 8 ft high then the answer is no, so bad luck Romeo!

Practice Exercise

1

Measure the sides of the triangle.
Show that Pythagoras' theorem works for this triangle.

....

....

2 Find the missing lengths.

(a)

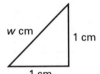

w cm   1 cm
1 cm

....

....

(b)

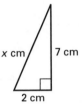

x cm   7 cm
2 cm

....

....

(c)

3 cm   7 cm
y cm

....

....

(d)

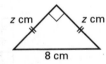

z cm z cm
8 cm

....

....

3 Use Pythagoras' theorem to find the height of this equilateral triangle.

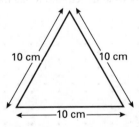

10 cm   10 cm
10 cm

....

....

....

Examination Questions

1. A square-based pyramid is joined to a cuboid to make the shape shown below.

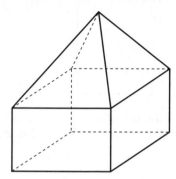

For the complete shape write down the number of

(a) faces

....

(b) edges

....

(c) vertices

....

(NEAB – specimen paper)

2. The diagram shows a net of a cuboid

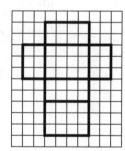

Use the grid below to show what the cuboid looks like when the net is folded.

(SEG, Summer 1998 – Paper 12)

Shape, Space
and Measures

**Topic 13
Shapes and
solids**

Foundation and Intermediate Tiers

Intermediate Tier Only

3. (a) Sketch a cube.

(b) Which **two** of these shapes are nets for a cube?

....

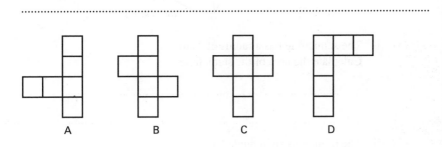

A   B   C   D

(NEAB, Summer 1997 – Paper 2)

4.

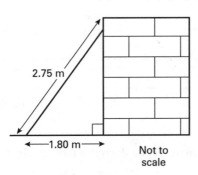

2.75 m

←1.80 m→

Not to
scale

A ladder, 2.75 m long, leans against a wall.
The bottom of the ladder is 1.80 m from the wall on level ground.

Calculate how far the ladder reaches up the wall.
Give your answer to an appropriate degree of accuracy.

....

....

....

....

(NEAB, Summer 1998 – Paper 2)

Topic 13
Shapes and solids

Examination Questions

5. The diagram shows a semicircle and a right-angled triangle

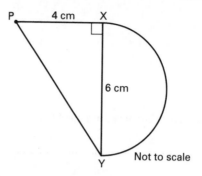

Not to scale

(a) (i) The semicircle has a radius of 3 cm.
Calculate the area of the semicircle.

....

....

(ii) The triangle is right angled at X.
PX = 4 cm and XY = 6 cm.
Calculate the length of PY.
You **must** show all your working.

....

....

....

(SEG, Winter 1998 – Paper 14)

6. The diagram shows a cross section through a roof on a barn.

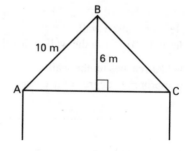

(a) Calculate
(i) the length AC

....

....

....

(ii) the area of triangle ABC

....

....

Examination Questions

The building is 25 metres long.

(b) Calculate the volume of the roof space.

....

....

7. Jane designs a ramp for wheelchair users.
This is its cross-sectional view.

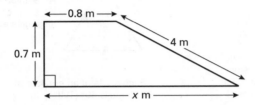

(a) Calculate the distance marked x m.
Give your answer to 1 decimal place.

....

....

(b) The width of the ramp is 1.5 metres.

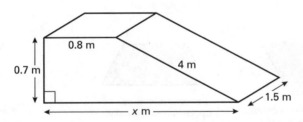

What volume of concrete is needed to build the ramp?

....

....

....

(NEAB – specimen paper)

Topic 14
Triangles and quadrilaterals

Summary

Triangles

An acute-angled triangle (all angles acute)

A right-angled triangle (one right angle)

An obtuse-angled triangle (one obtuse angle)

An isosceles triangle (one pair of sides equal and one pair of angles equal)

An equilateral triangle (all sides equal and all angles equal)

Each angle of an equilateral triangle is 60° (180° ÷ 3)

Note: A trapezium with non parallel sides of equal length is called an isosceles trapezium.

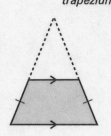

Quadrilaterals

Square (all sides and all angles are equal)

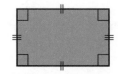

Rectangle (opposite sides equal and parallel and all angles equal)

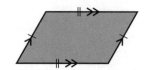

Parallelogram (opposite sides equal and parallel)

Rhombus (all sides equal, opposite sides parallel)

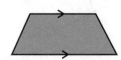

Trapezium (one pair of opposite sides parallel)

Kite (two pairs of adjacent sides equal)

Other polygons

Triangles and quadrilaterals are examples of polygons with 3 and 4 sides respectively.

You need to know the names of other polygons.

A regular polygon has all sides and all angles equal.

A regular triangle is an equilateral triangle.

A regular quadrilateral is a square.

*Note: All the pictures in the table are of **regular polygons** (i.e. all their sides are the same length).*

Number of sides	Name	Picture
3	triangle	
4	square	
5	pentagon	
6	hexagon	
7	heptagon	
8	octagon	
9	nonagon	
10	decagon	

Practice Exercise

1 Give the names of these triangles.

(a)

(b)
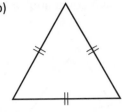

(c)
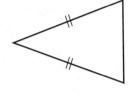

(d)
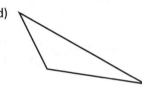

2 Give the names of these quadrilaterals.

(a)
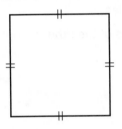

(b)
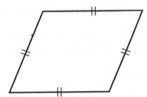

(c)
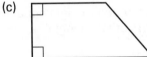

(d)

3 Match the pairs of descriptions.

3-sided shape with 2 equal sides	rhombus
quadrilateral with all sides equal	isosceles triangle
3-sided shape with one angle between 90° and 180°	obtuse-angled triangle
triangle with 3 lines of symmetry	rectangle
quadrilateral with right-angled corners	equilateral triangle

4 Name these regular polygons.

(a)
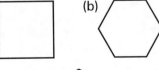

(b)

(c)

(d)

(e)

1 (a) Answer
....

1 (b) Answer
....

1 (c) Answer
....

1 (d) Answer
....

2 (a) Answer
....

2 (b) Answer
....

2 (c) Answer
....

2 (d) Answer
....

4 (a) Answer ....

4 (b) Answer ....

4 (c) Answer ....

4 (d) Answer ....

4 (e) Answer ....

Summary

About similar triangles

Similar triangles have equal angles (and their sides are in corresponding ratio).

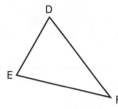

In the given triangles ABC and DEF,

$\angle ABC = \angle DEF$
$\angle BCA = \angle EFD$
$\angle CAB = \angle FDE$

so the triangles are similar.

Similarly, for similar triangles $\dfrac{AB}{DE} = \dfrac{BC}{EF} = \dfrac{AC}{DF}$.

About congruent triangles

Congruent triangles have equal angles and equal sides (i.e. they fit exactly over one another). In the case of triangles, there are 4 different sets of minimum conditions which give congruent triangles.

1   All the **S**ides of one triangle equal all the **S**ides of the other triangle. Remember **SSS** (side, side, side).

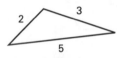
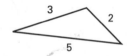

2   Two **S**ides and the **A**ngle between these sides of one triangle equal two **S**ides and the **A**ngle between these sides of the other triangle. Remember **SAS** (side, angle, side).

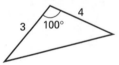
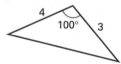

3   Two **A**ngles and one **S**ide of one triangle equal two **A**ngles and the corresponding **S**ide of the other triangle. Remember **AAS** (angle, angle, corresponding side).

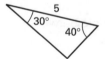

4   Each triangle is **R**ight angled. The **H**ypotenuse and one of the other **S**ides are equal. Remember **RHS** (right angle, hypotenuse, side).

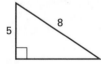
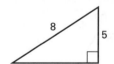

Practice Exercise

1 Use a ruler and protractor to make accurate scale drawings of the shapes (a)–(c)

(a)

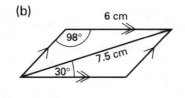

(b)

(c)

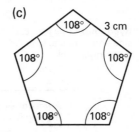

2 Say whether each pair of triangles is congruent and state the congruence condition you used.

(a)

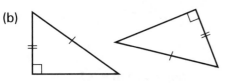

....

....

(b)

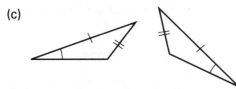

....

....

(c)

....

....

3 Make the links:

Two triangles with the same angles as each other	must be congruent
Two triangles with the same length sides as each other	could be congruent
Two triangles with the same perimeter but different areas	cannot be congruent

4 In the diagram AB is parallel to CD.
AB = OC = 15 cm. OB = 12 cm.

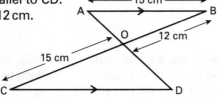

Not to scale

Calculate the length of CD.

....

....

Topic 14

Triangles and quadrilaterals

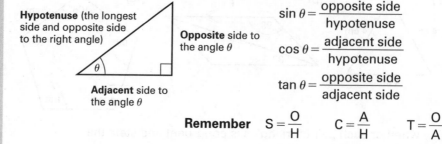

Summary

Working with trig ratios

The trig (short for trigonometric) ratios are defined like this:

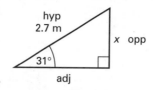

Hypotenuse (the longest side and opposite side to the right angle)

Opposite side to the angle θ

Adjacent side to the angle θ

$$\sin \theta = \frac{\text{opposite side}}{\text{hypotenuse}}$$

$$\cos \theta = \frac{\text{adjacent side}}{\text{hypotenuse}}$$

$$\tan \theta = \frac{\text{opposite side}}{\text{adjacent side}}$$

Remember $S = \dfrac{O}{H}$ $C = \dfrac{A}{H}$ $T = \dfrac{O}{A}$

or SOH   CAH   TOA

Finding the length of a side given one side and one angle

Find x in the figure below.

hyp
2.7 m

x opp

31°

adj

1   Label sides opp, adj and hyp.
2   Select the correct trig ratio.

3   Find the value of the selected trig ratio.
4   Use the trig ratio to make an equation.

5   Solve the equation.

opp $= x$, hyp $= 2.7$
you want opp and you have hyp so select sin

$\sin 31° = 0.515\,038\,1$

$\sin 31° = \dfrac{\text{opp}}{\text{adj}} = \dfrac{x}{2.7}$

$0.515\,038\,1 = \dfrac{x}{2.7}$

$x = 2.7 \times 0.515\,038\,1 = 1.39\,\text{m (3 sf)}$

Finding the size of an angle given two sides

Find the angle z in the figure below.

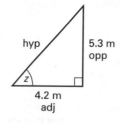

hyp

5.3 m
opp

z

4.2 m
adj

1   Label sides opp, adj and hyp.
2   Select the correct trig ratio.
3   Use the trig ratio to make an equation.

4   Use inverse tan to find the angle.

opp $= 5.3$, adj $= 4.2$
You have opp and adj so select tan

$\tan z = \dfrac{\text{opp}}{\text{adj}} = \dfrac{5.3}{4.2}$

$\tan z = 1.261\,904\,8$
$z = 51.6°$ (3 sf)

Note: *Before you use any trig ratios make sure that your calculator is operating in degrees.*

Practice Exercise

1

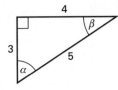

Say whether the following statements (a)–(f) are true or false.

(a) $\tan \alpha = \frac{3}{4}$

(b) $\cos \alpha = \frac{3}{5}$

(c) $\sin \alpha = \frac{4}{3}$

(d) $\tan \beta = \frac{3}{4}$

(e) $\cos \beta = \frac{4}{5}$

(f) $\sin \beta = \frac{4}{5}$

3 (a) Answer ....

3 (b) Answer ....

3 (c) Answer ....

3 (d) Answer ....

3 (e) Answer ....

3 (f) Answer ....

2

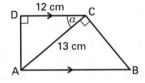

Find:

(a) AD ....

(b) $\cos \alpha$ ....

(c) AB ....

(d) BC ....

3

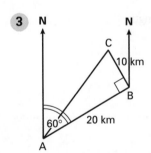

Explain why the bearing of A from B is 240°

....

....

What is the distance of C from A?

....

....

What is the bearing of C from A?

....

....

Examination Questions

1. (a) This diagram shows a shape with 5 sides.

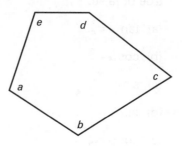

(i)   What is the mathematical name given to a shape with 5 sides?

....

(ii) Explain why the shape in the diagram is not regular

....

(NEAB, Summer 1997 – Paper 1, part question)

2.

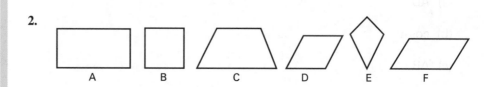

From the above shapes:

(a) List all of the shapes whose sides are all the same length

....

(b) List all of the shapes whose angles are all right angles

....

(c) List all of the shapes with two pairs of parallel sides

....

(d) Which shape has only one pair of parallel sides?

....

(e) What is the mathematical name given to shape D?

....

Examination Questions

Shape, Space
and Measures

Topic 14

**Triangles and
quadrilaterals**

Foundation and Intermediate Tiers

Intermediate Tier Only

3. These triangles are similar

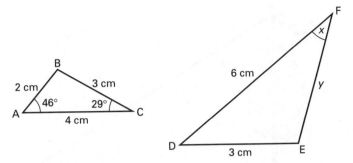

(a) What is the size of angle x?

.... degrees

(b) What is the length of y?

....

.... cm

(SEG – specimen paper)

4. The diagram shows part of the framework for a roof.

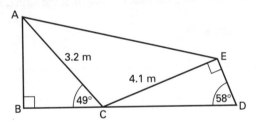

Triangles ABC and CED are right angled.
AC = 3.2 m   CE = 4.1 m
Angle ACB is 49°   Angle EDC is 58°

(a) Calculate the length BC.

....

....

....

(b) Calculate the length CD.

....

....

....

(NEAB, Winter 1998 – Paper 2)

Examination Questions

5. The diagram shows a kite, at K, flying directly above a tree.

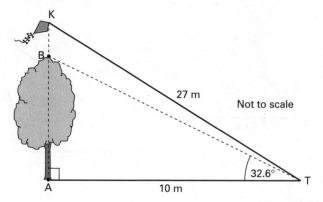

From T, the angle of elevation to the top of the tree is 32.6° and AT = 10 m.

(a) Calculate AB, the height of the tree.

....

....

....

.... m

When the kite is directly above the tree, the length of the string, KT, is 27 m.

(b) Calculate the angle KTA.

....

....

....

.... degrees

(SEG, Winter 1998 – Paper 13)

6. In the triangle XYL, AB is parallel to XY.
LA = 3 cm, LX = 8 cm and XY = 6 cm.
Find the length AB.

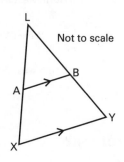

Not to scale

....

....

....

....

(NEAB – specimen paper)

Topic 14

**Triangles and
quadrilaterals**

Shape, Space and Measures

Topic 14
Measurement and drawings

*Note: **Kilo** is 1000*
***Cent** is 100*

Note: The sign '≈' means 'is approximately equal to'.

Points of the compass
Make sure that you know the eight points of the compass.

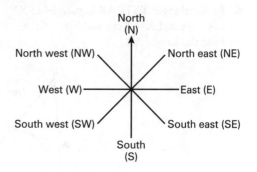

Basic units of measurement
The **metric units of length are:**

    10 mm (millimetres) = 1 cm (centimetre)
    100 cm = 1 m (metre)
    1000 m = 1 km (kilometre)

The **imperial units of length are:**

    12 in (inches) = 1 ft (foot)
    3 ft = 1 yd (yard)
    1760 yd = 1 mile

To convert imperial units of length to metric units of length and vice-versa, remember:

    1 inch ≈ 2.5 cm
    1 foot ≈ 30 cm
    5 miles ≈ 8 km

The **metric units of weight are:**

    1000 mg (milligrams) = 1 g (gram)
    1000 g = 1 kg (kilogram)
    1000 kg = 1 t (tonne)

The **imperial units of weight are:**

    16 oz (ounces) = 1 lb (pound)
    14 lb = 1 st (stone)
    8 st = 1 cwt (hundredweight)
    20 cwt = 1 ton

The **metric units of capacity are:**

    1000 ml (millilitres) = 1 l (litre)

The **imperial units of capacity are:**

    20 floz = 1 pt (pint)
    8 pt = 1 gal (gallon)

Practice Exercise

1 Look at the diagram.

(a) Which point is due east of A?

(b) Which point is north west of A?

(c) Which point is south west of B?

(d) Which point is north east of E?

(e) Mark point F on the diagram, south of D and south west of E.

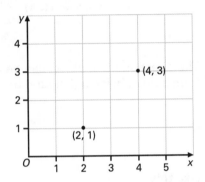

1 (a) Answer ....

1 (b) Answer ....

1 (c) Answer ....

1 (d) Answer ....

2 The two points marked on the diagram are opposite corners of a square.

Write down the co-ordinates of the other two corners.

2 Answer (............, ...)

(............, ...)

3 Arrange these in order of size, smallest first

1 foot   5 cm   3 km   1 mile   1 metre   10 cm   40 cm

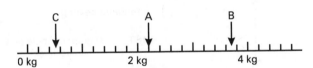

4

(a) What amount does arrow A show?

(b) What amount does arrow B show?

(c) What amount does arrow C show?

(d) Draw arrow D on the diagram to show 3.3 kg.

4 (a) Answer ....

4 (b) Answer ....

4 (c) Answer ....

5 Which is fastest?

A   1 km in 30 minutes

B   4 km in an hour

C   2 km in 30 minutes

D   1 km in 10 minutes

5 Answer ....

147

Shape, Space and Measures

Topic 14
Measurement and drawings

Summary

Points of the compass and bearings

Make sure that you know the eight points of the compass and how these relate to bearings

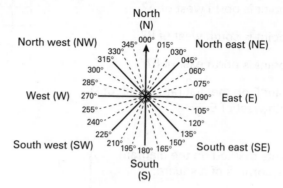

The direction of an object can be measured from a point using a (3 figure) bearing.

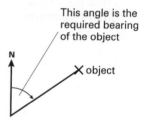

This angle is the required bearing of the object

Like this

The bearing of a boat from a lighthouse is 073°. Find the bearing of the lighthouse from the boat.

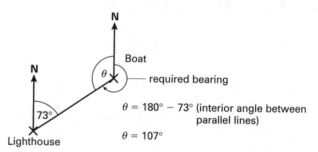

$\theta = 180° - 73°$ (interior angle between parallel lines)

$\theta = 107°$

The bearing of the lighthouse from the boat is $360° - 107° = 253°$

Basic units of measurement

Units of area

The area of a shape is measured by working out how many square units the shape covers.
The metric units of area are:

1 cm² = 1 cm × 1 cm = 10 mm × 10 mm = **100 mm²**
1 m² = 100 cm × 100 cm = **10 000 cm²**
1 km² = 1000 m × 1000 m = **1 000 000 m²**

Units of volume

The volume of a solid is measured by working out how many square units the shape contains.
The metric units of volume are:

1 cm³ = 1 cm × 1 cm × 1 cm = 10 mm × 10 mm × 10 mm = **1000 mm³**
1 m³ = 100 cm × 100 cm × 100 cm = **1 000 000 cm³**
1 km³ = 1000 m × 1000 m × 1000 m = **1 000 000 000 m³**

Practice Exercise

1 Add to the diagram:

   (a) a point B on a bearing of 060° from A

   (b) a point C on a bearing of 260° from A.

2

   (a) Which point has co-ordinates (−2, 3)?   *2 (a) Answer* ....

   (b) Which point has co-ordinates (1, −2)?   *2 (b) Answer* ....

   (c) Which point has co-ordinates (−2, −1)?   *2 (c) Answer* ....

   (d) Which point has co-ordinates (2, 1)?   *2 (d) Answer* ....

3 You travel 8 km in 1 hour.
Match the speeds with the units.

8	metres per minute
5	metres per second
$\dfrac{8 \times 1000}{60}$	miles per hour
$\dfrac{8 \times 1000}{60 \times 60}$	kilometres per hour

4 Complete the following:

   (a) $8\,cm^2 =$ .... mm^2 (d) $4\,m^3 =$ .... cm^3

   (b) .... $km^2 = 5\,000\,000\,m^2$ (e) .... $cm^3 = 1000\,mm^3$

   (c) $2.5\,m^2 =$ .... cm^2 (f) .... $km^3 = 2\,500\,000\,000\,m^3$

5 If the bearing of B from A is 060°, what is the bearing of A from B?

....

....

Shape, Space and Measures

Topic 15
Measurement and drawings

Note: Loci is the plural of locus!

Locus of a point

The locus of a point is a fancy name to describe the path the point makes when it has to follow certain rules.

1 **One fixed point**
   The locus of a point which is always the same distance, say 3 cm, from **one** given fixed point O, is a circle radius 3 cm centre O.

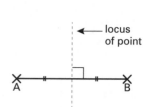

2 **Two fixed points**
   The locus of a point which is always the same distance from **two** given fixed points, say A and B, is the perpendicular bisector of the line joining A to B.

3 **One fixed line**
   The locus of a point which is always the same distance from **one** given fixed straight line is a pair of parallel lines joined by semicircles.

4 **Two fixed lines**
   The locus of a point which is always the same distance from **two** given fixed intersecting lines is the bisectors of the angles between the lines.

Constructions

You will need to know how to construct the following using ruler and compasses.

Perpendicular bisector of AB
With your compass point at A draw an arc.
With your compass point at B using the same radius draw another arc.
Join the points of intersection of these two arcs.
This is the perpendicular bisector of AB.

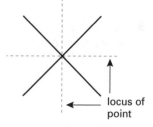

Angle bisector of ∠NPM
With your compass point at P draw an arc intersecting PM and PN at X and Y.
With your compass point at X draw an arc.
With your compass point at Y using the same radius draw another arc.
Join P and the point of intersection of these two arcs.
This is the bisector of the angle MPN.

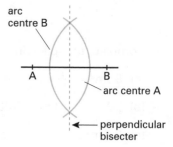
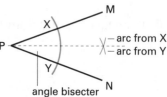

Practice Exercise

1 Draw the locus of points:

(a) 2 cm from the line AB

(b) equidistant from points A and C.

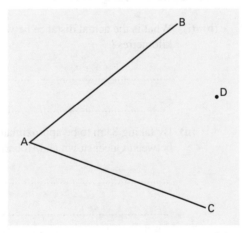

B ×

×A

×C

(c) Indicate the points which satisfy both of these conditions.

2 (a) Construct the perpendicular bisector of AD.

(b) Construct the bisector of angle BAC.

(c) Shade the region that is nearer to A than to D *and* nearer to AB than to AC.

3 Construct the following on a separate sheet of paper using a ruler and compasses:

(a) an angle of 45°

(b) an angle of 60°

(c) an angle of 30°.

Examination Questions

1. The diagram shows a map of Tasmania.

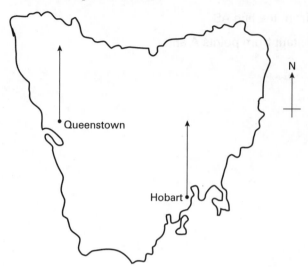

(a) What is the three figure bearing of Queenstown from Hobart?

....

The map has been drawn to a scale of 1 cm to 30 km

(b) (i) What is the actual distance between Queenstown and Hobart in
         kilometres?

....

....

(ii) By taking 8 km to be approximately 5 miles, calculate the distance
      between Queenstown and Hobart in miles.

....

....

(SEG – specimen paper)

Examination Questions

2. The diagram shows a map of a group of islands.
The map has been drawn to a scale of 1 cm to 5 km.

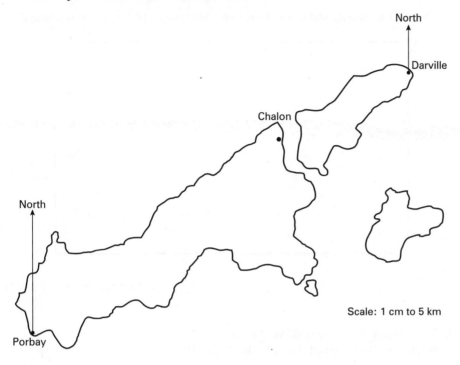

North

Darville

Chalon

North

Porbay

Scale: 1 cm to 5 km

(a) A straight road joins Porbay to Chalon.

    (i)   Use the map to find the length of this road in kilometres.

       ....

       ....

    (ii) Brian cycles from Porbay to Chalon along this road.
        He sets off at 0930 and cycles at an average speed of 18 kilometres per
        hour.
        At what time does he arrive in Chalon?

       ....

       ....

       ....

(b) A lighthouse is on a bearing of 080° from Porbay and 200° from Darville.
    Mark, with a cross, the position of the lighthouse on the map.

(SEG, Summer 1998 – Paper 14)

Topic 15

Measurement and drawings

Examination Questions

3. The diagram shows a car par with ticket machines at P and Q. People always use the ticket machine nearer to them.

Construct accurately and shade the region where people park who use machine P.

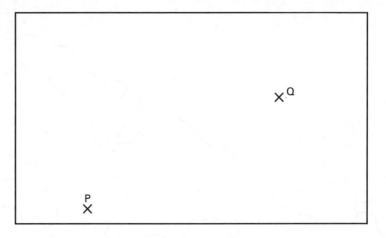

(NEAB, Winter 1997 – Paper 2)

4. The diagram shows the position of towns Blackburn (B), Holywell (H) and Whitchurch (W).

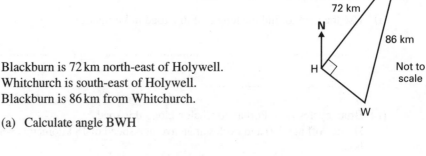

Blackburn is 72 km north-east of Holywell.
Whitchurch is south-east of Holywell.
Blackburn is 86 km from Whitchurch.

(a) Calculate angle BWH

....

....

....

....

(b) What is the three figure bearing of Blackburn from Whitchurch?

....

....

....

(NEAB – specimen paper, part question)

5. Two straight roads are shown in the diagram.
A new gas pipe is to be laid from Bere equidistant from the two roads.

The diagram is drawn to a scale of 1 cm to 1 km.

(a) Construct, on the diagram, the path of the gas pipe.

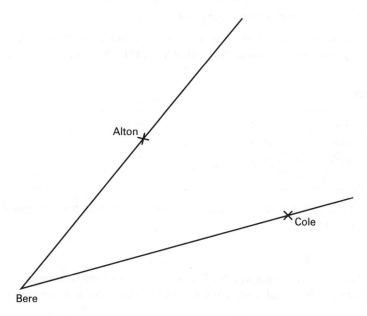

(b) The gas board needs a construction site depot.
The depot must be equidistant from Bere and Cole.
The depot must be less than 4 km from Alton.

(i) On the diagram draw loci to represent this information.

The depot must be nearer the road through Cole than the road through Alton.

(ii) Mark on the diagram with a cross a possible position for the site depot which satisfies all of these conditions.

(SEG – specimen paper)

Topic 16
Collection and representation

Note: You must make sure that your questions are not biased, personal or offensive if you want to get a good response rate.

Summary

Collecting data

You can collect data using observation, questionnaires or interviewing. When designing your own questionnaire you should use questions which require short definite answers preferably of the yes/no type!

Tally charts and frequency tables

When you have collected your (raw) data, you will need to organise it in some way such as in a **frequency table** with **tallies** to record each piece of data.

Like this

Hours of TV	Tally	Frequency
0 to less than 2	ⅢⅢ ⅢⅢ |||	13
2 to less than 3	ⅢⅢ ⅢⅢ ⅢⅢ ⅢⅢ		21
etc.		

Remember that the data you collect is only as good as the representative sample you use.

Displaying data

Once you have your data in a table then you are ready to represent it using some form of statistical diagram such as a pictogram or a bar chart.

Pictograms

A pictogram uses pictures to represent the frequency.

Like this

Hours of TV   Key: [ ] represents 2 people

0 to less than 2   [ ][ ][ ][ ][ ][ ][

2 to less than 3   [ ][ ][ ][ ][ ][ ][ ][ ][ ][

3 to less than 4   [ ][ ][ ][ ][ ]

4 or more   [ ][ ]

Bar charts

The frequency is represented by the lengths of bars.

Note: The bars may be horizontal or vertical.

Like this

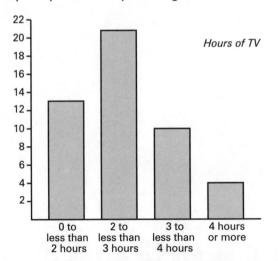

Practice Exercise

1 Complete the tally chart for the following data:

```
1 2 5 4 3 1 3 4 2 5 1 4 6 3 2 1 4 2 3
2 4 3 1 2 3 6 1 2 3 6 3 4 5 2 5 6 6 5
```

Number	Tally	Frequency
1		
2		
3		
4		
5		
6		

2 Rearrange the following letters and use the words you have found to label each diagram correctly.

HCATRBRA   TOPCGMIRA

AEPCRTHI   PNRHLEIGA

(a)

....

(b)

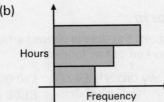

....

(c)

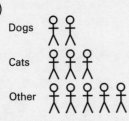

....

(d)

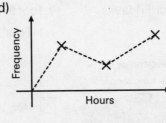

....

Handling Data

Topic 16
Collection and representation

Displaying data

Data can be represented using some form of statistical diagram such as a pictogram, bar chart, line graph or pie chart.

Like this

The amount of money in £s taken in 'Clever Cloggs' school tuck shop is shown in the table:

Day	Monday	Tuesday	Wednesday	Thursday	Friday
Money	£1.40	£4.20	£12.30	£15.00	£7.10

Show the data using a line graph and a pie chart.

Line graphs

The information can be easily shown on a line graph although intermediate values on the graph may not have any meaning!

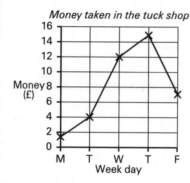

Pie charts

In a pie chart, the data is shared among 360° and the angle for each piece of data is worked out as follows:

Total money taken is £40.00   £40.00 is represented by 360°
                                £1.00 is represented by 360° ÷ 40 = 9°

Angle for Monday is	$1.40 \times 9°$	$= 12.6°$
Angle for Tuesday is	$4.20 \times 9°$	$= 37.8°$
Angle for Wednesday is	$12.30 \times 9°$	$= 110.7°$
Angle for Thursday is	$15.00 \times 9°$	$= 135°$
Angle for Friday is	$7.10 \times 9°$	$= 63.9°$
	Total	$= 360°$

Note: It is a good idea to check that your angles do add up to 360° before proceeding.

Practice Exercise

1 Complete the tally chart for the following data.

22	22	1	1	20	6	11	14	22	11	23	8	24
17	21	21	2	20	22	6	2	23	12	13	25	13
17	14	14	11	6	19	21	7	13	13	17	3	14
23	7	7	21	11	19	19	14	23	8	13	10	20
11	7	11	15	15	3	3	15	9	24	10	18	14
16	20	16	9	12	18	12	17	4	24	13	18	17

Number	Tally	Frequency
1–5		
6–10		
11–15		
16–20		
21–25		

2 (a) Complete the following to find the angles for the pie chart.

Favourite ice cream	vanilla	strawberry	chocolate	raspberry
Frequency	15	18	16	11

Total number of ice creams = ...

.... ice creams are represented by 360°

1   ice cream is represented by 360° ÷ .... = ...

Angle for vanilla is 15 × .... = ...

Angle for strawberry is 18 × .... = ...

Angle for chocolate is .... = ...

Angle for raspberry is .... = ...

(b) Use the information you have found in part (a) to complete the pie chart.

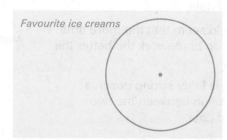

Favourite ice creams

Handling Data

Topic 16
Collection and representation

All about scatter diagrams

A scatter diagram is used to show whether or not there is a relationship between two variables. The distribution of points on the scatter diagram can be used to give an indication of the relationship or **correlation** between the two variables.

- If the points are randomly scattered you say there is **no correlation** between the two variables.

- If the points are close to a straight line you say there is **strong correlation**.

- If the points plotted are not close to a straight line you say there is **weak correlation**.

- If as one variable increases the other increases then you say there is **positive correlation**.

- If as one variable increases the other decreases then you say there is **negative correlation**

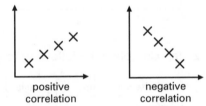

positive correlation   negative correlation

Line of best fit

Where the points plotted are close to a straight line then you can draw a line of best fit. The line of best fit should be drawn so that there are roughly as many points on one side of the line as the other.

Like this

The table gives the marks and time spent on a piece of homework undertaken by 6 pupils.

Pupil	A	B	C	D	E	F
Time (min)	60	55	30	10	40	55
Mark	9	8	6	1	6	7

Plot this data on a scatter diagram. Draw the line of best fit and comment on the correlation between the two sets of data.

It would seem that the more time spent on homework the better the mark.

There is fairly strong positive correlation between the two sets of data.

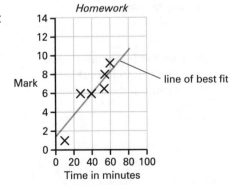

Note: *You can use your line of best fit to estimate one of the variables if you are given the other.*

Practice Exercise

1 Link the scatter diagram to its description. The first has been done for you.

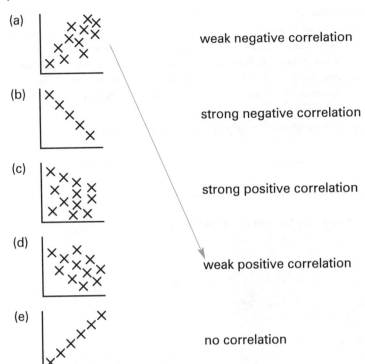

(a)

weak negative correlation

(b)

strong negative correlation

(c)

strong positive correlation

(d)

weak positive correlation

(e)

no correlation

2

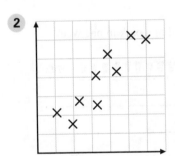

Draw a line of best fit on this scatter diagram.

3 Use the scatter diagram on page 160 of mark against time spent on homework to answer the following:

(a) Calculate the likely time spent on a piece of homework by a pupil gaining a mark of 4.

(b) Calculate the likely mark of a pupil spending 90 minutes on their homework.

(c) Which of your answers to (a) and (b) is the more accurate? Why?

3 (a) Answer ....

3 (b) Answer ....

Topic 16
Collection and representation

1. Don wants to write a report for his school magazine on how pupils travel to school. He asks pupils in his class, 'How do you travel to school?'

Here are their replies.

Peter, cycle	**John**, bus	**Alex**, bus	**Catrin**, bus	**Mark**, cycle	**Raj**, car
Emily, car	**Wade**, cycle	**Richard**, bus	**Valjit**, bus	**Ann**, bus	**Frank**, car
Chris, cycle	**Jon**, cycle	**Rita**, car	**Colin**, cycle	**Valerie**, car	**Iain**, car
Tom, bus	**Jim**, bus	**Lucy**, bus	**Tim**, bus	**Claire**, car	**Alan**, car

(a) What is wrong with asking only the pupils in Don's class?

....

....

(b) Show a better way for Don to record his data.

(NEAB – specimen paper)

2. The pictogram shows the number of ice creams sold in a park in one week

Key: represents 10 ice creams

(a) On which day were the most ice creams sold?

....

(b) How many ice creams were sold on Thursday?

....

(c) How many ice creams were sold altogether?

....

3. The chart below shows the temperatures at noon on a certain day in 11 countries.

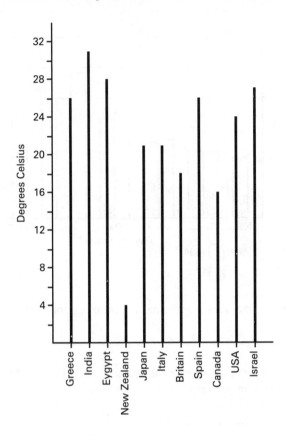

(a) Which country was the hottest?

....

(b) Which country was the coldest?

....

(c) Which countries had temperatures of less than 20 degrees Celsius?

....

(d) Which countries had the same temperature?

....

(e) Which country had the median temperature?

....

(NEAB – specimen paper)

4. The bar chart shows which day of the week shoppers went to a supermarket in 1994 and 1996.

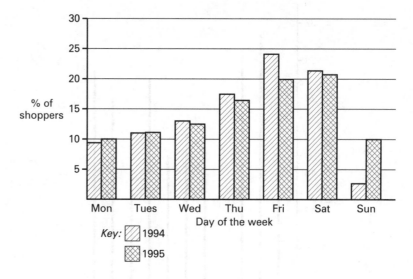

(a) Which day of the week was the most popular day for shopping in 1994?

....

(b) Did the shoppers choose different days to shop in 1996 compared with 1994? Give a reason for your answer.

....

....

(c) 'In 1996, about half the shoppers did their shopping at the end of the week (Friday, Saturday and Sunday).'

Is this statement true or false?
Show all your working.

....

....

....

(NEAB, Summer 1998 – Paper 1)

Examination Questions

5. In one week Ronnie rents out 90 items from his shop as shown in the table below.

Item	Frequency
Televisions	35
Videos	30
Computers	17
Other equipment	8

Complete the pie chart for all the week's rentals.

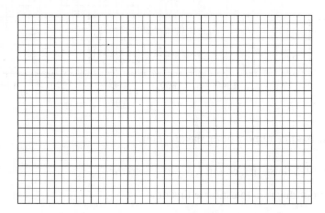

(NEAB, Summer 1998 – Paper 2)

6. The Mathematics scores and Science scores of 8 students are shown in the table.

Student	A	B	C	D	E	F	G	H
Mathematics score	44	18	51	60	25	10	35	40
Science score	34	21	46	50	18	15	29	39

(a) Use the data to plot a scatter diagram.

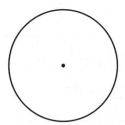

(b) What does the scatter diagram suggest about the connection between the scores in Mathematics and Science?

....

....

(SEG, Summer 1998 – Paper 12)

Examination Questions

7. Some of the world records for running the mile are shown below.
   The data are represented on the scatter diagram.

Glenn Cunningham	1934	247 sec.
Roger Bannister	1954	239 sec.
Michael Jazy	1965	234 sec.
John Walker	1975	230 sec.
Steve Cram	1985	226 sec.

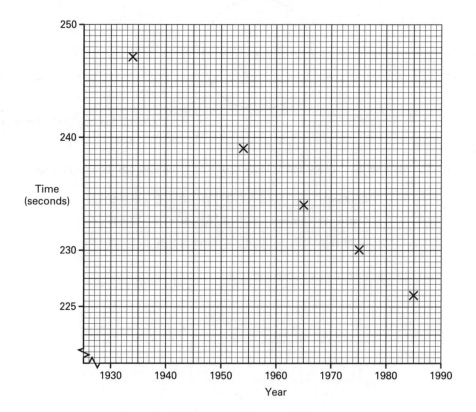

(a) Draw the line of best fit on the diagram.

(b) In 1979, Sebastian Coe ran a world record time.

Use your diagram to estimate this time.

....

....

(NEAB – specimen paper)

8. Each week during the summer season, a seaside resort recorded the rainfall in millimetres and the number of deck chair tickets sold.
The scatter diagram illustrates some of these recordings.

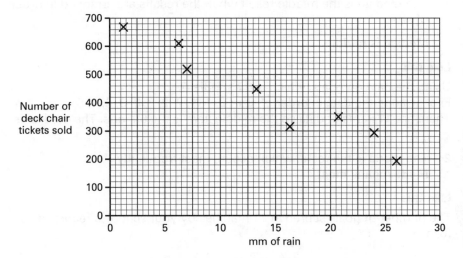

(a) What does the scatter diagram tell you about the connection between the rainfall and the number of deck chair tickets sold?

....

....

....

....

(b) On the diagram below, sketch what you might expect to get if you made a scatter diagram for 'the number of hours of sunshine' and 'the number of deck chair tickets sold' each week.

Number of
deck chair
tickets sold

Number of hours of sunshine

(NEAB – specimen paper)

Topic 17
Averages and spread

Note: *In general, if there are n numbers then the median is the* $\left(\dfrac{n+1}{2}\right)$*th one.*

Note: *Using grouped data, the group or class which occurs most frequently is called the modal class.*

The statistical average

There are three statistical averages.

1 The **median** is the middle result when the results are arranged in order of size.

   Median is **middle**.

Like this

Using the data on goals, which is the median?
First arrange the data in order of size: 0, 1, 1, 2, 2, 2, 3, 3, 4, 4, 5.
There are 11 items of data so the middle item is the 6th one. The median is 2.

2 The **mode** is the result which occurs most frequently.
   Mode means **most**.

Like this

The number of goals scored in 11 matches by your school is recorded as follows:

$$2, 4, 1, 0, 4, 3, 2, 2, 3, 5, 1$$

What is the mode?

The most frequent number is 2, so the mode is 2.

3 The **mean** is the sum of the data divided by the number of items of data.

   $$\text{Mean} = \frac{\textbf{sum of all the data}}{\textbf{number of items of data}}$$

Like this

Again using the data on goals find the mean number of goals.
The mean number of goals is

$$\frac{2+4+1+0+4+3+2+2+3+5+1}{11} = 2.45 \,(3\,\text{sf})$$

The range

The range is found by working out the difference between the highest value and the lowest value.

Like this

Again using the data on goals, find the range of the number of goals.

$$2, 4, 1, 0, 4, 3, 2, 2, 3, 5, 1.$$

Highest value = 5
Lowest value = 0
Range = highest value − lowest value = 5 − 0 = 5

Practice Exercise

1 For each set of numbers **(a)–(d)**
    (i) arrange them in order of size.
    (ii) find the median
    (iii) find the mode
    (iv) find the mean.

    (a) 2 2 3 3 3 4 4 4 4
        (i)   Order ....
        (ii) Median = ...
        (iii) Mode = ...
        (iv) Mean = ...

    (b) $\frac{1}{8}$ $\frac{1}{4}$ $\frac{1}{4}$ $\frac{1}{2}$ $\frac{1}{2}$ $\frac{1}{2}$ $\frac{3}{4}$
        (i)   Order ....
        (ii) Median = ...
        (iii) Mode = ...
        (iv) Mean = ...

    (c) 2 2 2 2 2 2
        (i)   Order ....
        (ii) Median = ...
        (iii) Mode = ...
        (iv) Mean = ...

    (d) (i) -5 -5 -5 -6 -6 -6 -6 -4 -4 -3
        (i)   Order ....
        (ii) Median = ...
        (iii) Mode = ...
        (iv) Mean =

2 Write down the range for each set of numbers in question 1.

    (a) Range = ...   (c) Range = ...

    (b) Range = ...   (d) Range = ...

3 Write down a set of numbers with mode = median = mean = 5.

    ....

4 Write down a set of numbers with mode = 6, median = 5 and mean = 4.

    ....

Topic 17 Averages and spread

Finding the mean

To find the mean from a frequency table you use the formula: $\text{Mean} = \dfrac{\sum f \times x}{\sum f}$

where $\sum$ is the greek letter sigma and stands for 'the sum of', x is the data value and f is the frequency.

Like this

The table gives the marks (x) scored in a Maths test. Find the mean mark.

Mark (x)	0	1	2	3	4	5
Frequency (f)	2	4	7	9	9	4

Sum of all the marks is
$\sum f \times x = (2 \times 0) + (4 \times 1) + (7 \times 2) + (9 \times 3) + (9 \times 4) + (4 \times 5) = 101$
Number tested is $\sum f = 2 + 4 + 7 + 9 + 9 + 4 = 35$

Mean mark is $\dfrac{\sum f \times x}{\sum f} = \dfrac{101}{35} = 2.89$ (3 sf)

Cumulative frequency graphs

Cumulative frequency graphs are found by plotting the cumulative frequencies at the upper values of the data. Then you join the points with a smooth curve.

Like this

Plot a cumulative frequency graph of the following data which shows the heights of 50 children measured to the nearest centimetre.

Height (cm)	$100 < h \leq 110$	$110 < h \leq 120$	$120 < h \leq 130$	$130 < h \leq 140$	$140 < h \leq 150$	$150 < h \leq 160$
Frequency	5	8	11	14	8	4

To plot the cumulative frequency graph you need to work out the cumulative frequencies by totalling (or accumulating) the frequencies in the table

Height (cm)	$100 < h \leq 110$	$110 < h \leq 120$	$120 < h \leq 130$	$130 < h \leq 140$	$140 < h \leq 150$	$150 < h \leq 160$
Frequency	5	8	11	14	8	4
Cumulative frequency	5	$5 + 8 = 13$	$13 + 11 = 24$	$24 + 14 = 38$	$38 + 8 = 46$	$46 + 4 = 50$

Note: Check that your final cumulative frequency is the same as the total.

Plot the cumulative frequency on the vertical axis and the upper value of the data (in this case height) on the horizontal axis and join the points with a smooth curve.

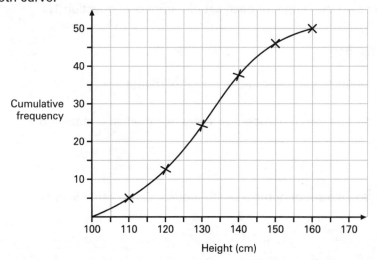

Practice Exercise

1 The table gives the marks (*x*) scored in an English test. Complete the table to find the mean mark.

Mark, x	Frequency, f	fx
0	0	$0 \times 0 = 0$
1	3	$1 \times 3 =$
2	11	
3	12	
4	5	
5	4	
	$\Sigma f =$	$\Sigma fx =$

$$\text{Mean} = \frac{\Sigma fx}{\Sigma f} = \frac{\cdots}{\cdots} = \cdots$$

Compare the mean of the English marks with the mean of the Maths marks on the opposite page. What do you notice?

....

....

2 The graph shows the cumulative frequency distribution of the Maths marks.

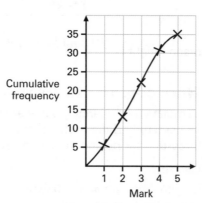

Complete the following table to work out the cumulative frequency of the English marks.

Plot the cumulative frequency distribution of the English marks on the same axes as the Maths marks.

Mark, x	Frequency, f	Cumulative frequency
0	0	0
1	3	3
2	11	
3	12	
4	5	
5	4	

Comment on your results.

....

....

Handling Data

Topic 17
Averages and spread

Summary

Finding the mean of grouped data

To find the mean of grouped data you must work out the frequency times the mid-interval value of each group.

$$\text{Mean} = \frac{\sum(f \times \text{mid-interval value})}{\sum f}$$

Like this

Find the mean of the heights (h) of 80 children in a school from the data in the table below.

Height, h (cm)	$80 \leq h < 90$	$90 \leq h < 100$	$100 < h \leq 110$	$110 \leq h < 120$	$120 \leq h < 130$
Frequency	4	12	18	27	19

You must work out the mid-interval value of each group then the frequency times the mid-interval value.

Height, h (cm)	Frequency (f)	Mid-interval value (x)	$f \times$ mid-interval value ($f \times x$)
$80 \leq h < 90$	4	85	$4 \times 85 = 340$
$90 \leq h < 100$	12	95	$12 \times 95 = 1140$
$100 \leq h < 110$	18	105	$18 \times 105 = 1890$
$110 \leq h < 120$	27	115	$27 \times 115 = 3105$
$120 \leq h < 130$	19	125	$19 \times 125 = 2375$
	$\sum f = 80$		$\sum(f \times \text{mid-interval value}) = 8850$

Mean height is $\dfrac{\sum(f \times \text{mid-interval value})}{\sum f} = \dfrac{8850}{80} = 111 \ (3\,\text{sf})$

More cumulative frequency graphs

Cumulative frequency graphs are useful to show the spread of data and can be used to find the **median** (middle position), **quartiles** (first quarter and three-quarter positions) and **interquartile range** for a distribution.

Like this

For the data on page 170 which shows the heights of 50 children measured to the nearest centimetre find the median, quartiles and the interquartile range.

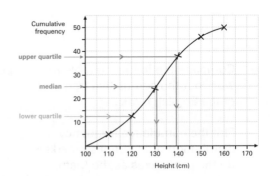

From your graph you can read off the following values:
The **median** is the 25th ($\frac{1}{2}$ of 50, the total frequency) value, approximately 131 cm.
The **lower quartile (LQ)** is the 12.5th ($\frac{1}{4}$ of 50) value, approximately 118 cm.
The **upper quartile (UQ)** is the 37.5th ($\frac{3}{4}$ of 50) value, approximately 139 cm.

The **interquartile range = upper quartile − lower quartile**
= 139 cm − 118 cm = 21 cm.

Practice Exercise

1 The table shows the heights of some seedlings grown in a greenhouse.
   Complete the table to find the mean height.

Height (cm)	Frequency, f	Mid-interval value, x	Frequency × mid-value
0 up to 2	8	1	$8 \times 1 = 8$
2 up to 6	12		
6 up to 10	13		
10 up to 20	8		
20 up to 40	5		
	$\Sigma f = \ldots\ldots$		$\Sigma fx = \ldots\ldots$

$$\text{Mean} = \frac{\Sigma fx}{\Sigma f} = \frac{\ldots\ldots}{\ldots\ldots} = \ldots\ldots$$

2 The following cumulative frequency curve gives the waiting time
   (in minutes) at a short-stay car park.

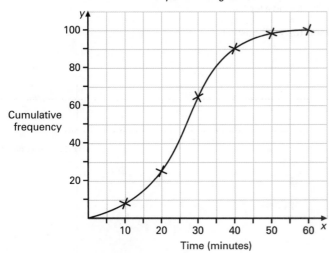

Car park waiting times

Use the graph to calculate:

(a) the median waiting time ....

(b) the upper quartile ....

(c) the lower quartile ....

(d) the interquartile range ....

Explain why the interquartile range is a good measure of range.

....

....

Topic 17
Averages and spread

Examination Questions

1. Graham and Wendy go tenpin bowling.

(a) Graham's first eight scores are:

$$5, \quad 8, \quad 8, \quad 5, \quad 5, \quad 6, \quad 6, \quad 5$$

What is his mean score?

....

....

....

(b) Wendy's first eight scores are:

$$4, \quad 9, \quad 5, \quad 2, \quad 9, \quad 3, \quad 2, \quad 9$$

(i) What is her modal score?

....

(ii) What is the range for Wendy's scores?

....

(c) Who is the better bowler?

Give a reason for your answer.

....

....

....

(NEAB – specimen paper)

2. Birdpool Park held its annual fishing competition in September.
   The number of fish caught by each of fifteen competitors in the time allowed was as follows:

   $$1, \quad 2, \quad 2, \quad 4, \quad 4, \quad 7, \quad 7, \quad 8, \quad 9, \quad 9, \quad 9, \quad 10, \quad 10, \quad 11, \quad 11$$

   (a) What is the modal number of fish caught?

   ....

   (b) What is the median number of fish caught?

   ....

   The number of fish caught by five more competitors were:

   $$2, \quad 10, \quad 7, \quad 11, \quad 7$$

   (c) For the twenty results now available calculate:

   (i) the mode;

   ....

   ....

   (ii) the median,

   ....

   ....

   ....

   (SEG – specimen paper)

3. (a) Pauline measures the length of some English cucumbers.
   The lengths in centimetres are:

   $$27, \quad 28, \quad 29, \quad 30, \quad 31, \quad 31, \quad 32, \quad 33, \quad 35, \quad 37, \quad 39$$

   (i) What is the range of the length of these cucumbers?

   ....

   (ii) What is the mean length of these cucumbers?

   ....

   ....

   Pauline measures the lengths of some Spanish cucumbers. The range of the lengths of these cucumbers is 6 cm and the mean is 30 cm.

   (b) Comment on the differences in these two varieties of cucumber.

   ....

   ....

   (SEG, Winter 1998 – Paper 14)

Topic 17
Averages
and spread

4. Fiaz records the number of words in each sentence of a magazine as shown in the following table.

Class interval	Frequency
1–5	13
6–10	24
11–15	22
16–20	15
21–25	13
26–30	8
31–35	3
36–40	1
41–45	0
46–50	1

(a) From the table:

   (i) write down the modal class

   ....

   (ii) write down the class interval in which the median lies.

   ....

(b) Calculate an estimate of the mean number of words in each sentence.

....

....

....

....

....

....

Examination Questions

5. Year 11 pupils at Newtown School took part in a survey.
The results are shown in the table below.

Time to travel to school (t minutes)	Number of pupils
$0 < t \leqslant 5$	5
$5 < t \leqslant 10$	29
$10 < t \leqslant 20$	57
$20 < t \leqslant 30$	69
$30 < t \leqslant 45$	33
$45 < t \leqslant 75$	7
Over 75	0

Calculate the estimated mean travelling time of the pupils at Newtown School.

....

....

....

....

(NEAB – specimen paper)

6. The finishing times of 360 people who took part in a sponsored run are recorded.
The following cumulative frequency graph shows these results.

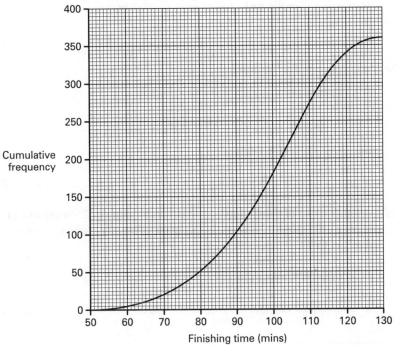

(a) What is the median finishing time?

....

(b) What is the interquartile range?

....

(SEG – specimen paper)

Topic 17
Averages and spread

7. The length of life of 100 batteries of a certain make were recorded. The table shows the results.

Length of life (hours)	<10	<15	<20	<25	<30	<35	<40
Cumulative frequency	0	2	9	50	86	96	100

(a) Draw a cumulative frequency graph to illustrate these data.

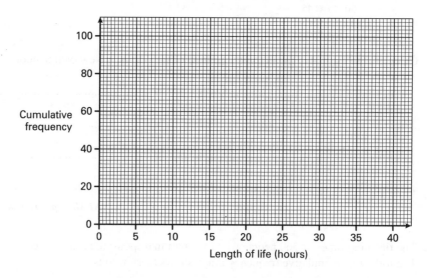

(b) How many batteries had a life of more than 32 hours?

....

(c) Use your graph to estimate:

  (i) the median;

  ....

  (ii) the interquartile range;

  ....

(d) Another make of battery has a median length of life of 25 hours and an interquartile range of 7 hours. Is this make of battery likely to be more reliable than the first?
Circle your answer yes/no.
Give a reason for your answer.

....

....

....

(SEG, Summer 1998 – Paper 14)

Examination Questions

8. The weight of tea in a sample of 100 tea bags is shown in the table below.

Weight of tea in tea-bag (w grams)	Number of tea-bags	Cumulative frequency
$2.9 < w \leqslant 3.0$	1	
$3.0 < w \leqslant 3.1$	5	
$3.1 < w \leqslant 3.2$	34	
$3.2 < w \leqslant 3.3$	43	
$3.3 < w \leqslant 3.4$	13	
$3.4 < w \leqslant 3.5$	3	
$3.5 < w \leqslant 3.6$	1	

(a) (i) Complete the cumulative frequency table.

   (ii) Draw a cumulative frequency diagram for the sample of tea bags.

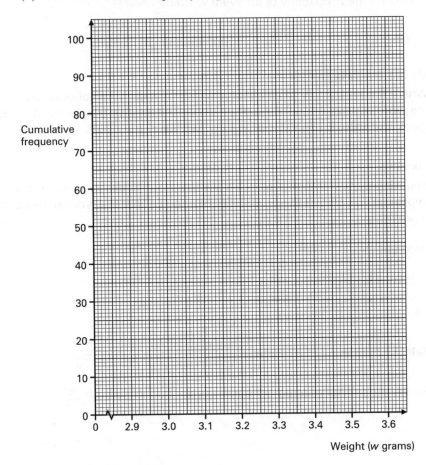

(b) The tea bags are packed in boxes of 80 tea bags.
On the side of the box it says '250 g'.
Do you think that '250 g' is a fair description of the total weight of the tea in the 80 tea bags in the box? Give a reason for your answer.

....

....

....

....

(NEAB – Specimen page)

Topic 18 Probability

Summary

Probability

Probability is a measure of the likelihood of a result happening. All probabilities can be expressed on a scale of 0 to 1 and probabilities can be expressed as fractions, decimals or percentages (so it might be helpful to revise these).

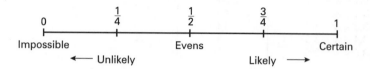

In general the probability of an event written P(event)

$$P(\text{event}) = \frac{\text{number of successful events}}{\text{total number of events}}$$

Relative frequency

Where the probability of an event is based on experimental evidence then the word relative frequency is often used. The relative frequency of an event gives an approximate value of the probability of the event.

Like this

You record the number of red cars passing your house one morning. Find an approximate value of the probability of a red car passing your house one morning.

Here are your results:

Number of red cars	23
Total number of cars	100

Note: *The probability can also be given as a decimal (0.23) or a percentage (23%).*

Note: *The more cars you record the better the relative frequency of a red car passing will approximate to the probability of a red car passing your house.*

Relative frequency of a red car $= \dfrac{\text{number of red cars}}{\text{total number of cars}} = \dfrac{23}{100}$

So the probability of a red car passing your house is about $\dfrac{23}{100}$

Practice Exercise

1 Complete the following diagram.

```
0                    .............        .............
├─────────────────────┼─────────────────────┤
.............        .............        Certain
```

2 Complete the table.

Fraction	Decimal	Percentage
$\frac{1}{2}$	....	50%
....	0.25	....
....	....	20%
$\frac{3}{5}$	....	....
....	0.75	....
$\frac{9}{10}$	....	....
....	....	45%
....	0.22	....

3 The table shows the sales of crisps in a shop one weekend.

Flavour	Cheese and onion	Plain	Salt and Vinegar	Chicken	Smokey bacon	Other
Sales	14	19	11	5	5	1

Say whether each of the statements (a)–(e) is true or false.

(a) The relative frequency of plain crisps is $\frac{19}{50}$

3 (a) Answer ....

(b) The relative frequency of cheese and onion crisps is $\frac{14}{55}$

3 (b) Answer ....

(c) The relative frequency of chicken crisps is the same as the relative frequency of smokey bacon crisps.

3 (c) Answer ....

(d) The relative frequency of salt and vinegar crisps is $\frac{11}{55}$

3 (d) Answer ....

(e) The relative frequency of salt and vinegar crisps is $\frac{1}{5}$

3 (e) Answer ....

Topic 18 Probability

Summary

Total probability

The sum of all possible probabilities of an event is equal to 1 so that

P(event occurring) = 1 – P(event not occurring)

or   **P(event not occurring) = I – P(event occurring)**

so that if the probability of doing my maths home work on time is 0.9 then the probability of not doing my maths homework on time is $1 - 0.9 = 0.1$

Expected probability

The expected number of times of getting a particular result is equal to the number of times multiplied by probability.

Like this

The probability of a rainy day in April is 0.4. How many rainy days would you expect to get in April?

There are 30 days in April, so expected number of rainy days is $30 \times 0.4 = 12$
You could expect 12 rainy days in April.

Showing probability

Probabilities of two events can be shown using a possibility space diagram.

Like this

Two dice are rolled. Show all the possible results in a table.

There are 36 possible results. In a table the results look like this.

		1	2	3	4	5	6
				1st dice			
	1	1,1	2,1	3,1	4,1	5,1	6,1
	2	1,2	2,2	3,2	4,2	5,2	6,2
2nd dice	3	1,3	2,3	3,3	4,3	5,3	6,3
	4	1,4	2,4	3,4	4,4	5,4	6,4
	5	1,5	2,5	3,5	4,5	5,5	6,5
	6	1,6	2,6	3,6	4,6	5,6	6,6

Possibility space diagram

Practice Exercise

1 The probability that a train arrives on time is 0.45.
The probability that a train arrives late is 20%.
What is the probability that it arrives early?
Explain how you reach your answer.

....

....

....

2 A square spinner is spun and a dice is rolled.

Complete the possibility space for the spinner and the dice.

			Spinner		
		Red (R)	Yellow (Y)	Green (G)	Blue (B)
	1	1,R	1,Y	1,G	1,B
	2	2,R			
Dice	3				
	4				
	5				
	6				

Use your possibility space to calculate:

(a) the probability of the spinner landing on yellow

2 (a) Answer ....

(b) the probability of throwing a five with the dice

2 (b) Answer ....

(c) the probability of throwing a three with the dice and the spinner landing on green

2 (c) Answer ....

(d) the probability of the spinner landing on blue and throwing a six with the dice.

2 (d) Answer ....

3 A dice is rolled and a coin is tossed. If a head is obtained then the score on the dice is doubled.
(a) Complete the following table.

		Dice					
		1	2	3	4	5	6
	H	2					
Coin	T	1					

(b) Use your table to calculate

(i) the probability of a score of 1

3 (b) (i) Answer ....

(ii) the probability of an even score

3 (b) (ii) Answer ....

(iii) the probability of a score of 12.

3 (b) (iii) Answer ....

(c) Which is the most likely score?

3 (c) Answer ....

Summary

More showing probability

Probabilities of more than one event can also be shown using a tree diagram.

Like this

A fair coin is tossed 3 times. Show all the possible results on a tree diagram.
$P(H)$ = probability of throwing a head, $P(T)$ = probability of throwing a tail

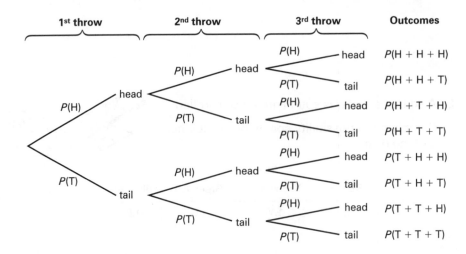

Mutually exclusive events

Mutually exclusive events can't happen at the same time, for example selecting an ace and a king when picking one card from a normal pack of playing cards.

If A and B can't happen at the same time then the probability of either one or the other happening is given by:

$$P(A \text{ or } B) = P(A) + P(B)$$

Like this

In a mixed bag of sweets the probability of picking a peppermint is 0.2 and the probability of picking a fruit drop is 0.3. What is the probability of picking a peppermint or fruit drop in any one go?

The events can't happen at the same time so they are mutually exclusive and the probability of picking a peppermint **or** a fruit drop is

$$P(\text{peppermint}) + P(\text{fruit drop}) = 0.2 + 0.3 = 0.5$$

Independent events

Independent events do not depend on each other, for example scoring an 'A' in Maths and winning your tennis match.

If A and B are independent events:

$$P(A \text{ and } B) = P(A) \times P(B)$$

Like this

A coin is tossed and a dice is rolled. What is the probability of obtaining a head and a six?

The results do not depend on each other so they are independent events and the probability of obtaining a head **and** a six = $P(\text{head}) \times P(\text{six}) = \dfrac{1}{2} \times \dfrac{1}{6} = \dfrac{1}{12}$

Practice Exercise

1 Say whether the events (a)–(d) are mutually exclusive or not.

(a) Throwing a one and an even number on a dice.

1 (a) Answer ....

(b) Throwing a six and an even number on a dice.

1 (b) Answer ....

(c) Choosing a heart and a diamond from a pack of cards.

1 (c) Answer ....

(d) Choosing a king and a heart from a pack of cards.

1 (d) Answer ....

2 Explain the difference between dependent and independent events.

....

....

....

....

3 A bag contains 4 red cubes and 5 blue cubes. A cube is taken from the bag and its colour noted. It is then returned to the bag. A second cube is then taken from the bag and its colour noted.

(a) Complete the following tree diagram for choosing 2 cubes.

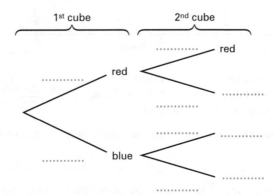

(b) Use your tree diagram to calculate:

(i) the probability of picking a red cube first followed by a blue cube.

3 (b) (i) Answer ....

(ii) the probability of picking 2 blue cubes.

3 (b) (ii) Answer ....

(iii) the probability of picking a red cube and a blue cube in either order.

3 (b) (iii) Answer ....

Handling Data

Topic 18
Probability

Examination Questions

1. Jack has these five cards.

   CERTAIN   EQUALLY LIKELY   LIKELY
   UNLIKELY   IMPOSSIBLE

   (a) Which card should he choose to complete these statements

      (i) If I toss a coin the probability that it comes down heads and the probability

           that it comes down tails are ....

      (ii) If I leave home early it is .... I will be late for
           school.

   (b) To answer part (a) (i), Jack picked a card at random.

      (i) What is the probability that he picked the correct card?

      ....

      (ii) What is the probability that he picked the wrong card?

      ....

                                                        (NEAB – specimen paper)

2. Below are five words that describe probability.
   (a) Write each word in the right place next to the probability scale.
       The first one is done for you.

Evens	Unlikely	Certain	Likely	Impossible
	$\frac{1}{4}$	$\frac{1}{2}$	$\frac{3}{4}$	
0				1

                              Evens

   (b) Yvonne has eight buttons as shown.
       Each button has 2 holes or 3 holes or 4 holes.
       Yvonne takes a button at random.

      (i) What is the probability that she takes a button with two holes?

      ....

      (ii) What is the probability that she takes a button with 2 holes or with 4
           holes?

      ....

                                                        (SEG, Summer 1998 – Paper 12)

3. Brenda has a bag of fruit sweets.
   There are 4 lemon, 1 orange, 8 strawberry and 7 pear sweets.
   Brenda chooses one sweet at random.

   What is the probability that it is:

   (a) the orange sweet?

   ....

   (b) a pear sweet?

   ....

   (c) not a pear sweet?

   ....

   (NEAB, Summer 1997 – Paper 2)

4. (a) A fair coin is thrown 20 times. It lands heads 12 times.
       What is the relative frequency of throwing a head?

   ....

   The coin continues to be thrown. The table shows the number of heads
   recorded for 20, 40, 60, 80 and 100 throws.

Number of throws	20	40	60	80	100
Number of heads	12	18	30	42	49

   (b) Draw a graph to show the relative frequency of throwing a head for these data.

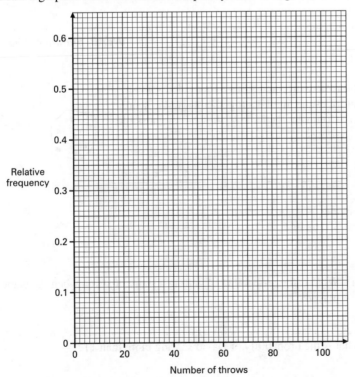

   (c) Estimate the relative frequency of throwing a head for 1000 throws.

   ....

   (SEG, Winter 1998 – Paper 14)

Examination Questions

5. Two fair spinners are used for a game.
   The scores from each spinner are added together.

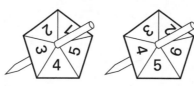

(a) Complete this table to show all possible totals for the two spinners.

	2	3	4	5	6
1	3	4			
2	4	5			
3					
4					
5					
6					

(b) What is the probability of scoring

   (i) a total of 3?

   ....

   (ii) a total of more than 8?

   ....

   ....

   (NEAB, Summer 1998 – Paper 1)

6. David throws a dice and spins a four sided spinner.
   He multiplies the numbers together to get his score.
   (a) (i) Complete the table to show all the possible
   scores.

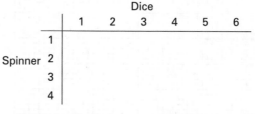

		Dice					
		1	2	3	4	5	6
	1						
Spinner	2						
	3						
	4						

   (ii) What is the probability of getting a score of seven when the game is
        played?

   ....

(b) What is the probability of David scoring more than 11?

   ....

   ....

   (SEG, Summer 1998 – Paper 11)

7. The table shows the colour and make of 20 cars.

		Colour of car	
		White	**Blue**
Make of car	**Vauxhall**	7	4
	Ford	3	6

(a) A car is chosen at random.
What is the probability that it is a blue Ford?

....

(b) A white car is chosen at random.
What is the probability that it is a Vauxhall?

....

(SEG, Winter 1998 – Paper 14)

8. When a model is fired in a kiln, the probability that it shrinks is 0.95.
When taken out to cool, the probability that it cracks is 0.04.

(a) What is the probability that when a model is fired it does **not** shrink?

....

(b) A model is fired in a kiln, then taken out to cool.
Complete the tree diagram by writing all the missing probabilities on the
appropriate branches

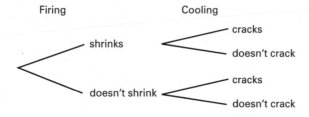

Firing   Cooling

shrinks — cracks / doesn't crack

doesn't shrink — cracks / doesn't crack

(c) Calculate the probability that the model shrinks and also cracks.

....

....

(NEAB, Summer 1997 – Paper 1)

9. The probability that I am late for work on a Monday is 0.4.
The probability that I am late for work on a Tuesday is 0.2.
What is the probability that in one particular week

(a) I am late for work on **both** Monday and Tuesday,

....

....

....

(b) I am late for work on Monday **but** on time on Tuesday,

....

....

....

(c) I am on time on **both** Monday and Tuesday,

....

....

....

(d) I am late for work on Monday **or** Tuesday but **not** both days?

....

....

....

....

(NEAB – specimen paper)

10. A dice is biased as follows:
     the probability of scoring a 6 is 0.4
     the probability of scoring a 5 is 0.2

(a) The dice is thrown once.
     Calculate the probability of scoring a 5 or 6.

....

....

(b) The dice is thrown twice and the scores are added together.
Calculate the probability of getting a total of 11.

....

....

....

SEG – specimen paper

11. A box contains cubes.
Each cube is coloured and numbered.
The table shows the probability of colour and number when a cube is taken from the box at random.

		Colour of cube	
	Red	**White**	**Blue**
1	0.1	0	0
2	0.1	0.1	0.1
3	0	0.2	0.2
4	0.1	0	0.1

Number on cube

(a) There are 12 white cubes in the box.
How many blue cubes are in the box?

....

....

(b) A cube is taken from the box at random.
What is the probability that it is red or number 4 or both?

....

....

SEG – specimen paper

Number

Topic 1: The rules of number

page 7

1 a $0.5, 50\%, \frac{50}{100}, \frac{1}{2}, \frac{5}{10}$

$\frac{1}{4}, \frac{25}{100}, 25\%, 0.25, \frac{5}{20}$

$5\%, \frac{5}{100}, 0.05, \frac{1}{20}, \frac{2}{40}$

$\frac{1}{5}, \frac{2}{10}, 0.2, 20\%, \frac{20}{100}$

  b $\frac{1}{4}$

  c 25%

2

	Statement	True or false
	$12\% \text{ of } £15 = \frac{12}{100} \times £15$	True
	$12\% \text{ of } £15 = \frac{£15}{12}$	False
	$12\% \text{ of } £15 = £1.80$	True
	$12\% \text{ of } £15 = \frac{£15}{100} \times 12$	True
	$12\% \text{ of } £15 = \frac{£15}{12} \times 100$	False
	$12\% \text{ of } £15 = \frac{£12}{15} \times 100$	False

page 9

1 Any numbers a and b such that:

  a $47 < a < b < 48$

  b $2.3 < a < b < 2.4$

  c $0.25 < a < b < 0.267$

  d $0.037 < a < b < 0.043$

2 **Column 1   Column 2**

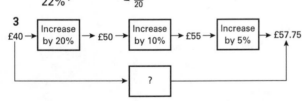

3

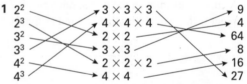

An increase of 20% followed by an increase of 10% followed by an increase of 5% is not the same as an increase of 35%.

page 11

1 Any fraction $\frac{a}{b}$ such that $\frac{2}{3} < \frac{a}{b} < \frac{3}{4}$

2 **a** and **d**

3 Cost is $117\frac{1}{2}\%$ ($100\% + 17\frac{1}{2}\%$ VAT)
So $117\frac{1}{2}\%$ of the cost of the washing machine is £528.75
1% of the cost of the washing machine is
$\frac{£528.75}{117.5} = £4.50$
100% of the cost of the washing machine is
$£4.50 \times 100 = £450$
Cost of washing machine excluding VAT is £450

4 **b**, **d** and **e**

Topic 2: More number

page 17

1 a 500 metres   c 1700 p = £17
  b £2300   d 256 000

2 23 600

3 $25 \times £752 = £18\,800$

4 Estimate: $5 \times \sqrt{7} \approx 5 \times \sqrt{9} = 5 \times 3 = 15$
Calculator: $5 \times \sqrt{7} = 13.2287 \ldots = 13.23$ (2 dp)

5

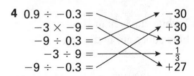

ingredients in a recipe — nearest 10 miles
prices in a supermarket — nearest centimetre
your height — nearest penny
your weight — nearest half kilogramme
distance to London — nearest five grammes

page 19

1 *Example:* $-6 + 1 + -3 + 7 + -1 + 2 = 0$

2 To make 100 ml of salad dressing, you need 80 ml oil and 20 ml vinegar.

3 The ratio of males to females is 7 : 3

4 248

5 a ✓   b ✗   c ✗   d ✗   e ✓

page 21

1 3040 (3 sf); 3039.7 (1 dp); 3040 (nearest whole number); 3000 (1 sf)
3 and 3039

2 The other number is halved

3 $0.0063, 6.3 \div 10^2, 0.63 \times 10^3, 63 \times 100, 6.3 \times 10^4$

4 $0.9 \div -0.3 =$ -30
   $-3 \times -9 =$ $+30$
   $-9 \div 0.3 =$ -3
   $-3 \div 9 =$ $-\frac{1}{3}$
   $-9 \div -0.3 =$ $+27$

Topic 3: Describing number

page 27

1 2^2 $3 \times 3 \times 3$ 9
   2^3 $4 \times 4 \times 4$ 4
   3^2 2×2 64
   3^3 3×3 8
   4^2 $2 \times 2 \times 2$ 16
   4^3 4×4 27

2 Multiples of 3: 3, 6, 9, 12, 15, 18, 21, 24, 27, 30, 33, 36, 39, 42, 45, 48, 51, 54, 57, 60, 63, 66, 69, 72, 75, 78, 81, 84, 87, 90, 93, 96, 99
Multiples of 5: 5, 10, 15, 20, 25, 30, 35, 40, 45, 50, 55, 60, 65, 70, 75, 80, 85, 90, 95, 100
Multiples of 9: 9, 18, 27, 36, 45, 54, 63, 72, 81, 90, 99
Multiples form patterns in the table, e.g. multiples of 3 make diagonal lines, multiples of 5 make vertical lines

3 Factors of 180: 1, 2, 3, 4, 5, 6, 9, 10, 12, 15, 18, 20, 30, 36, 45, 60, 90, 180
1, 4, 9 and 36 are square numbers

page 29

1 4.5×10^7

2 $240 = 2 \times 120$
$= 2 \times 2 \times 60$
$= 2 \times 2 \times 2 \times 30$
$= 2 \times 2 \times 2 \times 2 \times 15$
$= 2 \times 2 \times 2 \times 2 \times 3 \times 5$
$= 2^4 \times 3 \times 5$

3 $2 = \sqrt{4}$; $3 = \sqrt{9}$; $4^2 = 16$; $9^2 = 81$

4 a 432 000   b 206   c 0.008 15

page 31

1 ab^2, bab, b^2a

$a^2b^2, ab \times ab, (ab)^2, \sqrt{a^4b^4}, \dfrac{a^3b^3}{ab}$

$a^2b, ba^2, a \times a \times b$

$ab, \dfrac{a^2}{a} \times \dfrac{b^2}{b}, \sqrt{a^2b^2}, \dfrac{(ab)^2}{ab}$

2 $0.00048, 2.4 \times 10^{-3}, 4.8 \times 10^{-3}, 0.48, 2.4, 240,$
$4.8 \times 10^2, 2.4 \times 10^3$

3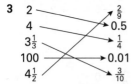

4 a The highest common factor (HCF) of two numbers is the largest integer which is a factor of both numbers.
  b The lowest common multiple (LCM) of two numbers is the lowest number for which both numbers are factors.

Topic 4: Application of number

page 37

1 The time taken by the train is 3 hours 5 minutes. The average speed is approximately 70 miles an hour (i.e. 210 miles ÷ 3 hours).
2 2 inches, 10 cm, 10.01 cm, 120 mm, 1 foot, 1 metre, 120 cm, 4 feet
3 Hours worked
$= 3\frac{1}{2} + 3\frac{1}{2} + 4 + 3 + 4 + 2\frac{1}{2} + 3\frac{1}{2} + 4\frac{1}{2} + 3 = 31\frac{1}{2}$ hours
Amount Jane earns
$= 31.5 \times £15.95 = £502.43$ (to nearest penny)

page 39

1 Small size: 1 m*l* costs £1.29 ÷ 100 = £0.0129
Large size: 1 m*l* costs £3.10 ÷ 250 = £0.0124
Best buy is the large size
Check
Small size: 1 penny buys 100 ÷ 129 = 0.775 m*l*
Large size: 1 penny buys 250 ÷ 310 = 0.806 m*l*
Best buy is large size
2 Discount $= \dfrac{5}{100} \times £57.45 = £2.87$ (to nearest penny)

Price paid = £57.45 − £2.87 = £54.58
3 b gives the correct answer

page 41

1 Tax paid at 20% = 0.2 × £3900 = £780
Tax paid at 23% = 0.23 × (£16 500 − £3900) = £2898
Total tax paid = £780 + £2898 = £3678
2 First find the volume of cuboid in cm³.
To find the mass (in g) you multiply the volume (in cm³) by the density (in g/cm³).
3 Interest for 1st year $= \dfrac{3}{100} \times £100 = £3$

Amount at beginning of 2nd year = £100 + £3 = £103

Interest for 2nd year $= \dfrac{3}{100} \times £103 = £3.09$

∴ Amount at end of 2nd year = £103 + £3.09 = £106.09
4 a £100 × (1.03)² = £106.09
  b Answers are the same. Multipliers for percentage increase can be used to calculate compound interest.

Algebra

Topic 5: The language of algebra

page 49

1 An expression is a series of terms linked by + and − signs
An equation is an expression which is equal to a number or another expression
A formula is a statement expressed in words or symbols
2 An expression has no equals sign; an equation must have terms, either pure number or expressions on either side of the equals sign.

3 a ab **b** $a - b$ (or $b - a$) **c** $4a$ **d** $\dfrac{b}{3}$ **e** a^2

4 a $y + 1$ years old **b** £$3x$ **c** £$(c - 15)$ **d** xy cm²

page 51

1 Like terms: $x, 3x, 5x, -2x$; $2y, 7y, -\frac{1}{2}y, \frac{1}{3}y$; $z, 4z$; $xy, 3xy, -yx$; $xyz, 2xyz, \frac{1}{2}zyx$
2 a $6y$ **c** a^2b^2 (or $abab$)   **e** $4x + 8$
  b $2ab$ (or $ba + ab$)   **d** $3x$ **f** $y^2 - 3y$

3 $3(x - 6)$ $18 - 3x$ → $-3(-6 + x)$
$3(6 - x)$ $3x + 18$ → $-3(x + 6)$
$3(x + 6)$ $-3x - 18$ → $-3(-x - 6)$
$3(-x - 6)$ $3x - 18$ → $-3(-x + 6)$

4 Let the number be x, the answer y.
Then $y = \left(\dfrac{2x + 6}{2}\right) - x = x + 3 - x = 3$

5 ab^2

page 53

1 Area of A $= x^2$; Area of B $= 8x$; Area of C $= 5x$;
Area of D = 5 × 8 = 40
Total area $= x^2 + 8x + 5x + 40$
$= x^2 + 13x + 40$
2 $(x + 12)^2 = (x + 12)(x + 12) = x^2 + 12x + 12x + 144$
$= x^2 + 24x + 144$
3 a $(x + 7)(x + 2) = x^2 + 7x + 2x + 14 = x^2 + 9x + 14$
  b $(x - 3)(x + 8) = x^2 - 3x + 8x - 24 = x^2 + 5x - 24$
  c $(x - 5)(x - 11) = x^2 - 5x - 11x + 55 = x^2 - 16x + 55$
4 a $x^2 + 5x + 4 = (x + 1)(x + 4)$
  b $x^2 + 6x - 7 = (x + 7)(x - 1)$
  c $x^2 - x - 6 = (x - 3)(x + 2)$
  d $x^2 - 11x + 24 = (x - 3)(x - 8)$

Topic 6: Making graphs

page 59

1 a (1, 1), (2, 2), (3, 3), (4, 4)
  b (0, 5), (1, 4), (2, 3), (3, 2)
  c (1, 0), (2, 1), (3, 2), (4, 3)
  d Example: (5, 5); (4, 1); (5, 4)
2

page 61

1 a $(-4, 4)$, $(-2, 2)$, $(0, 0)$, $(2, -2)$
b $(-8, 0)$, $(-6, 1)$, $(-4, 2)$, $(-2, 3)$
c $(-4, 7)$, $(-2, 1)$, $(0, -5)$, $(2, -11)$
d $(4, -4)$; $(0, 4)$, $(4, -17)$

2

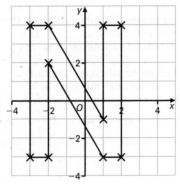

3 a

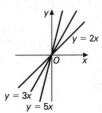

b

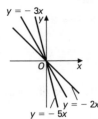

c

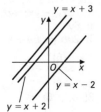

d

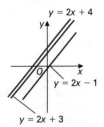

page 63

1 a

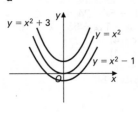

b

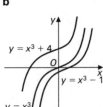

c

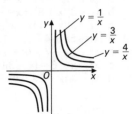

d

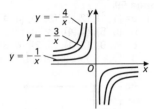

2 a $\dfrac{2}{x}$ (B)   **b** x^3 (C)   **c** $(x-2)(x-3)$ (A)

Topic 7: Using graphs

page 67

1 a €3.50   **c** €14.50   **e** £5.00
b €11.00   **d** £2.25   **f** £8.75
2 a 11 lb   **b** 16.5 lb   **c** 4.5 kg   **d** 7.4 kg

page 69

1 C
2 a 12:45   **b** 45 minutes
3

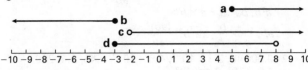

4 a $x \geqslant 3$ **c** $x > -3$
b $x \leqslant -1$ **d** $-5 < x \leqslant 2$

page 71

1 *Smallest gradient* $3y = x - 1$
$y = \dfrac{x}{2} + 10$
$5y = 8x$
Largest gradient $y = 2x + 3$

2 a D   **b** A   **c** B   **d** C

3

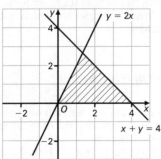

4 a $m = 3$, $c = 2$ **d** $m = \frac{1}{2}$, $c = 1$
b $m = -2$, $c = 7$ **e** $m = -2$, $c = 3$
c $m = 2$, $c = -\frac{1}{2}$

Topic 8: Using algebra

page 77

1 a $3a = 30$ **c** $4c - 6 = 2$
b $5b + 12 = 20$ **d** $\dfrac{d}{2} + 3 = 4\frac{1}{2}$

2 $a + b = 5$; $ab = 6$; $a - c = 3$; $abc = 0$; $\frac{1}{2}b = 1$;
$ad = -12$; $\dfrac{d}{b} = -2$; $abd = -24$; $a^b = 9$

3 *Biggest* $3(x + 2) = 21$, $3x + 2 = 17$, $3x - 2 = 13$,
$3(x - 2) = 9$ *Smallest*

4 10 m²

page 79

1 a 1 kg   **b** 5 kg   **c** 2 kg   **d** 5 kg   **e** 5 kg   **f** 3 kg
2 A and C
3 $3x + 75 = 360$
$3x = 285$
$x = 95$
4 $a + c = 3\frac{1}{2}$; $bc = 1$; $ad = -1$; $ad + bc = 0$;
$a(b + d) = 5$; $a^b = 9$; $b^a = 8$; $a(b - d) = 7$

page 81

1 a Either $(x - 3) = 0$ or $(x + 7) = 0$
$x = 3$ or $x = -7$
b Either $(x + 7) = 0$ or $(2x - 5) = 0$
$x = -7$ or $x = \frac{5}{2}$
c $(x + 5)(x - 3) = 0$
Either $(x + 5) = 0$ or $(x - 3) = 0$
$x = -5$ or $x = 3$
d $(x - 7)(x + 4) = 0$
Either $(x - 7) = 0$ or $(x + 4) = 0$
$x = 7$ or $x = -4$

2 $x^2 - 7x - 12 = 0$; $x = 4$, $x = 3$
$x^2 + x - 12 = 0$; $x = -4$, $x = 3$
$x^2 - x - 12 = 0$; $x = 4$, $x = -3$
$x^2 + 7x + 12 = (x + 4)(x + 3)$; $x = -4$, $x = -3$
3 a $x = 3$, $y = 5$ **b** $x = 2$, $y = -3$

Topic 9: More using algebra

page 85
1 a 2, 4, 8, 16, …   **c** 1, 1, 2, 3, 5, …
  b 1, 4, 9, 16, …   **d** 2, 4, 6, 8, …
2 a 19, 23, 27, 31   **c** 48, 96, 192, 384
  b $-3, -5, -7, -9$ **d** $1\frac{1}{8}, \frac{9}{16}, \frac{9}{32}, \frac{9}{64}$
3 a Add 4   **c** Multiply by 2
  b Subtract 2   **d** Divide by 2

page 87
1 $4n$; 4, 8, 12, 16, … $3n + 2$; 5, 8, 11, 14
  $n + 3$; 4, 5, 6, 7, … $6n$; 6, 12, 18, 24, …
  $n + 4$; 5, 6, 7, 8, …
2 nth term $= -3n + 21$
3 a $5 > 3$ **c** $3^2 > 6$
  b $-2 < 4$ **d** $0.25 > 0.2$
4 $y - c = mx$
$$\frac{y - c}{m} = x$$
$$x = \frac{y - c}{m}$$

page 89
1 A
2

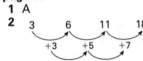

  nth term $= 3 + 3(n - 1) + 1(n - 1)(n - 2)$
           $= 3 + 3n - 3 + n^2 - 3n + 2$
           $= n^2 + 2$
3 Sequence: 4, 12, 24, 40, …
  1st differences: 8, 12, 16, …
  2nd differences: 4, 4
  nth term $= 4 + 8(n - 1) + 2(n - 1)(n - 2)$
           $= 4 + 8n - 8 + 2n^2 - 6n + 4$
           $= 2n^2 + 2n$
4 a $x > 4$ **b** $x \leqslant 6$ **c** $x > \frac{5}{2}$
5 A

Shape, Space and Measures

Topic 10: Angle properties

page 97
1 a anticlockwise   **b** clockwise
2 a $\frac{1}{4}$ turn   **c** $\frac{3}{4}$ turn   **e** $\frac{1}{4}$ turn   **g** $\frac{2}{3}$ turn
  b $\frac{1}{2}$ turn   **d** $\frac{1}{2}$ turn   **f** $\frac{1}{3}$ turn
3 a $90°$ **b** $180°$ **c** $90°$ **d** $270°$
4 $a° + b° + c° + d° = 360°$

page 99
1 a $f = 135°$, $g = 45°$, $h = 135°$ **d** $q = 57°$
  b $i = 90°$ **e** $r = 73°$, $s = 92°$
  c $j = 80°$, $k = 100°$, $l = 80°$, $m = 80°$, $n = 100°$,
     $o = 80°$, $p = 100°$
2 a $a = 108°$; angles on a straight line
     $c = d$; alternate angles
     $b = 72°$; vertically opposite angles
     $e = 72°$; corresponding angles
3 a False   **c** True   **e** True
  b False   **d** False   **f** False

4 a If DA and CB were parallel, then
     $A\hat{D}C + D\hat{C}B = 180$. In this case
     $A\hat{D}C + D\hat{C}B = 65° + 121° = 186°$, therefore DA
     and CB are not parallel.
  b $A\hat{B}C = 59°$; interior angles
     $D\hat{A}B = 115°$; interior angles

page 101
1 a $900°$ **b** $1440°$
2 a $(n - 2) \times 180° = (6 - 2) \times 180° = 720°$
  b Hexagon consists of 4 triangles,
       so angle sum $= 4 \times 180° = 720°$

  c $120°$ ($720° \div 6$)
3 a False   **c** True   **e** True
  b False   **d** False

Topic 11: Length, area and volume

page 107
1 a Perimeter $= 24 + 1 + 24 + 1 = 50$ cm
  b Perimeter $= 12 + 2 + 12 + 2 = 28$ cm
  c Perimeter $= 3 + 8 + 3 + 8 = 22$ cm
  d Perimeter $= 6 + 4 + 6 + 4 = 20$ cm
2 a Area $= 6 \times 4 = 24$ cm^2
  b Area $= 12 \times 1 = 12$ cm^2
  c Area $= 5 \times 5 = 25$ cm^2
  d Area $= 10 \times \frac{1}{2} = 5$ cm^2
3 a 24   **b** e.g. 6 cm $\times$ 2 cm $\times$ 2 cm
4 a Volume $= 3 \times 2 \times 8 = 48$ cm^3
  b Volume $= 9 \times 4 \times 2\frac{1}{2} = 90$ cm^3

page 109
1 C and D
2 Area of A $= 6 \times 10 = 60$ cm^2
  Area of B $= 6 \times 7 = 42$ cm^2
  Total area $= 60 + 42 = 102$ cm^2
3 a 51 cm^2 **b** 152 cm^2

page 111
1 Area of parallelogram = base $\times$ height
  Area of trapezium = half height $\times$ sum of parallel
  sides
  Volume of cylinder = area of base $\times$ height
2 *Smallest area* C, E, B, F, D, A *Largest area*
3 a $\frac{1}{2}(3 \times 4) \times 10 = 60$ cm^2
  b $6 \times 3 \times 10 = 180$ cm^2
  c $\frac{4}{2}(8 + 11) \times 10 = 380$ cm^2
  d $\pi \times 6^2 \times 10 \times 1130$ cm^2 (3 sf)
4 Lengths: $a + b + c$, $2a + 2b$, $4(a + b + c)$
  Areas: πa^2, $ab + ac$, $a^2 + b^2$
  Volumes: abc, a^2b

Topic 12: Symmetry and transformations

page 117
1

2 a order 2   **b** order 2
3

mirror

4

1 a 3   **c** infinite number
  b 6   **d** 5

2

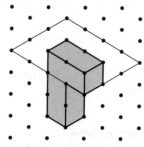

3 a T_2
  b T_3
  c T_1
  d T_4
  e

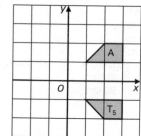

4

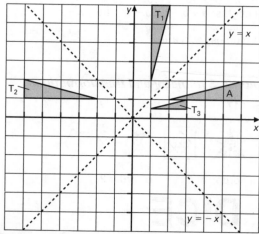

1 a, b

c Reflection in the line $x = 0$
d T_3 is an enlargement of A with scale factor $\frac{1}{2}$ centre (0, 0).
e The co-ordinates of A after a translation with vector $\begin{pmatrix} 3 \\ 2 \end{pmatrix}$ are (5, 3), (9, 3) and (9, 4).

2 a

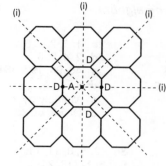

b Let x = interior angle of regular octagon
Angle sum at any vertex = $2x + 90° = 360°$
So $2x = 270°$ and $x = 135°$

Topic 13: Shapes and solids

1 Acute; A, H
Obtuse; B, D, F, G
Reflex; C, E, I, J

2

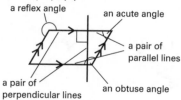

3

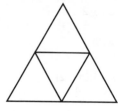

1 a Triangular prism

b Cuboid

c Square-based pyramid

d Cube

2 a

Name of shape	No. of faces	No. of vertices	No. of edges
Cube	6	8	12
Cuboid	6	8	12
Triangular prism	5	6	9
Triangular pyramid	4	4	6
Square pyramid	5	5	8

b No. of faces + No. of vertices = No. of edges + 2
c No; e.g. cylinder

page 131

1 Sides of triangle 2.1 cm, 2.8 cm and 3.5 cm
$2.1^2 + 2.8^2 = 12.25$

$\sqrt{12.25} = 3.5$, so Pythagoras' theorem works.

2 a $w^2 = 1^2 + 1^2 = 2$
$w = \sqrt{2} = 1.41$ cm

b $x^2 = 2^2 + 7^2 = 53$
$x = \sqrt{53} = 7.28$ cm

c $y^2 = 7^2 - 3^2 = 40$
$y = \sqrt{40} = 6.32$ cm

d $z^2 = \frac{1}{2} \times 8^2 = 32$
$z = \sqrt{32} = 5.66$ cm

3 Let h = height of triangle
Then $10^2 = 5^2 + h^2$
$h^2 = 75$
$h = \sqrt{75} = 8.66$ cm (3 sf)

Topic 14: Triangles and quadrilaterals

page 137

1 a acute-angled triangle
b equilateral triangle
c isosceles triangle
d obtuse-angled triangle

2 a square
b rhombus
c trapezium
d parallelogram

3 Obtuse-angled triangle; 3-sided shape with one angle between 90° and 180°
Isosceles triangle; 3-sided shape with two equal sides
Rhombus; quadrilateral with all sides equal
Rectangle; quadrilateral with right-angled corners
Equilateral triangle; triangle with three lines of symmetry

4 a Square
b hexagon
c decagon
d heptagon
e triangle

page 139

1 a

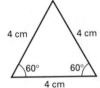

b

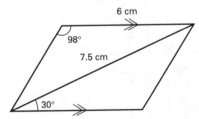

c

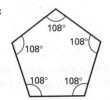

2 a Yes; all sides equal (SSS)
b Yes; right-angled, hypotenuse and one other side equal (RHS)
c No

3 Two triangles with the same angles as each other could be congruent.
Two triangles with the same length sides as each other must be congruent.
Two triangles with the same perimeter but different areas cannot be congruent.

4 $\dfrac{CD}{AB} = \dfrac{CO}{BO}$;

$CD = \dfrac{CO}{BO} \times AB = \dfrac{15 \times 15}{12} = 18.75$ cm (2 dp)

page 141

1 a False
b True
c False
d True
e True
f False

2 a $AD = \sqrt{13^2 - 12^2} = 5$ cm

b $\cos \alpha = \dfrac{12}{13}$

c $AB = 13 \div \cos \alpha = \dfrac{13^2}{12} = 14.1$ cm (3 sf)

d $BC = \sqrt{(14.083 \ldots^2 - 13^2)} = 5.42$ cm (3 sf)

3 Bearing of A from B = 180° + 60° = 240°
Distance of C from A = $\sqrt{20^2 + 10^2} = \sqrt{500}$
= 22.4 km (3 sf)
$\tan C\hat{A}B = \frac{10}{20}$ so $C\hat{A}B = 26.56°$
Bearing of C from A = 60° − 26.56 …° = 33.43 …°
= 033.4° (3 sf)

Topic 15: Measurement and drawings

page 147

1 a B **b** D **c** E **d** B
e

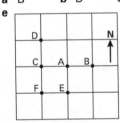

2 (2, 3) and (4, 1)
3 5 cm, 10 cm, 1 foot, 40 cm, 1 metre, 1 mile, 3 km
4 A = 2.2 kg, B = 3.7 kg, C = 0.5 kg
5 D

page 149

1

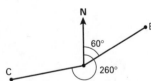

2 a B **b** D **c** C **d** A
3 8 kilometres per hour; 5 miles per hour;
$\dfrac{8 \times 1000}{60 \times 60}$ metres per second;
$\dfrac{8 \times 1000}{60}$ metres per minute

4 a $8\,\text{cm}^2 = 800\,\text{mm}^2$
 b $50\,\text{km}^2 = 50\,000\,000\,\text{m}^2$
 c $2.5\,\text{m}^2 = 25\,000\,\text{cm}^2$
 d $4\,\text{m}^3 = 4\,000\,000\,\text{cm}^3$
 e $1\,\text{cm}^3 = 1000\,\text{mm}^3$
 f $2.5\,\text{km}^3 = 2\,500\,000\,000\,\text{m}^3$
5 Bearing of A from B = 240°

page 151

1

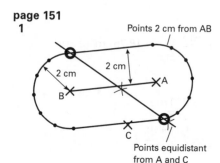

O Points that satisfy both instructions

2

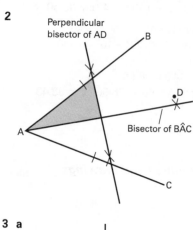

3 a

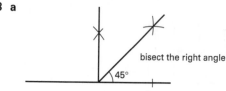

bisect the right angle

b

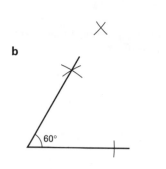

60°

c

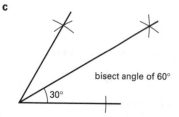

bisect angle of 60°

30°

Handling data

Topic 16: Collection and representation

page 157

1

Number	Tally	Frequency
1	卌 I	6
2	卌 III	8
3	卌 III	8
4	卌 I	6
5	卌	5
6	卌	5

2 a Pie chart   **c** Pictogram
 b Bar chart   **d** Line graph

page 159

1

Number	Tally	Frequency
1–5	卌 III	8
6–10	卌 卌 III	13
11–15	卌 卌 卌 卌 IIII	24
16–20	卌 卌 卌 II	17
21–25	卌 卌 卌 I	16

2 a Total number of ice creams = 60
 60 ice creams are represented by 360°
 1 ice cream is represented by 360° ÷ 60 = 6°
 Angle for vanilla $= 15 \times 6 = 90°$
 Angle for strawberry $= 18 \times 6 = 108°$
 Angle for chocolate $= 16 \times 6 = 96°$
 Angle for raspberry $= 11 \times 6 = 66°$
                              Total $= \overline{360°}$

b

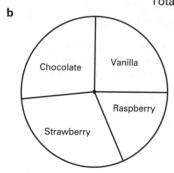

page 161

1 a Weak positive correlation
 b Strong negative correlation
 c No correlation
 d Weak negative correlation
 e Strong positive correlation

2

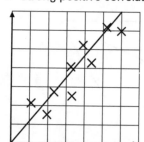

3 a 20 minutes
 b 11 marks
 c Answer **b** is more accurate as there are more points plotted and the line is likely to be a better fit in this area.

Topic 17: Averages and spread

page 169

1 a i 2 2 3 3 3 4 4 4 4   **iii** Mode = 4

    ii Median = 3   **iv** Mean = 3.2 (1 dp)

   b i $\frac{1}{8}$ $\frac{1}{4}$ $\frac{1}{4}$ $\frac{1}{2}$ $\frac{1}{2}$ $\frac{1}{2}$ $\frac{3}{4}$ **iii** Mode = $\frac{1}{2}$

    ii Median = $\frac{1}{2}$ **iv** Mean = 0.4 (1 dp)

   c i 2 2 2 2 2 2   **iii** Mode = 2

    ii Median = 2   **iv** Mean = 2

   d i −6, −6, −6, −6, −5, −5, −5, −4, −4, −3

    ii Median = −5   **iv** Mean = −5

    iii Mode = −6

2 a Range = 2   **c** Range = 0

   b Range = $\frac{5}{8}$ **d** Range = 3

3 Examples: 5 5 5 5 or 7 6 5 5 5 4 3

4 Example: 6 6 5 1 2

page 171

1

Mark, x	Frequency, f	fx
0	0	$0 \times 0 = 0$
1	3	$1 \times 3 = 3$
2	11	$2 \times 11 = 22$
3	12	$3 \times 12 = 36$
4	5	$4 \times 5 = 20$
5	4	$5 \times 5 = 20$
	$\Sigma f = 35$	$\Sigma fx = 101$

Mean = $\dfrac{\Sigma fx}{\Sigma f} = \dfrac{101}{35} = 2.89$

Although the Mathematics marks have a greater range than the English, the mean mark for both tests is the same.

2

Mark, x	Frequency, f	Cumulative frequency
0	0	0
1	3	3
2	11	14
3	12	26
4	5	31
5	4	35

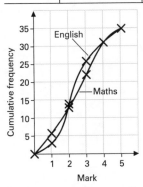

See comment for question 1.

page 173

1

Height (cm)	Frequency, f	Mid-interval value, x	Frequency × mid-value
0 up to 2	8	1	8
2 up to 6	12	4	48
6 up to 10	13	8	104
10 up to 20	8	15	120
20 up to 40	5	30	150
	$\Sigma f = 46$		$\Sigma fx = 430$

Mean = $\dfrac{\Sigma fx}{\Sigma f} = \dfrac{430}{46} = 9.34$ cm (3 sf)

2 a 28 minutes   **c** 33 minutes

   b 20 minutes   **d** 13 minutes

   IQR is a good measure of range because it excludes rogue values.

Topic 18: Probability

page 181

1

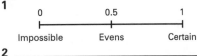

2

Fraction	Decimal	Percentage
$\frac{1}{2}$	0.5	50%
$\frac{1}{4}$	0.25	25%
$\frac{1}{5}$	0.20	20%
$\frac{2}{5}$	0.40	40%
$\frac{3}{4}$	0.75	75%
$\frac{9}{10}$	0.9	90%
$\frac{9}{20}$	0.45	45%
$\frac{2}{9}$	0.22	22%

3 a False   **c** True   **e** True

   b True   **d** True

page 183

1 $1 - (0.45 + 0.2) = 0.35$

2

		Spinner		
		Red (R)	Yellow (Y)	Green (G)	Blue (B)
Dice	1	1, R	1, Y	1, G	1, B
	2	2, R	2, Y	2, G	2, B
	3	3, R	3, Y	3, G	3, B
	4	4, R	4, Y	4, G	4, B
	5	5, R	5, Y	5, G	5, B
	6	6, R	6, Y	6, G	6, B

   a $\frac{6}{24} = \frac{1}{4}$ **b** $\frac{4}{24} = \frac{1}{6}$ **c** $\frac{1}{24}$ **d** $\frac{1}{24}$

3 a

		Dice					
		1	2	3	4	5	6
Coin	H	2	4	6	8	10	12
	T	1	2	3	4	5	6

   b i $\frac{1}{12}$ **ii** $\frac{9}{12} = \frac{3}{4}$ **iii** $\frac{1}{12}$

   c Scores of 2, 4 and 6 are equally most likely

page 185

1 a Yes   **b** No   **c** Yes   **d** No

2 Independent events do not affect each other, dependent events do.

3 a

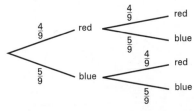

   b i $\frac{4}{9} \times \frac{5}{9} = \frac{20}{81}$ **ii** $\frac{5}{9} \times \frac{5}{9} = \frac{25}{81}$

   iii $\frac{4}{9} \times \frac{5}{9} + \frac{5}{9} \times \frac{4}{9} = \frac{40}{81}$

Number

Topic 1: The rules of number

1 a $200 \div 3.9 = 51.28 \ldots$ So 52 rails are needed
  b 1.67 m

2 a One thousand seven hundred and fifty
  b 50
  c 2000

3 a $\frac{5}{20} = \frac{1}{4}$
  b $\frac{1}{5} \times 20 = 4$ pieces

4 a 6.08 m = 608 cm; 7.50 m = 750 cm
    Carpet left = 750 − 608 = 142 cm
  b $6.08 \div 1.65 = 3.684 \ldots$
    3 bookcases can be put along the wall

5 Percentage of girls in class 9B $= \frac{15}{30} \times 100 = 50\%$
  Percentage of girls in class 9C $= \frac{17}{39} \times 100 = 43.6\%$
  So class 9B has the higher proportion of girls

6 a 600   **b** 6000   **c** 60

7 a 0, 0.058, 0.085, 0.55, 0.555, 0.56, 1
  b i 0.54   **ii** 0.8

8 $\frac{120}{100} \times 15 = \frac{6}{5} \times 15 = 18$ oranges

9 a 1992 sale price is 87.5% (100% − 12.5%)
    of 1990 price
    1992 price = £88 000 × 0.875 = £77 000
  b 1996 sale price is 101.5% (100% + 1.5%)
    of 1990 price
    1996 price = £88 000 × 1.015 = £89 320
    Value of Elm Tree House has increased by
    £89 320 − £88 000 = £1320

10 21 × 65.9 p = 1383.9 p = £13.84 (to nearest penny)

11 $\frac{8}{4}$, 5

12 0.6, 0.666, 0.$\dot{6}$, 0.67, 0.7

13 a Fraction of arable land
$$= 1 - \left(\frac{1}{6} + \frac{5}{18}\right) = 1 - \left(\frac{3+5}{18}\right) = 1 - \frac{8}{18} = \frac{10}{18} = \frac{5}{9}$$
  b Area of arable land
$$= \frac{5}{9} \times 324 = 5 \times 36 = 180 \text{ hectares}$$

14 Discount = 13.80 − 12.30 = £1.50
    $1.50 \div 13.80 = 0.1086 \ldots = 11\%$ (2 sf)

15 Sale price is 80% of original price
    1% of original price = £25 ÷ 80 = £0.3125
    100% of original price = 100 × £0.3125 = £31.25

16 Sale price is 90% of original price
    1% of original price = £32.40 ÷ 90 = £0.36
    100% of original price = 100 × £0.36 = £36

Topic 2: More number

1 759 000

2 a Mohini rounded to one significant figure:
    $21 \times 29 \approx 20 \times 30 = 600$
  b 1980 = 2000 (1 sf); 43 = 40 (1 sf)
    $1980 \div 43 \approx 2000 \div 40 = 50$

3 $\sqrt{6 \times 9} = \sqrt{54} = 7.348 \ldots = 7$ (nearest whole number)

4 a Mixed fruit needed for 6 scones
$$= \frac{6}{24} \times 100 = 25 \text{ g}$$
  b Flour needed for 40 scones
$$= \frac{40}{24} \times 600 = 1000 \text{ g} = 1 \text{ kg}$$

5 a −8, −5, −2, −1, 0, 2, 4
  b $-8 + -5 + -2 + -1 + 0 + 2 + 4 = -10$

6 a 3 : 4
  b $\frac{3}{7} = 0.4285 \ldots = 43\%$ (2 sf) are girls

7 $645\,166 \div 4 = 161\,291.5 = 161\,000$ (3 sf) people are retired

8 $\frac{3}{4} \times$ £80 million = £60 million was given to swimming

9 Distance travelled on 1 litre of diesel
    $= 559 \div 53.7 = 10.4096 \ldots = 10.4$ miles (3 sf)

10 $5 \times -6 + -10 = -30 + -10 = -40$

11 Time taken to deliver 1 litre = 20 ÷ 8 = 2.5 s
    Time taken to deliver 70 litres = 70 × 2.5 = 175 s
                 = 3 min 55 s

12 a 24.860 526 32
  b $\frac{4.7 \times 20.1}{5.6 - 1.8} \approx \frac{5 \times 20}{6 - 2} = \frac{80}{4} = 20$

13 a Gallons of petrol used = 7764 ÷ 37 = 209.837 …
    Litres of petrol used = 4.55 × 209.837 …
    Money spent on petrol = 52 × 4.55 × 209.837 …
             = 49 647.632 … p = £496.48
  b Gallons of petrol used $\approx 8000 \div 40 = 200$
    Litres of petrol used $\approx 200 \times 5 = 1000$
    Money spent on petrol $\approx 50 \times 1000$
              = 50 000 p = £500

14 a Units used $= \dfrac{(42.91 - 10.33) \times 100}{7.49} = 434.979 \ldots$
    = 435 (nearest whole unit)
  b Total bill = quarterly charge + cost of electricity used
    = £10.33 + £(7.49 × 578 ÷ 100)
    = £10.33 + £43.2922
    = £53.62 (nearest penny)

15 Rounding to 1 sf, $876 \div 32 \approx 900 \div 30 = 30$

16 a 5   **b** −2

17 239.15 s

Topic 3: Describing number

1 a 74 + 26 = 100   **c** 73 × 74 = 5402
  b 73 − 23 = 50   **d** 56

2 a i 4   **ii** 8

3 a 9   **b** 8

4 6

5 Joseph

6 4, 16

7 a $2^5 = 2 \times 2 \times 2 \times 2 \times 2 = 32$
  b $5^2 = 25$
    Difference = 32 − 25 = 7

8 Time taken for light to travel from nearest star
    $= 4.0 \times 10^{13} \div 3.0 \times 10^5 = 1.33 \times 10^8$ s
$$1.3 \times 10^8 \text{ s} = \frac{1.3 \times 10^8}{60 \times 60 \times 24 \times 365}$$
$$= \frac{1.3 \times 10^8}{31\,536\,000} = 4.23 \text{ years (3 sf)}$$
    Distance to nearest star = 4.23 light years (3 sf)

9 $\sqrt{5} - \sqrt[3]{10} = 2.236 \ldots - 2.1544 \ldots = 0.0816$
    = 0.08 (2 dp)

10 Thickness of one sheet = 5 ÷ 500 = 0.01
                        $= 1 \times 10^{-2}$ cm

11 a $3^2 \times 3^5 = 3^{(2+5)} = 3^7$
  b $3^6 \div 3^2 = 3^{(6-2)} = 3^4$

12 a HCF of 216 and 168 is 24
  b 2.4 m

13 $\sqrt{200} = \sqrt{2 \times 100} = 10\sqrt{2}$
    $\sqrt[3]{2000} = \sqrt[3]{2 \times 1000} = 10\sqrt[3]{2}$
    $\sqrt{2} > \sqrt[3]{2}$ so $\sqrt{200} > \sqrt[3]{2000}$

14 a Percentage retired

$$= \frac{1.04 \times 10^7}{5.80 \times 10^7} \times 100 = 17.93 \ldots = 18\% \text{ (2 sf)}$$

   b Population of Europe $= 0.138 \times 5.72 \times 10^9$
$$= 7.8936 \times 10^8 = 7.89 \times 10^8 \text{ (3 sf)}$$

15 a 3.5×10^{16} miles

   b Time taken $= \dfrac{3.5 \times 10^{16}}{5.9 \times 10^{12}} = 5932.20 \ldots$

$$= 6000 \text{ years (1 sf)}$$

Topic 4: Application of number

1 a $5 \times 35\text{p} = 175\text{p} = £1.75$
    Change from £5 $= £5.00 - £1.75 = £3.25$
  b Jason can buy $500 \div 35 = 14.28 \ldots = 14$ bars
  c Number of chocolate bars $= 1100 \div 55 = 20$ bars

2 a i Coaches need $= 197 \div 46 = 4.28 \ldots = 5$
   ii Total paid $= 197 \times £2.60 = £512.20$
     Cost to hire 1 coach $= £512.20 \div 5 = £102.44$
  b Average speed $= 132 \div 3 = 44$ mph

3 a 0750
  b Time taken by 0839 train is 1 hour 39 minutes
    Time taken by 0900 train is 2 hours 12 minutes
    So journey is 33 minutes longer

4 a Cost for 3 days $= £12 + (3 \times £15.40)$
$$= £12 + £46.20 = £58.20$$
  b Number of days hired
$$= \frac{£135.20 - £12}{£15.40} = \frac{£123.20}{£15.40} = 8 \text{ days}$$

5 a 2:10 pm
  b 1 hour 55 minutes
  c $\frac{3}{4} \times £8.00 = £6.00$

6 a 20 p + 20 p + 20 p;
    20 p + 20 p + 10 p + 10 p;
    20 p + 10 p + 10 p + 10 p + 10 p;
    10 p + 10 p + 10 p + 10 p + 10 p + 10 p
  b 25 minutes

7 a $£450 = 450 \times 3.4 = 1530$ Singapore Dollars
  b 27 Singapore Dollars $= 27 \div 3.4 = 7.94 \ldots$
$$= £8 \text{ (nearest pound)}$$

8 Small size: 1 m*l* costs $50 \div 72 = 0.694\text{p}$
  Medium size: 1 m*l* costs $90 \div 135 = 0.6\text{p}$
  Medium size is better value for money

9

x	5	10	20
y	45	180	720

10 $28\,\text{m/s} = 28 \times 60 \times 60 = 100\,800\,\text{m/h} = 100.8\,\text{km/h}$
$$= 100\,\text{km/h (2 sf)}$$

11 Taxable income $= £27\,000 - £3525 = £23\,475$
  Tax paid at 20% $= 0.2 \times £3200 = £640$
  Tax paid at 25% $= 0.25 \times (£23\,475 - £3200) = £5068.75$
  Total tax paid $= £5068.75 + £640 = £5708.75$

12 a 2 hours 30 minutes $= 2.5$ hours
    Distance $= 2.5 \times 80 = 200$ miles
  b New journey time $= 200 \div 100 = 2$ hours
    So 30 minutes will be saved on journey time

13 $P = 66.2 \times 10^6 \left(1 + \dfrac{3}{100}\right)^5$

$$= 66.2 \times 10^6 \times 1.03^5 = 76.7 \times 10^6 = 76.7 \text{ million}$$

14 Volume $= 5 \times 5 \times 10 = 250\,\text{cm}^3$
  Density $= 354\,\text{g} \div 250\,\text{cm}^3 = 1.416 = 1.42\,\text{g/cm}^3 \text{ (3 sf)}$

Algebra

Topic 5: The language of algebra

1 a 7 and 10
  b i 12 and 13   **ii** 24

2 a 15°C   **b** 0°C   **c** −15°C

3 a $-x + 13y$ **b** $2x + 10$

4 a $2x + 2y$ **b** $5pq$

5 $2x + 10 + 3x + x + 120 + 2x - 20 = 8x + 110$

6 a $(2x - 4)(x + 6) = 2x^2 + 12x - 4x - 24$
$$= 2x^2 + 8x - 24$$
  b i $2x(x - 2y)$ **ii** $(x + 12)(x - 2)$

7 a $3x^3 - 5x$ **b** $6x^2 - x - 2$

8 a i $8y$ **ii** $6y + 6$ **iii** $y = 3$
  b $2x + 4 = 8x - 2$, $6x = 6$ ∴ $x = 1$
    Area of rectangle $= 2(x + 2) = 2 \times 3 = 6\,\text{cm}^2$

9 a t^8 **b** p^4 **c** a^4

Topic 6: Making graphs

1 a

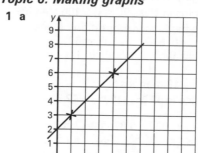

  b $a = 3$

2 a

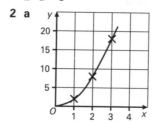

  b $x = 2.45$

3

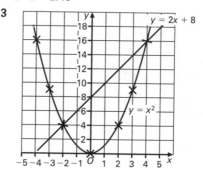

Points of intersection $(-2, 4)$ and $(4, 16)$

4

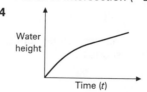

Topic 7: Using graphs

1 a

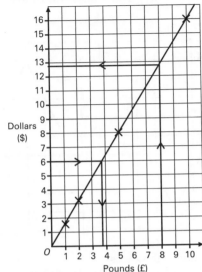

b ii $12.80   **ii** £3.75

2

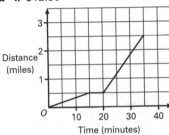

3 a, c

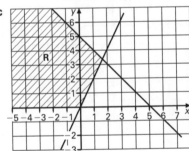

b The solution of the equation $2x = 5 - x$ is given by the x co-ordinate of the point of intersection of the two lines.

4 a Let c = charge, t = time
Equation for line $c = \frac{1}{2}t + 10$

b $\frac{1}{2}t + 10 \leqslant 84$
$\frac{1}{2}t \leqslant 74$
$t \leqslant 148$
Maximum time that could be spent on repair is 148 minutes

5 a 55 miles
b Average speed between 0950 and 1000 is the same as average speed between 0930 and 1030 = 45 mph
c Between 1040 and 1140

6 a   **b** 0954

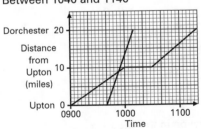

7 $x = 1.5$

Topic 8: Using algebra

1 a $s = 2t + 32 = (2 \times -7) + 32 = 18$
  b $t = \frac{1}{2}(s - 32) = \frac{1}{2}(40 - 32) = 4$
  c $18.9 = 20$ (1 sf); $s = (2 \times 20) + 32 = 72$
2 $2(3x + 5) = 4x + 7$
      $6x + 10 = 4x + 7$
          $2x = -3$
            $x = -1\frac{1}{2}$
3 a i Area of $P = 4 \times 2x = 8x\,\text{cm}^2$
    ii Perimeter of $P = 2x + 4 + 2x + 4 = 4x + 8\,\text{cm}$
  b $4x + 8 = 12x + 2$
        $8x = 6$
         $x = \frac{3}{4}$
4 $h = ut + \frac{1}{2}at^2 = (12.9 \times 5) + (\frac{1}{2} \times -9.8 \times 5^2)$
               $= 64.5 - 122.5 = -58\,\text{m}$
5 $x = 3, y = \frac{1}{2}$
6 $x = 2\frac{1}{2}, y = -1$

7 a

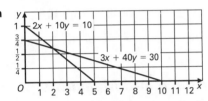

b Cost of 1 litre of petrol is £0.60

Topic 9: More using algebra

1 a 31   **b** -17
2 a 10
  b i No. of black tiles = ($2 \times$ pattern number) + 2
    ii 102
3 a 17   **b** 11
4 a i 7
    ii nth term = first term + $(n - 1) \times 7$
       10th term = $2 + (10 - 1) \times 7 = 2 + 63 = 65$
  b i 118
    ii nth term = $4 + (n - 1) \times 6 = 4 + 6n - 6 = 6n - 2$

5 a

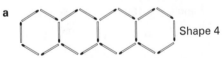

Shape 4

  b i

Shape number	1	2	3	4	5
Number of matchsticks	6	11	16	21	26

    ii Each term is 5 more than the last term
    iii No. of matchsticks in shape 9 = $(9 \times 5) + 1$
                            $= 45 + 1 = 46$

6 50
7 a 38
  b No. of outside edges = $4n + 6$
8 a 31
  b $5n + 2$
  c $n^2 + n$
9 a i n^2 **ii** $4n^2$
  b For any number n, either $n + 1$ or $n + 2$ is an even number. An even number multiplied by an odd number is always even. Therefore every term in $(n + 1)(n + 2)$ must be even.

10 $V = \frac{1}{3}\pi r^2 h$

$\dfrac{3V}{\pi h} = r^2$

$r = \sqrt{\dfrac{3V}{\pi h}}$

11

Value of x	Value of x^3	
2	8	too small
3	27	too big
2.8	21.952	too small
2.9	24.389	too big
2.85	23.149	too big

Solution lies between 2.8 and 2.85, so $x = 2.8$ (1 dp)

12

Value of x	Value of $x^3 - x$	Comment
3.5	39.375	too big
3.4	35.904	too big
3.3	32.637	too small
3.35	34.245	too small

Solution lies between 3.35 and 3.4, so $x = 3.4$ (1 dp)

13 a i $2r(r + h)$ **ii** $2x^2 - 5x - 12$

   b i $b = 75$ **ii** $M = b + \sqrt{\dfrac{P}{a}}$

Shape, Space and Measures

Topic 10: Angle properties

1 a 1500   **b** 90°

2 a $p = 56°$, $q = 124°$

   b $r = s = 60°$

   c $t = 102°$

3 a i obtuse angle   **ii** isosceles

   b 35°

   c 35°, $\hat{CDP}$ and $\hat{BPD}$ are alternate angles

4 $x = 117°$, $y = 27°$

5 a i trapezium   **ii** $x = 30°$

   b $y = 60°$

   c 720°

6 a $x = \dfrac{360}{8} = 45°$

   b exterior angle $= \dfrac{360}{5} = 72°$,

       interior angle, $y = 180° - 72° = 108°$

7 a $x = \dfrac{360}{8} = 45°$ **b** $y = \frac{1}{2}(180 - 45) = 67.5°$

Topic 11: Length, area and volume

1 a i Perimeter $= 4 + 4 + 4 + 4 = 16$ cm

    ii Area $= 4 \times 4 = 16$ cm²

   b 8 cm

2 a 10 cm²   **b** 6 cm

3 12 000 cm³ (or 12 l)

4 Area $= \pi r^2 = \pi \times 7.5^2 = 176.7$ cm² (1 dp)

5 a Volume $= \frac{1}{3}\pi r^2 h + \frac{1}{2}(\frac{4}{3}\pi r^3) = \frac{1}{3}\pi r^2(h + 2r)$

      $= 497$ cm³ (3 sf)

   b Slant height of cone, $l = \sqrt{9^2 + 5^2} = 10.295\ldots$

      Surface area $= \pi r l + \frac{1}{2}(4\pi r^2) = \pi r(l + 2r)$

      $= 319$ cm² (3 sf)

6 a i Circumference $= \pi d = \pi \times 7 = 22.0$ cm (1 dp)

    ii Area $= \pi r^2 = 38.5$ cm² (1 dp)

   b Volume $= \dfrac{\pi d^2 h}{4} = 38.5 \times 10 = 385$ cm³ (3 sf)

7 Area of A $= 4.5 \times 5 = 22.5$ cm²

   Area of B $= \dfrac{4.5}{2}(2.1 + 8) = 22.7$ cm² (1 dp)

   Shape B has the larger area

8 Area of base $= 1000 \div 20 = 50$ cm²

   $r^2 = \dfrac{50}{\pi} = 15.915\ldots$ so $r = \sqrt{15.915\ldots} = 3.98$ cm (3 sf)

9 Area of parallelogram $= 6 \times 3 = 18$ cm²

   Volume of ice cream $= 18 \times 12 = 216$ cm³

Topic 12: Symmetry and transformations

1 a i P(2, 3)

    ii P′(2, −3)

   b

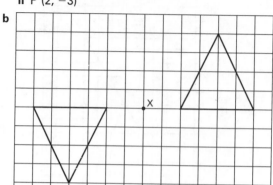

2 a Reflection in the x axis

   b Rotation 90° anticlockwise about (0, 0)

   c Enlargement, scale factor 3, centre (5, 4)

3 a i Rotation

    ii Translation

   b

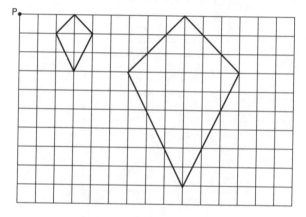

4 a, b,
  c i
  c ii 1

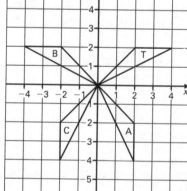

5

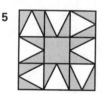

6 a Reflection in the line $y = x$

   b Enlargement, scale factor 2, centre (−7, 1)

Topic 13: Shapes and solids

1 a 9   **b** 16   **c** 9

2

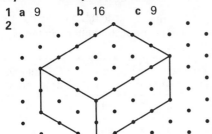

3 a

           b B and C

4 Height $= \sqrt{2.75^2 - 1.80^2} = 2.08\,m$ (3 sf)

5 b i Area $= \frac{1}{2}\pi r^2 = 14.14\,cm^2$ (2 dp)
     ii PY $= \sqrt{6^2 + 4^2} = 7.21\,cm^2$ (2 dp)

6 a i AC $= 2 \times \sqrt{10^2 - 6^2} = 16\,m$
     ii Area of ABC $= \frac{1}{2} \times 16 \times 6 = 48\,m^2$
   b Volume of roof space $= 48 \times 25 = 1200\,m^3$

7 a $x = 0.8 + \sqrt{4^2 - 0.7^2} = 4.7\,m$ (1 dp)
   b Area of cross-section $= \frac{0.7}{2}(0.8 + 4.7) = 1.925\,m^2$
     Volume $= 1.925 \times 1.5 = 2.9\,m^3$ (1 dp)

Topic 14: Triangles and quadrilaterals

1 a Pentagon
   b Its sides/angles are not equal

2 a B, D
   b A, B
   c A, B, D, F
   d C
   e rhombus

3 a 29°   **b** $y = 4.5\,cm$

4 a BC $= 3.2 \cos 49° = 2.10\,m$ (1 dp)
   b CD $= \dfrac{4.1}{\sin 58°} = 4.83\,m$ (1 dp)

5 a AB $= 10 \tan 32.6 = 6.4\,m$ (1 dp)
   b $\widehat{KTA} = \cos^{-1}\dfrac{10}{27} = 68.3°$ (1 dp)

6 $\dfrac{AB}{XY} = \dfrac{LA}{LX}$ so AB $= \dfrac{LA}{LX} \times XY = \dfrac{3 \times 6}{8} = 2.25\,cm$

Topic 15: Measurement and drawing

1 a 300°
   b i $4 \times 30 = 120\,km$ **ii** $120 \times \frac{5}{8} = 75$ miles

2 a i $8.4 \times 5 = 42.0\,km$
     ii Time taken $= 42/18 = 2\frac{1}{3}$ hours
        $= 2$ hours 20 minutes
        Brian arrives at $0930 + 0220 = 1150$

   b

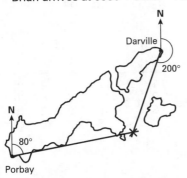

3

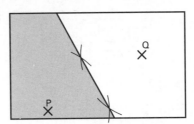

4 a $\widehat{BWH} = \sin^{-1}\dfrac{72}{86} = 56.8°$

   b $\widehat{HBW} = 33.2°$
     Bearing of B from W $= 45° - 33.2° = 011.8°$

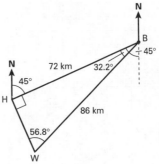

5

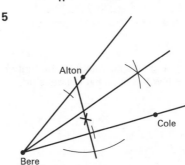

Topic 16: Collection and representation

1 a One class is not a representative sample of
     whole school, e.g. the age of pupils may well
     affect how they travel to school.
   b Tally table

How pupils travel to school	No. of pupils
Car	⦀⦀ ⦀⦀⦀
Cycle	⦀⦀ ⦀
Bus	⦀⦀ ⦀⦀

2 a Sunday   **b** 150   **c** 1160

3 a India
   b New Zealand
   c New Zealand, Britain, Canada
   d Greece and Spain; Japan and Italy
   e USA (24 °C)

4 a Friday
   b Yes, more people shopped on Sunday in 1996
     because Sunday opening was more common.
   c True: % shopping on Friday, Saturday,
     Sunday $= 20 + 21 + 10 = 51\%$

5

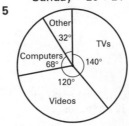

6 a

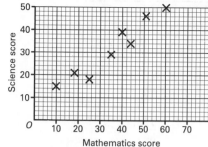

b Strong positive correlation

7 a

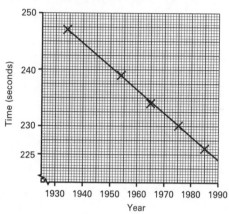

b 227 s

8 a There is strong negative correlation; the higher the rainfall, the fewer deck chair tickets sold.

b

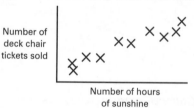

Topic 17: Averages and spread

1 a Mean score = 6
  b i Modal score = 9 **ii** Range = 9 − 2 = 7
  c Graham is the better bowler, he is more consistent and his mean score is higher.
2 a Mode = 9
  b Median = 8
  c i Mode = 7 **ii** Median = 7.5
3 a i Range = 39 − 27 = 12 **ii** Mean length = 32 cm
  b Spanish cucumbers are generally shorter than English cucumbers and have less variation in their lengths.
4 a i Modal class = 6–10
   ii Median (50th value) is in class interval 11–15

  b Mean $= \dfrac{\Sigma(f \times \text{mid-interval value})}{\Sigma f}$

   $= \dfrac{1487}{100}$

   $= 14.87$ words

5 Estimated mean travelling time

   $= \dfrac{\Sigma(f \times \text{mid-interval value})}{\Sigma f}$

   $= 22.34775 = 22$ minutes (to nearest minute)

6 a Median finishing time = 101 minutes
  b IQR = 103 − 89 = 14 minutes

---

7 a *See page 207 for answer*
  b 100 − 92 = 8
  c i Median = 25 hours **ii** IQR = 27 − 23.5 = 3.5
  d No: because IQR is larger the battery lifetimes are more spread.

8 a i

Weight of tea in tea-bag (w grams)	Number of tea-bags	Cumulative frequency
$2.9 < w \leqslant 3.0$	1	1
$3.0 < w \leqslant 3.1$	5	6
$3.1 < w \leqslant 3.2$	34	40
$3.2 < w \leqslant 3.3$	43	83
$3.3 < w \leqslant 3.4$	13	96
$3.4 < w \leqslant 3.5$	3	99
$3.5 < w \leqslant 3.6$	1	100

  ii *See page 207 for answer*
  b Median weight of tea-bag = 3.22 g, so median weight of tea in box = 80 × 3.22 = 257.6 g
   IQR = 3.27 − 3.17 = 0.1 g, so IQR for box = 80 × 0.1 = 8 g
   Yes '250 g' is a fair description – most boxes (approx. 90%) contain more than 250 g

Topic 18: Probability

1 a i Equally likely **ii** Unlikely
  b i $\frac{1}{5}$ **ii** $\frac{4}{5}$
2 a

(number line: 0, $\frac{1}{4}$, $\frac{1}{2}$, $\frac{3}{4}$, 1 — Impossible, Unlikely, Evens, Likely, Certain)

  b i $\frac{3}{8}$ **ii** $\frac{5}{8}$
3 a $\frac{1}{20}$ **b** $\frac{7}{20}$ **c** $\frac{13}{20}$
4 a $\frac{12}{20} = \frac{3}{5}$
  b

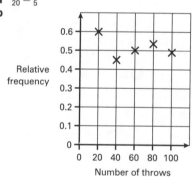

  c 0.5
5 a

	2	3	4	5	6
1	3	4	5	6	7
2	4	5	6	7	8
3	5	6	7	8	9
4	6	7	8	9	10
5	7	8	9	10	11

  b i $\frac{1}{25}$ **ii** $\frac{6}{25}$
6 a i

		Dice				
		1	2	3	4	5	6
Spinner	1	1	2	3	4	5	6
	2	2	4	6	8	10	12
	3	3	6	9	12	15	18
	4	4	8	12	16	20	24

  ii 0
  b $\frac{8}{24} = \frac{1}{3}$
7 a $\frac{6}{20} = \frac{3}{10}$ **b** $\frac{7}{10}$

8 a 0.05

b
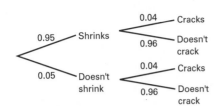

Firing   Cooling

0.95 — Shrinks
0.04 — Cracks
0.96 — Doesn't crack

0.05 — Doesn't shrink
0.04 — Cracks
0.96 — Doesn't crack

c $0.95 \times 0.04 = 0.038$

9 a $0.4 \times 0.2 = 0.08$
b $0.4 \times 0.8 = 0.32$
c $0.6 \times 0.8 = 0.48$
d $0.4 \times 0.8 + 0.6 \times 0.2 = 0.32 + 0.12 = 0.44$

10 a $0.4 + 0.2 = 0.6$
b $(0.4 \times 0.2) + (0.2 \times 0.4) = 0.16$

11 a Total number of cubes in box $= \dfrac{12}{0.3} = 40$

Number of blue cubes $= 0.4 \times 40 = 16$
b 0.4

Topic 17 Question 7 a

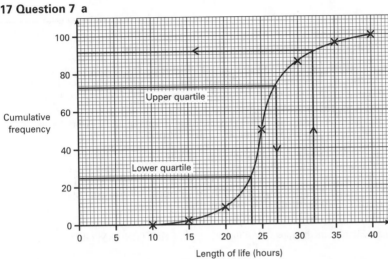

Topic 17 Question 8 a ii

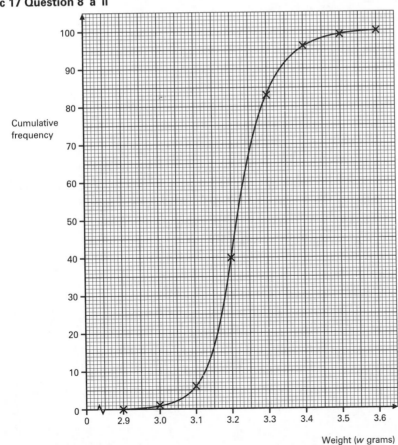

Acknowledgements

The publishers thank the following Examination Boards for permission to reproduce copyright material:

Southern Examining Group (SEG)
Northern Examinations and Assessment Board (NEAB)

Thanks to Tony Banks and John Readman for their invaluable contributions at review.
Thanks to the team at Stanley Thornes, in particular Adrian Wheaton, Malcolm Tomlin and Lorna Godson.

© Paul Metcalf, Liz Hamilton and Anne Haworth 1999
The right of Paul Metcalf, Liz Hamilton and Anne Haworth to be identified as authors of this work has been asserted by them in accordance with the Copyright, Designs and Patents Act 1988.

First published 1999 by
Stanley Thornes (Publishers) Ltd, Ellenborough House, Wellington Street, CHELTENHAM GL50 1YW

ISBN 0 7487 4512 2

Typeset by Tech Set Ltd, Gateshead

Printed and bound in Spain by Mateu Cromo